TECHNIQUES OF CHEMISTRY

ARNOLD WEISSBERGER, *Editor*

VOLUME I

PHYSICAL METHODS OF CHEMISTRY

PART IA
Components of Scientific Instruments

TECHNIQUES OF CHEMISTRY

ARNOLD WEISSBERGER, *Editor*

TECHNIQUES OF CHEMISTRY

VOLUME I

PHYSICAL METHODS
OF CHEMISTRY

INCORPORATING FOURTH COMPLETELY REVISED AND AUGMENTED
EDITION OF TECHNIQUE OF ORGANIC CHEMISTRY,
VOLUME I, PHYSICAL METHODS OF ORGANIC CHEMISTRY

Edited by

ARNOLD WEISSBERGER
AND
BRYANT W. ROSSITER
Research Laboratories
Eastman Kodak Company
Rochester, New York

PART IA
Components of Scientific Instruments

WILEY-INTERSCIENCE

A DIVISION OF JOHN WILEY & SONS Inc.
New York · London · Sydney · Toronto

Library of Congress Catalog Card Number: 77-114920

ISBN 0 471 92724 4

Printed in the United States of America

10 9 8 7 6 5 4 3 2 1

PLAN FOR
PHYSICAL METHODS OF CHEMISTRY

AUTHORS OF PART I

LEROY L. BLACKMER

Research Laboratories, Eastman Kodak Company, Kodak Park, Rochester, New York

CURTIS E. BORCHERS

Department of Chemistry, Northwestern University, Evanston, Illinois

JOHN FIGUERAS

Research Laboratories, Eastman Kodak Company, Kodak Park, Rochester, New York

MURRAY C. GODDARD

Research Laboratories, Eastman Kodak Company, Kodak Park, Rochester, New York

ROBERT J. LOYD

Department of Chemistry, Northwestern University, Evanston, Illinois

LEON F. PHILLIPS

Department of Chemistry, University of Canterbury, Christchurch, New Zealand

DAVID R. SIMONSEN

Manufacturing Experiments, Kodak Park, Rochester, New York

DONALD E. SMITH

Department of Chemistry, Northwestern University, Evanston, Illinois

NEW BOOKS AND NEW EDITIONS OF BOOKS OF THE TECHNIQUE OF ORGANIC CHEMISTRY SERIES WILL NOW APPEAR IN TECHNIQUES OF CHEMISTRY. A LIST OF PRESENTLY PUBLISHED VOLUMES IS GIVEN BELOW.

TECHNIQUE OF ORGANIC CHEMISTRY
ARNOLD WEISSBERGER, *Editor*

INTRODUCTION TO THE SERIES

Techniques of Chemistry is the successor to the Technique of Organic Chemistry Series and its companion—Technique of Inorganic Chemistry. Because many of the methods are employed in all branches of chemical science, the division into techniques for organic and inorganic chemistry has become increasingly artificial. Accordingly, the new series reflects the wider application of techniques, and the component volumes for the most part provide complete treatments of the methods covered. Volumes in which limited areas of application are discussed can be easily recognized by their titles.

Like its predecessors, the series is devoted to a comprehensive presentation of the respective techniques. The authors give the theoretical background for an understanding of the various methods and operations and describe the techniques and tools, their modifications, their merits and limitations, and their handling. It is hoped that the series will contribute to a better under-standing and a more rational and effective application of the respective techniques.

Authors and editors hope that readers will find the volumes in this series useful and will communicate to them any criticisms and suggestions for improvements.

Research Laboratories   ARNOLD WEISSBERGER
Eastman Kodak Company
Rochester, New York

PREFACE

Physical Methods of Chemistry succeeds, and incorporates the material of, three editions of *Physical Methods of Organic Chemistry* (1945, 1949, and 1959). It has been broadened in scope to include physical methods important in the study of all varieties of chemical compounds. Accordingly, it is published as Volume I of the new Techniques of Chemistry Series.

Some of the methods described in *Physical Methods of Chemistry* are relatively simple laboratory procedures, such as weighing and the measurement of temperature, refractive index, and determination of melting and boiling points. Other techniques require very sophisticated apparatus and specialists to make the measurements and to interpret the data; x-ray diffraction, mass spectrometry, and nuclear magnetic resonance are examples of this class. Authors of chapters describing the first class of methods aim to provide all information that is necessary for the successful handling of the respective techniques. Alternatively, the aim of authors treating the more sophisticated methods is to provide the reader with a clear understanding of the basic theory and apparatus involved, together with an appreciation for the value, potential, and limitations of the respective techniques. Representative applications are included to illustrate these points, and liberal references to monographs and other scientific literature providing greater detail are given for readers who want to apply the techniques. Still other methods that are successfully used to solve chemical problems range between these examples in complexity and sophistication and are treated accordingly. All chapters are written by specialists. In many cases authors have acquired a profound knowledge of the respective methods by their own pioneering work in the use of these techniques.

In the earlier editions of *Physical Methods* an attempt was made to arrange the chapters in a logical sequence. In order to make the organization of the treatise lucid and helpful to the reader, a further step has been taken in the new edition—the treatise has been subdivided into technical families:

Part I   Components of Scientific Instruments, Automatic Recording and Control, Computers in Chemical Research
Part II   Electrochemical Methods
Part III Optical, Spectroscopic, and Radioactivity Methods

Part IV   Determination of Mass, Transport, and Electrical-Magnetic Properties

Part V   Determination of Thermodynamic and Surface Properties

The changes in subject matter from the Third Edition are too numerous to list in detail. We thank previous authors for their continuing cooperation and welcome the new authors to the series. New authors of Part I are Dr. Leroy L. Blackmer, Dr. Curtis E. Borchers, Dr. John Figueras, Mr. Murray C. Goddard, Mr. Robert J. Loyd, Dr. Leon F. Phillips, and Dr. Donald E. Smith.

We are also grateful to the many colleagues who advised us in the selection of authors and helped in the evaluation of manuscripts. They are for Part I: Mr. D. C. Barton, Dr. E. R. Brown, Mr. M. C. Goddard, Mr. W. K. Grimwood, Mr. H. O. Hoadley, Mrs. A. Kocher, Dr. W. R. Ruby, and Mr. J. G. Streiffert.

The senior editor expresses his gratitude to Bryant W. Rossiter for joining him in the work and taking on the very heavy burden with exceptional devotion and ability.

ARNOLD WEISSBERGER

January 1970   BRYANT W. ROSSITER
Research Laboratories
Eastman Kodak Company
Rochester, New York

CONTENTS

COMPONENTS OF SCIENTIFIC INSTRUMENTS

TECHNIQUES OF CHEMISTRY

ARNOLD WEISSBERGER, *Editor*

VOLUME I

PHYSICAL METHODS OF CHEMISTRY

PART IA
Components of Scientific Instruments

Chapter **I**

INTRODUCTION

Leon F. Phillips

---

1 GENERAL DESIGN CONSIDERATIONS

The Role of Instrumentation in Chemistry

Not very long ago it was possible to do interesting and useful work in most areas of chemistry with little help from instrumentation. The classical sequence of preparation, analysis, and characterization of new substances which formed the basis of chemical research programs would sometimes include the measurement of an ultraviolet spectrum or magnetic moment, but measurements of this nature were usually regarded as incidental to the main objectives of the research. Mass spectrometers and infrared spectrometers, to name two of the most useful modern chemical instruments, were difficult to operate, and were in the province of physicists and a few borderline physical chemists. Even the measurement of an absorption spectrum in the visible region was a tedious operation. Magnetic resonance in its present form had still to be invented. A generation ago organic chemists as a group were just beginning to realize the amount of insight to be gained from purely physical measurements: the change that has occurred since then has been virtually a revolution. An indication of the readiness with which physical instruments and methods are now adopted is provided by a comparison of the time lags between invention and large-scale chemical application of mass spectrometry (about 40 years), nuclear magnetic resonance (about 10 years), and Mössbauer spectroscopy (about three years). It has become appreciated that the first people to work in a new field, or to apply a new instrumental technique in an old field, are those who make the most interesting discoveries, and it is only a slight exaggeration to say that if a new

1

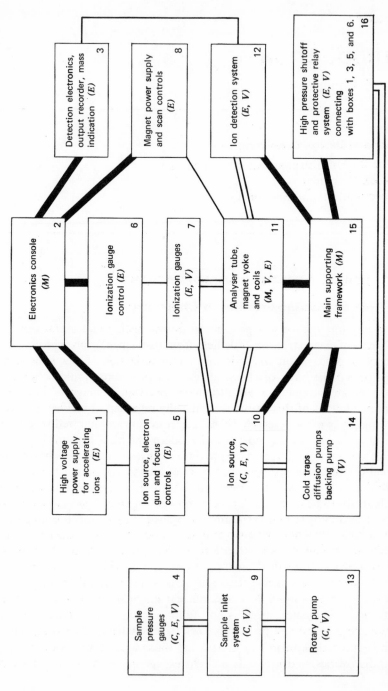

Fig. 1.1 Block diagram of a mass spectrometer, with components classified according to their mechanical (*M*), electrical (*E*), vacuum system (*V*), or chemical handling (*C*) functions. ▬▬ mechanical support; ═══ vacuum connection; ——— electrical connection.

type of spectroscopy were to be announced on a Monday chemists in the vicinity would be running the spectra of their latest compounds by the end of the week and a commercial instrument for the purpose would be advertised during the following month. Even a new way of using an old technique, as in the automation of x-ray structure determination, or of combining two techniques, as in optical rotary dispersion, can yield important dividends. It follows from this discussion that the education of a chemist at the present time is incomplete unless it includes training in instrumentation that is at least sufficient to enable the student to understand the operating principles and to recognize the potentialities and limitations of any instrument that he is likely to encounter. The need for a systematic approach to instrumentation is demonstrated by the observation that a complete catalog of the scientific instruments used in chemistry would contain items ranging in complexity from a thermometer to a cyclotron. It is the main purpose of this introduction to point out the features that are common to all instruments, of whatever degree of complexity, and to consider the general factors that govern the choice of a suitable design for an instrument which is to be built or bought. In the chapters that follow a number of specific topics relating to instrument design and construction are discussed in detail. It is hoped that our account will be of value not only to people whose responsibility it is to acquire or build scientific equipment but also to those who employ equipment that is already available. Uncritical users of "black boxes" generally pay for their lack of understanding by failure to exploit an instrument's full performance or to detect errors that arise from exceeding an instrument's capabilities.

Block Diagrams

Many scientific instruments are simple in form and have an obvious mode of operation; many others, unfortunately, are not in this category. The first step toward understanding any complex entity is to analyse it into its components. One way of doing this with a scientific instrument is to classify the components in terms of their functions. Such a classification, for example, might include categories for mechanical components, optical components, vacuum systems, electrical supplies and connections, electronics, and chemical handling systems. A block diagram of a reasonably complex instrument (a mass spectrometer) based on this type of classification is shown in Fig. 1.1. This kind of diagram is useful in elucidating the gross structure of an instrument, as an aid to devising a suitable physical layout for a large construction, and as the basis of a flow chart to determine the best order of construction and assembly when a new instrument is to be built.

The two basic functions of instruments are measurement and control. Measurement is the more fundamental, since a physical quantity such as temperature or magnetic field intensity must be measured to determine whether it differs from the required value before it can be controlled. This leads us to a different way of constructing a block diagram in which the emphasis is on the flow of signals (i.e., information) from the system whose properties are being measured to the output of the instrument. The resulting diagrams are more general and correspondingly more abstract in character than Fig. 1.1. A typical block diagram of this type for a chemical instrument is given in Fig. 1.2, in which the chemical system is represented by a circle and the components of the instrument itself are represented by rectangles.

A signal consists of a change in the value of some measurable quantity, such as light intensity, temperature, or electric current, and to detect such a change it is necessary to have a standard of comparison. For this reason the signal paths in Fig. 1.2 are shown as double lines, one line for the varying quantity and one for the standard or reference signal. In electrical instruments the reference signal is usually, though not invariably, provided by a point at earth (zero) potential. The *transducers* are devices for transferring signals, or their information content, from one form or medium to another; for example, a thermocouple is a transducer for converting information in the form of a temperature difference to equivalent information in the form of a voltage difference; a photocell is a transducer for converting a difference in light intensity into a voltage or current difference; a pen recorder is a transducer for converting a voltage or current signal into a change in the position of a line drawn on a chart. In recent years a great variety of extremely powerful signal-handling techniques has been developed in the field of electronics and most instruments are now built to exploit this development as much as possible. Information is most often conveyed from one part of an instrument to another in the form of electrical signals so that a device such as a thermocouple or photocell, which produces an electrical signal, is normally used as an input transducer, whereas a pen recorder, or galvanometer, which gives a visual readout of an electrical signal, is commonly used as an output transducer. In consequence of the predominance of electronic signal-handling methods some basic understanding of electronics on the part of the experimenter is desirable. The *signal modifier* of Fig. 1.2 would in most cases be an amplifier of electrical signals with the function of converting

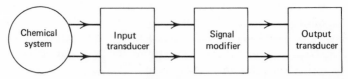

Fig. 1.2   Block diagram of an instrument for measuring some property of a chemical system. Signal paths are shown by arrows.

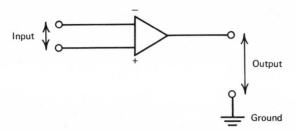

Fig. 1.3 Conventional amplifier symbol. (Often the (+) input lead is directly connected to ground.) A signal applied to the (+) input produces an output signal of the same sign. A signal applied to the (−) input produces an output signal of the opposite sign.

the relatively feeble voltage or current from the input transducer into a signal powerful enough to operate the output transducer. This should be accomplished with no loss of information due to noise or distortion along the way. Other possible functions of a modifier include the averaging of a signal over a period of time, the chopping of a steady voltage or current to produce an alternating signal, the rectification of an alternating signal to produce a steady voltage or current, and pulse shaping and pulse-height discrimination. It is often useful to distinguish an amplifier by using the conventional triangular symbol of Fig. 1.3. Some other modifiers, notably those used in digital logic circuitry, also have their own conventional symbols, which are described in Chapter IV.

Even for an instrument as simple as a thermometer the analysis implied by Fig. 1.2 is possible in principle; here the small mass of mercury is essentially a transducer for converting a temperature change into a volume change, the long capillary is a modifier for converting the volume change to a change of length, and the engraved scale is an output transducer for converting the length change into a readable change of so many degrees. In this case the analysis is hardly more than an academic exercise, but in the design or understanding of a complex piece of equipment it is an essential first step.

As an example of the use of block diagrams in the design of a moderately complicated piece of equipment, let us suppose that we require instrumentation to measure the progress of a chemical reaction as a function of time. The chemical system will consist of the reaction vessel and its contents and a transducer is needed to respond to a change in the nature of the contents. To be more specific, suppose that the reaction is accompanied by a color change (e.g., the reaction of iodine with acetone or of nitric oxide with oxygen) and that the transducer is to respond to the change in optical density at some suitable wavelength. Most commercial spectrophotometers are not designed to allow the optical density at one wavelength to be recorded as a function of time, and so we decide to build an apparatus for the purpose.

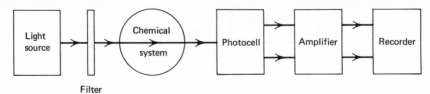

Filter

Fig. 1.4 Block diagram of an instrument for observing light absorption by a chemical system.

Our first ideas give rise to the block diagram shown in Fig. 1.4 in which the combination of light source, optical filter (a modifier for light signals), and photocell constitutes the input transducer.

It now becomes apparent from the diagram that no path has been provided for a comparison signal, and in order to measure a change in optical density it would be necessary to remove the reaction vessel periodically and replace it with an identical vessel in which no reaction had occurred. We can improve this arrangement by splitting the light beam into two parts, as in Fig. 1.5, and arranging for a rotating or vibrating shutter—a "light chopper"—to present the two light beams to the photocell alternately. The resulting apparatus should be adequate to measure a change in optical density of a few percent with sufficient accuracy for kinetic studies. To complete the experimental system we should also include a thermostat to fix the temperature of the reaction mixture, power supplies for the amplifier, photocell, and any other electronic units that become involved, a rectifier to convert the alternating signal that results from our use of a light chopper into a steady signal for the chart recorder, and connections to the mains for thermostat, recorder, and power supplies. We might also wish to introduce one or more *feedback loops* to improve the stability of the measuring system; for example, the intensity of the comparison signal received by the photocell could be used

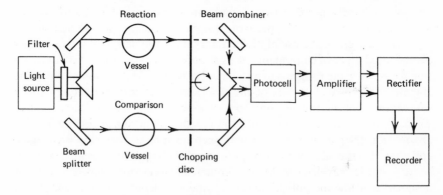

Fig. 1.5 Addition of a comparison light signal to the apparatus of Fig. 1.4.

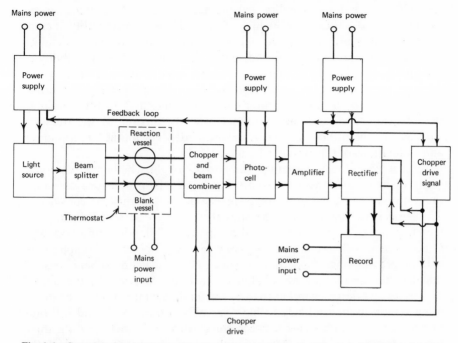

Fig. 1.6 Complete block diagram for the apparatus begun in Fig. 1.4. Main signal paths indicated by heavy lines.

to control the amount of power supplied to the light source in such a way that an increase in intensity would result in a decrease in power and vice versa. The negative feedback would then have the effect of holding the comparison signal at a constant value. The same principle is involved in the operation of the thermostat and in any other automatic control system. A block diagram that includes all of the features mentioned so far is shown in Fig. 1.6.

Specifications and Economics

Once a decision has been made to acquire a new piece of equipment, one of the first questions to follow is whether to build it or whether to buy a commercial instrument. In general it is better to buy a commercial instrument if one can be found to meet the desired specifications. Indeed, with instruments that are in large-volume production the commercial instrument is likely to be less expensive than anything an individual could build to give the same performance, particularly if he includes the value of his time in the calculation. Factors in favor of building rather than buying include the lack of a commercial machine that could give the required performance at a reasonable price, the possibility that the development of a new instrument would itself constitute a worthwhile advance, the ready availability of components from which the instrument could be assembled, the availability of good workshop facilities and technical assistance, and the possibility of actually saving time by beginning to build immediately rather than going through the sequence of obtaining price quotations, placing the order, waiting through the manufacturer's delivery time, and finally obtaining delivery from a distant factory. Obviously, the answer to the question whether to build or buy in any particular case depends on the circumstances and inclinations of the individual scientist.

When a piece of scientific equipment is to be bought, whether as a complete entity or as a component for something larger, the problem of obtaining the optimum combination of performance and price must be considered. The basic performance characteristics that need to be specified and will largely govern the price to be paid are precision, stability, and accuracy. Other factors, such as compactness, convenience of operation, compatibility with other components, speed, resistance to corrosive atmospheres, ease of maintenance, and long-term reliability, which are governed by the skill of the instrument designer rather than by the fundamental nature of the measuring system itself, are likely to have less effect on the price and will thus provide a basis for choosing between competitive instruments. Of the three main factors precision is a measure of the range of values within which the result of a single measurement can be located, stability (or reproducibility) is a measure of the range over which the result of successive measurements can be expected to wander because of changes within the instrument itself, and accuracy is a measure of the range of values about the true value which is likely to be found when successive measurements are made with different instruments of the same type. Ideally these three quantities should be of similar magnitude, since there is nothing to be gained by having one or two of the ranges specified within very narrow limits if one of the other ranges is relatively large. To give a simple example of such an unbalanced specification, it means very little in practice that the output of a mains-operated power supply, relative to an internal voltage standard, is stable to 0.001% with respect to line-voltage fluctuations, if the standard reference voltage has a temperature coefficient of 0.01% per degree. Again, if an instrument is to serve as a component of a larger apparatus, then there is usually no point in specifying characteristics that are appropriate to a level of precision of the order of, say, 0.01%, if some other factor limits the overall accuracy to ±1%. In other words, for optimum performance and price the components of a large apparatus should all be of similar precision, stability, and accuracy. Exceptions to this rule occur when a component is needed for a number of projects in addition to the one immediately at hand or when, as with a slidewire potentiometer, it is possible to obtain high precision at a relatively insignificant cost.

To illustrate the ideas of the preceding paragraph let us return to the block diagram of Fig. 1.6 and consider how it could be transformed into a working piece of apparatus. On the basis of the over-all specification we have to deduce the level of performance to be demanded of the various building blocks and then to judge the optimum ratio of price to precision, versatility, ruggedness, and all the other characteristics that are desirable for the individual components. The cost of the completed instrument in terms of time, effort, and money will depend on the decisions made at this stage.

Two useful classifications of the building blocks can now be made. The first separates them into *general-purpose* equipment, such as a recorder, which is not permanently attached to one apparatus but is likely to have many other services to perform, and *specialized* equipment such as a particular configuration of beam splitter, light chopper, and photocell, which is unlikely to be of further use in its present form once the experiment is over. Obviously it is easier to justify a large expenditure for an item with many potential uses. The second classification distinguishes "things to build" and "things to buy."

Of the items in Fig. 1.6 the recorder and thermostat easily qualify as general purpose equipment which should be bought. Many different chart recorders are available commercially, with numerous possible combinations of chart speed, sensitivity (typically 10 mV full scale), and speed of response. At the level of precision we have envisaged for this instrument, of the order of $\pm 1\%$, such a recorder is suitable and not too expensive. Similarly, a relatively inexpensive thermostat, able to maintain its temperature reliably constant within 0.2°C, should be adequate for most purposes. These items might be already on hand from some previous experiment or they might be available for borrowing. However, the optical system, from light source to photocell, would almost certainly have to be assembled from commercially available components and metal or plastic parts which may have to be machined especially for the purpose. Here, for example, it should be possible to economize without sacrificing performance by choosing plastic or easily worked metals such as aluminum or brass in preference to difficult metals like stainless steel, by using a well-chosen Corning glass filter in preference to an expensive interference filter, or by selecting a low-cost photomultiplier in preference to a vacuum photocell (see Chapter VI) so that there will be more than enough sensitivity available to allow inexpensive optical components to be employed. Finally, the electronic components—amplifier, rectifier, chopper drive, and power supplies—could for this level of precision be built quite easily on the basis of information contained in this book. Alternatively, one or more of these units could be bought, for example the power supplies or amplifiers, the expense being justified on the grounds that they are general-purpose equipment. Much must depend on the amount of technical assistance available and on the relative weightings given to the different forms of expenditure, that is, of time, effort, or money, when various approaches to the construction problem are being considered. If some items are bought and others built, care will be needed to ensure that the different units are compatible electrically and even that they will fit together conveniently in the same framework.

If high over-all precision is required, an apparatus usually, though not inevitably, becomes both elaborate and expensive. Thus, instead of the chart recorder of Fig. 1.6, we might use a digital voltmeter that reads to four or five significant figures, with some sort of printout facility to provide a permanent record or to allow a large accumulation of data to be processed by computer. As a result the cost of our output transducer might increase by a factor of 3 or more. Similar increases in cost could be expected for the other components, all of which would need to be improved considerably if the high precision of the output transducer were not to be wasted. In this situation it should be remembered that certain types of measurement often achieve excellent precision at a relatively modest cost. Notable examples are ordinary weighing, the measurement of potential differences near 1 V with a slide-wire potentiometer, measurement of signal frequency by comparison with a broadcast frequency standard, and measurement of linear displacement with the precision screw thread of a lathe bed or a micrometer. It happens that this last type of measurement could easily be applied to improving the precision of the apparatus we have been considering. We should arrange for the amount of light passing through the reaction vessel to be controlled with a micrometer-driven shutter; this shutter would be adjusted to equalize the intensity of the two beams received by the photomultiplier, and the amplifier and rectifier, in combination with a chart recorder or a sensitive meter, would serve merely to detect departures from equality in the two beams. To follow the progress of the reaction it would probably be most convenient to set the shutter aperture at a preselected value, note the time at which the meter or recorder reading passed through zero, and then reset the shutter and wait for another zero reading. The accuracy of this method would be limited mainly by the accuracy of calibration of the micrometer reading in terms of the amount of light passing through the aperture.

The preceding discussion illustrates the factors to be borne in mind during the first stages of instrument design. Conversely, when approaching a new instrument for the first time, it is helpful to remember that similar factors must have been considered by the original designer and that he must have begun his work with a block diagram, if not on paper, at least in his mind's eye.

Even if one is only occasionally involved in problems of instrumentation, it is important to remember that a great deal of effort is being expended continuously by manufacturers of scientific equipment with the aim of producing more precise, stable, convenient, or inexpensive measuring devices. Therefore it is a sound plan to have the institution or research group maintain a collection of manufacturers' catalogs and to be on the regular mailing lists of major manufacturers of complete instruments and discrete components that are likely to be useful for solving future problems. In addition, it invariably pays to consult the advertisements as well as the text in such publications as the *Review of Scientific Instruments, Journal of Scientific Instruments, Applied Optics, Physics Today, Scientific Research, Chemical and Engineering News, Journal of Chemical Education, Nature, Science,* and *International Electronics,* to name some of the most useful sources of new information about the components of scientific instruments.

References

Bair, E. J., *Introduction to Chemical Instrumentation*, McGraw-Hill, New York, 1962.

Wilson, E. Bright, Jr., *An Introduction to Scientific Research*, McGraw-Hill, New York, 1952.

Chapter **II**

MECHANICAL

Leroy L. Blackmer

---

1   INTRODUCTION

In the field of modern instrumentation there is a trend toward ever-increasing complexity with concomitant demands on precision, speed, and reliability. An expensive piece of equipment can fail completely because of catastrophic failure of a single component such as an improperly mounted resistor. On the other hand, inadequate mechanical and thermal stability can adversely affect performance with an end result that may be worse than complete failure. Other frequently overlooked aspects involve the interaction between the operator and the instrument (i.e., human engineering) and the maintenance of apparatus after it has been put into operation. Diagnosis of improper performance and correction of faults are sometimes nearly impossible tasks in poorly designed instruments.

Foremost among the requirements for optimum performance, low failure rates, and ease of maintenance is attention to the details of mechanical design. Within the domain of "mechanics" fall such diverse considerations as the operation of dynamic mechanical devices, the arrangement of parts and their interconnections, structural design of supporting members, and insulation from ambient interference [1, 2].

A full accounting of mechanical design procedures is far beyond the scope of one volume, but much can be learned from reliability studies of military equipment [3, 4, 5]. Such equipment, however, is usually designed for extreme conditions seldom encountered in the laboratory. It is the aim of this chapter to point out some of the more important fundamental aspects of mechanical and related problems that frequently arise in the design of instruments for nonmilitary use [6, 7].

2   ELECTRICAL ANALOGIES

A cursory study of the parameters involved in instrument design reveals that the same mathematical formulations often apply to a wide range of

phenomena. The parameters of interest appear as coefficients in the differential equation that describes the behavior of a particular system. Historically,
the equations of motion of mechanical systems were developed long before
the equations for electrical circuits. However, since electrical circuit theory
has developed to the state in which much is generally known about complex
circuits, a tendency has evolved to treat mechanical, thermal, and acoustic
quantities in the same fashion as electrical quantities [8, 9]. All energetic
interactions must be measured with respect to a fixed frame of reference. By
using this reference as a "system ground" and "wire connections" to represent
the coupling between the various elements of a system equivalent mechanical
circuits can be derived. Such "circuits" are analogous in every way to electrical
circuits, provided the elements are suitably correlated in function. Analogies
are particularly useful for designing resonant systems and are also helpful
in dealing with self-generated and external ambient conditions. Analytical
solutions are known for a wide variety of electrical circuit configurations
and, with appropriate substitution of variables, can be directly applied to
mechanical circuits. For more complex systems empirical measurements
are usually simpler to make with electrical analogs than with mechanical
devices. The circuit approach can also provide deeper insight into system
behavior and coupling modes that might otherwise be overlooked.

Quasi-static Linear Analogies

Many mechanical components operate in a quasi-static state that can be
described by first-order, linear differential equations. The force F required
to move an object in a viscous medium, for example, is related to the time
rate of displacement or velocity $v = dx/dt$. If the motion is linear and uniform
or at most only slowly varying in time, the driving force is

$$F = R_M \frac{dx}{dt} = R_M v. \tag{2.1}$$

The coefficient R_M represents the mechanical mass and is a constant of the
system. It is represented by the dashpot in the mechanical diagram of
Fig. 2.1a. By equating the driving force and velocity, respectively, to electrical
potential difference and current, the analogous circuit of Fig. 2.1b is obtained.
Since displacement must always be measured with respect to a reference
point, shown here as the circuit ground, some care is required in applying
the force-potential analogy to more complex systems.

Another simple but important example of the quasi-static state arises in
calculating the temperature rise in a junction transistor. From the fundamental equation of heat conduction the rate of thermal energy transfer
across unit area is proportional to the temperature gradient. The power
generated in the junction can be considered to flow through the thermal

Table 2.1 Static Coefficients

Coefficient	Variables	Equation	Power Dissipation
Electrical resistance (R) volts/coulomb/sec	Voltage (V) Current (I) Charge (q)	$V = RI = R\dfrac{dq}{dt}$	I^2R
Viscous friction (R_M) Newton/meter/sec	Force (F) Velocity (v) Displacement (x)	$F = R_M v = R_M\dfrac{dx}{dt}$	v^2R_M
Rotary friction (R_θ) Newton/meter/rad/sec	Torque (T_θ) Angular velocity (ω) Angular displacement (θ)	$T_\theta = R_\theta\omega = R\dfrac{d\theta}{dt}$	ω^2R_θ
Acoustic or pneumatic resistance (R_A) Newton/meter^5/sec	Pressure (p) Volume velocity (u)	$p = R_A u = R_A\dfrac{dq}{dt}$	u^2R_A
Thermal resistance (R_T) °C/joule/sec	Temperature (T) Power (P) Energy (W)	$T = R_T P = R_T\dfrac{dw}{dt}$	

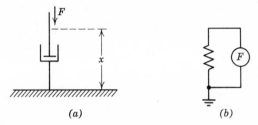

Fig. 2.1   Viscous friction elements.

paths shown in Fig. 2.2—junction to case, case to heat sink, and heat sink to ambient—like current in a set of series-connected resistors. Kirchhoff's laws (See Chapter III, Section 2) may be applied to the equivalent circuit, thus yielding the temperature at the junction,

$$T_J = R_{JC}P + R_{CS}P + R_{SA}P + T_A$$
$$= (R_{JC} + R_{CS} + R_{SA})P + T_A = R_T P + T_A, \qquad (2.2)$$

where the subscripts are indicated in the circuit diagram. As in an equivalent electrical circuit, the total thermal resistance between junction and ambient is the sum of the individual resistances.

Some other commonly occurring linear coefficients are listed in Table 2.1. Though less easy to visualize and construct as an equivalent physical element, the reciprocal resistance, or conductance, is equally applicable. In either case the coefficients represent energy dissipation and, except for the thermal energy, the power is given by the products I^2R, v^2R_M, etc.

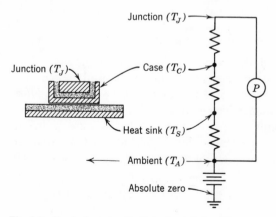

Fig. 2.2   Equivalent circuit of steady state heat flow.

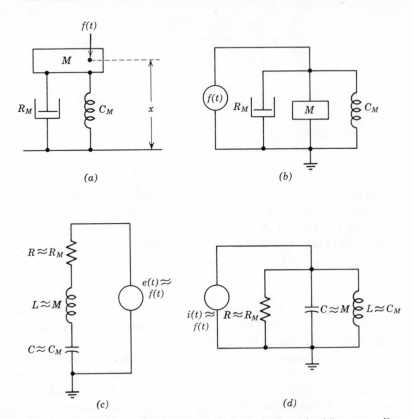

Fig. 2.3 Circuit analogies, (a) a mechanical system; (b) the mechanical "circuit" corresponding to (a); (c) the series (or direct) analogous circuit; and (d) the parallel (or inverse) analogous circuit.

Oscillatory System Analogies

Transient and steady-state analyses of oscillating systems involve the concepts of inertia represented in mechanical devices by mass and of restoring force represented by compliance. Figure 2.3a illustrates a typical suspension system which consists of a mechanical resistive element R_M and a compliant spring member C_M with one degree of freedom. If the mass M is subjected to a sinusoidal driving force of amplitude f_0 and angular frequency ω, the equation of motion is given by Newton's law [10],

$$M\frac{d^2x}{dt^2} + R_M\frac{dx}{dt} + \frac{x}{C_M} = f_0 \cos \omega t. \qquad (2.3)$$

where x is the displacement measured from a stationary reference frame and

R_M is the mechanical resistance discussed above. The compliance coefficient C_M is defined within elastic limits of the spring by Hooke's law,

$$f = \frac{x}{C_M}.$$ (2.4)

It is the reciprocal of the spring constant or force required to produce an incremental unit displacement.

In the force-potential analogy forces in parallel add algebraically, as do potential differences in a series electrical circuit. Thus compliance is mathematically equivalent to capacitance and mass is equivalent to inductance. By direct comparison with the equations for electrical circuits (see Chapter III, Section 2) the parallel mechanical configuration (Fig. 2.3b) translates to a series electrical circuit (Fig. 2.3c).

Mass possesses kinetic energy given by $\frac{1}{2}Mv^2$, where $v = dx/dt$; energy associated with an inductance is of the same form, namely $\frac{1}{2}Li^2$. A compliant structure stores potential energy $x^2/2C$, as does a charged capacitor.

Another usable analogy for rectilinear mechanical systems can be obtained by writing the equation of motion in terms of velocity, $v = dx/dt$.

$$M\frac{dv}{dt} + R_M v + \frac{1}{C_M}\int^t v\, dt_x = f_0 \cos \omega t.$$ (2.5)

From Table 2.2 force, mass, and compliance appear here in the same mathematical form, respectively, as do current, capacitance, and inductance in a parallel electrical circuit. Mechanical resistance corresponds to the reciprocal of electrical resistance. The mechanical configuration translates directly to the parallel "circuit" (Fig. 2.3d). This analogy, however, called the inverse analogy, fails in the frequency domain because mass-capacitance and compliance-inductance are not true analogs. The effects of mass become greater with increasing frequency, whereas the effects of capacitance become less. A similar relation exists between compliance and inductance.

Analogous quantities similar to those for rectilinear motion may also be compiled for mechanical rotational and acoustic systems. Some of these quantities are listed in Table 2.2. Solutions of the equivalent circuits yield the static and dynamic response characteristics of the system along with information of impedance and phase (see Chapter III, Section 2).

3 GENERATION OF MECHANICAL MOTION

Devices capable of generating mechanical motion range from simple freely falling weights, clock springs, and pendulums to complex systems with a degree of sophistication limited only by the ingenuity of the designer.

Table 2.2

	Inertial Coefficients			Compliant Coefficients		
	Direct Electrical Analogy	Inverse Electrical Analogy	Kinetic Energy (W)	Direct Electrical Analogy	Inverse Electrical Analogy	Potential Energy
Electrical	$e = L\dfrac{d^2q}{dt^2}$	$i = C\dfrac{de}{dt}$	$\frac{1}{2}Li^2$	$e = \dfrac{q}{C}$	$i = \dfrac{1}{L}\displaystyle\int e\,dt$	$\dfrac{q^2}{2C}$
Linear mechanical	$f = M\dfrac{d^2x}{dt^2}$	$f = M\dfrac{dv}{dt}$	$\frac{1}{2}Mv^2$	$f = \dfrac{x}{C_M}$	$f = \dfrac{1}{C_M}\displaystyle\int v\,dt$	$\dfrac{x^2}{2C_M}$
Rotary mechanical	$T_\theta = I\dfrac{d^2\theta}{dt^2}$	$T_\theta = I\dfrac{d\omega}{dt}$	$\frac{1}{2}I\omega^2$	$T_\theta = \dfrac{\theta}{C_T}$	$T_\theta = \dfrac{1}{C_T}\displaystyle\int \theta\,dt$	$\dfrac{\theta^2}{2C_T}$
Acoustic		$p = M_A\dfrac{du}{dt}$		$p = \dfrac{V}{C_A}$		

The majority of the requirements encountered in instrument design, however, can be satisfied by the relatively straightforward application of commercially available components. In this section the fundamental aspects of some of the more important means of generating controlled motion are discussed.

Since any motion, no matter how complicated, can always be resolved into vector components, it is convenient to classify the primary source as rotational, translational, or vibrational. Such motions can be directly converted from one mode to another, provided the source has sufficient power capacity.

Generation and Control of Rotational Motion

Motor Selection Criteria

The electric motor is one of the most versatile and easily controlled sources of rotational motion, but optimum choice of a motor for a specific use can be a formidable task. So-called standard motors are listed by the National Electrical Manufacturers Association [11] and are available in a wide range of ratings, performance characteristics, and sizes. The selection factors and typical applications given in Table 2.3 may be used as a rough guide to narrow the area of possible choice of instrument motors [12]. To satisfy more stringent requirements in critical applications a check-off list such as that shown in Table 2.4 is often useful. Similar data sheets are available from most manufacturers. From such data it is frequently possible for the manufacturer to modify standard designs to meet specific requirements.

Motor ratings, including the familiar horsepower ratings, are ambiguous unless all the operating conditions are known. For a given type of electrical power the most important consideration is the degree to which the torque/speed specification of the motor can be matched to the driven load, after taking the duty cycle into account. The time required to accelerate a system to the desired speed and the power transferred to the system during acceleration are related to the polar moments of inertia (the inertial coefficient I in Table 2.2). Since inertia is given by the expression

$$I = \sum MK^2 = MK^2 = \frac{WK^2}{g},\qquad(2.6)$$

the quantity WK^2 is frequently used in calculating performance factors. M and W are, respectively, the lumped mass and the weight of the rotating element, g is the gravitational constant, and K is the radius of gyration. The power that can be generated in a motor of given size is ultimately limited by the maximum temperature rise that can be tolerated. It depends on winding, hysteresis, and frictional losses, the rate at which energy is delivered to the load, thermal resistance of the frame and mounting, and the type of cooling. In most commercial motors the allowable temperature rise is limited by insulation and lubrication problems to 40°C.

Table 2.3 Instrument Motors (after Mathews)*

Type	Typical Application	Standard Phase	Starting Torque % Full Load	% Regulation	Response	Stall Acceleration	Speed Range % Full Load	Dynamic Braking	Maximum Power (hp)
Induction Motors									
Shaded pole	General purpose fans, blowers	1	100	6	F	L	35–100	Dc	$\frac{1}{6}$
Distributed winding	fans, blowers	1	150	4	G	M	35–100	Dc	$\frac{3}{4}$
Torque motor	pen drives, control	1	200	—	G	M	35–100	Cs	$\frac{3}{4}$
Low inertia servo	pen drives	1, 2	300	40	E	H	0–100	Cs	$\frac{3}{4}$
Synchronous Motors									
Permanent magnet	Chart drives	1	100	—	G	L	—	Inherent	$\frac{1}{2000}$
Reluctance	Chart drives	1	150	—	F	L	—	Dc	$\frac{3}{4}$
Hysteresis	Turntables Capstans	1	100	—	F	L	—	Dc	$\frac{3}{4}$
Polarized	Light choppers Mechanical rectifiers	1	100	—	F	L	—	Dc	$\frac{3}{4}$
Stepper	Low-speed stepper/ servo	1	100	—	E	M	—	Inherent	$\frac{3}{4}$
Dc Motors									
Shunt wound	Adjustable speed drives	—	200	10	F	L	10–100	As	$\frac{3}{4}$
Series wound	High torque loads	—	250	H	G	M	0–100	As	$\frac{3}{4}$
Compound wound	Adjustable speed drives	—	300	25	F	L	10–100	As	$\frac{3}{4}$
Printed circuit	Stepper/servo	—	300	40	E	H	0–100	As	$\frac{3}{4}$

E, excellent; F, fair; G, good; H, high; L, low; M, medium; As, armature shorting; Cs, capacitor shorting; Dc, direct current.

* Copyright, 1968, *Machine Design*, reprinted by permission.

Table 2.4 Motor Selection Guide

Power source
   Volts: Nominal _____   Regulation _____
              Frequency _____   Ripple _____   Harmonic content _____
   Watts: No load _____   Full load _____   Stall _____
   Current: No load _____   Full load _____   Stall _____
   Phase: _____

Motor type: □   dc   □   induction   □   synchronous
                □   reluctance   □   hysteresis   □   permanent magnet
                □   servo   □   other _____

Torque (in ounces):   at _____   rpm   Stall _____   Start _____

Rotation: □   unidirectional   □   reversible
          regulation _____

Duty cycle: □   Intermittent time on _____   □   Continuous
                     Time off _____

Temperature: Ambient _____   °C   Rise _____   °C

Mechanical:
   Frame: □   open   □   enclosed   □   noncooled   □   self-cooled
   Bearings: □   sleeve   □   ball   □   other _____
   Gear reduction _____
   Mounting: □   flange   □   ring   □   other _____
   Connections: □   terminals   □   leads

Life expectancy _____
Special features _____

Maximum speeds of electric motors are limited by bearing friction and wind resistance to some thousands of revolutions per minute. When much higher rotational speeds are needed, the only recourse in the present state of the art is to the use of air or gas as both bearing and prime mover.

Motor–Generator Principles

In addition to selecting electric motors to perform special, though perhaps routine, tasks for which specific designs are called for, the instrument designer is sometimes faced with the problem of using devices at hand. With a knowledge of basic motor-generator principles and properties of electrical machines, it is often possible to adapt existing equipment to different modes of operation. Motors and generators obey the same fundamental laws and in certain cases their functions can be interchanged. Simple devices can be easily constructed or modified to serve as brakes, clutches, indicators, and in a variety of other applications.

The designations and properties of various types of electric motor, such as those listed in Table 2.3, originate in the physical methods employed to convert electrical to mechanical energy. In elementary dc machines the process is governed by the Lorentz force law, which states that a positive point charge q moving with a velocity $\mathbf{v}$ in an electrostatic field of intensity $\mathbf{E}$ and a magnetic induction field of intensity $\mathbf{B}$ is subject to a force

$$\mathbf{F} = q(\mathbf{E} + \mathbf{v} \times \mathbf{B}). \tag{2.7}$$

Although electrostatic forces play an important role in many transducers, useful energy conversion is dependent primarily on magnetic forces, that is, on the second term of (2.7). The magnetic force is in a direction perpendicular to both the velocity and induction field vectors.

If the charge velocity arises from current I flowing in a conducting filament supplied by a battery, for example, the force transmitted to the filament through metallic binding forces on the charge carriers is

$$\mathbf{F} = \int I \, d\mathbf{l} \times \mathbf{B}. \tag{2.8}$$

Here $d\mathbf{l}$ is a vector increment of the current filament and the integral is taken over the length of wire in which the induction exists. The induction field may be supplied by suitably shaped permanent magnets or by electromagnets. The vector cross product implies that only that component of the field $\mathbf{B}$, orthogonal to the current filament, is effective in generating a force.

Figure 2.4a shows an elementary version of a simple motor, frequently called a Faraday generator and the forerunner of the "printed circuit" motor. A current filament of radial length a exists between the axis of rotation and the periphery of the disk in which the electric circuit is completed through a sliding contact. The induction field is assumed to be axial and uniform over the disk. Under these conditions an incremental radial segment Δr at distance r from the axis is subject to a torque $IBr \, \Delta r$. The total torque is

$$T_\theta = \int IBr \, dr = \tfrac{1}{2}IBa^2, \tag{2.9a}$$

and from Table 2.2 the power delivered by magnetic forces is

$$\frac{dW}{dt} = \omega T_\theta = \tfrac{1}{2}I\omega Ba^2. \tag{2.10a}$$

Another arrangement is shown in Fig. 2.4b. A single turn coil supported by a nonmagnetic cylinder of length l and radius a is free to rotate in a uniform magnetic field perpendicularly directed to the axis of rotation. Current supplied through a split ring commutator and fixed brushes maintains the same direction with respect to magnetic flux lines as the rotor coil passes

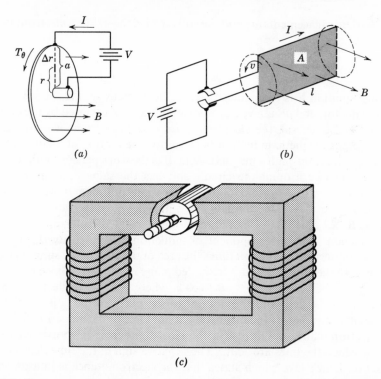

Fig. 2.4 Elementary motor generators: (*a*) the Faraday disk in uniform magnetic field; (*b*) rotating coil with commutator in uniform magnetic field; (*c*) rotating coil with magnetic flux field supplied by a stator coil.

through the field. It represents the precursor of a drum-wound armature machine. The torque at any position is given by

$$T_\theta = 2IBla \sin \theta \qquad (2.9b)$$

and the power by

$$P_{(mag)} = 2i\omega Bla \sin \theta, \qquad (2.10b)$$

where θ is the angle between the normal to the plane of the loop and the direction of the field. Forces on the end segments of the wire are oppositely directed and produce no net torque.

As soon as a conductor begins to move in a way that gives it a component of velocity perpendicular to the magnetic field it is said to "cut" lines of magnetic flux and the charges within it are subject to additional force components. These forces are in a direction opposite to that of the external current supply. The summation of the products of force per unit charge times the charge displacements around the coil is called the induced electromotance ε, where

$$\varepsilon = \oint \mathbf{E} \cdot d\mathbf{l} = \int_S \left[\nabla \mathrm{x} (\mathbf{v} \times \mathbf{B}) - \frac{\partial B}{\partial t} \right] \cdot d\mathbf{S}. \qquad (2.11a)$$

In this equation $\mathbf{E}$ is the induced electric-field intensity, $\mathbf{v}$ is the velocity of the conductor, and $d\mathbf{S}$ is a vector element of the area enclosed by the circulation of $\mathbf{E}$. In general, the electromotance originates from two sources—a time-variant magnetic induction field and/or the motion of a conductor of arbitrary shape through a magnetic field. It is the work per coulomb required to move charge around the circuit and has the same units as potential difference, the volt. For rigid loop configurations it is often more convenient to use the Faraday induction law $\varepsilon = -d\phi/dt$, where the flux of induction $\phi = \int_S B \cdot dS$. The flux of induction is the integrated scalar product of the instantaneous normal component of induction-field intensity through the area circumscribed by the coil times the area of the coil. In the simplified case in Fig. 2.4b the area is that of the shaded plane rectangle A. Since the field is assumed to be constant, $\phi = BA \cos \theta$, where θ is the angle between the direction of the field and the normal to the plane of the coil. As the coil rotates it sweeps across the magnetic lines of force of the induction field, and the electromotance developed in the closed circuit is proportional to the rate at which the lines are "cut." The negative sign of the time derivative is based on Lenz's law, which states that the electromotance is in a direction to oppose the action producing it.

In the machine in Fig. 2.4a the magnetic field is assumed to be uniform over the disk and constant in time so that by Stokes's theorem (2.11a) reduces to

$$\varepsilon = \oint \mathbf{E} \cdot dl = \oint \mathbf{v} \times \mathbf{B} \cdot dl. \qquad (2.11b)$$

The electromotance developed in a radial element Δr of the disk rotor is $vB \, \Delta r = \omega Br \, \Delta r$, and the power supplied by the source when the disk is rotating becomes

$$P_{(\text{source})} = \int I\omega Br \, dr + I^2 R = \tfrac{1}{2} i\omega Ba^2 + I^2 R, \qquad (2.12a)$$

where R is the ohmic resistance of the current filament. The first term is just the mechanical power developed (2.10a).

In a similar fashion, either from the general expression or from Faraday's law, the electric power required by the rotating plane loop of Fig. 2.5 is

$$P_{(\text{source})} = 2I\omega Bla \sin \theta + I^2 R. \qquad (2.12b)$$

Although practical motors designed for dc operation are more complicated than these simple examples, the same general conclusions apply. On the

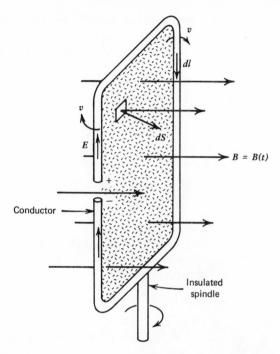

Fig. 2.5 Electromotance in a coil moving in a time-variant magnetic field.

application of voltage V the rotating member speeds up until the power supplied by the electric source is just equal to the sum of the mechanical power it produces plus the Joule losses (i.e., electric energy dissipated as heat in resistive elements). At this point the speed becomes constant, and without a load it is the highest speed at which the motor can run. Only a small current is required:

$$i = \frac{V - \varepsilon}{R}. \tag{2.13}$$

If the machine is mechanically loaded, the speed tends to decrease; a corresponding decrease in electromotance is due to the lower rate at which the rotating coil "cuts" magnetic lines of force. This results in a relatively large increase in current and mechanical output. Hence a variable load has little effect on speed if the resistance in the rotor winding is low.

If the rotor is mechanically driven at a speed such that the induced electromotance is greater than the battery supply voltage, the direction of current flow is reversed and the machine becomes a generator from which electric power can be drawn. The induced current may be used to charge the battery or to power other devices. There is no fundamental difference between simple dc motors and generators and they can be used interchangeably.

Direct-current motors differ chiefly in the means by which the magnetic field is established. Some modern designs employ permanent magnets. Alternatively, the field may be generated by wound stator coils connected in shunt, in series, or in shunt-series combination with the armature supply or connected to a separate power source.

Another important class of interactions occurs when the direction of the magnetic field and the current in the rotating loop vary at the same rate. Figure 2.4c shows a simple machine in which the field is generated by a fixed coil wound on pole pieces that surround the rotor. Current to the latter is supplied through slip rings. It is a fundamental principle of magnetic-field theory that when mechanical work is done by such a system of current loops the instantaneous energy stored in the field also increases. The mechanical and electrical energies are equal and both are supplied by the current sources. Thus the incremental changes in energy ΔW, as the loop rotates through angle $\Delta\theta$, are related by the expression

$$\Delta W(\text{mechanical}) = \Delta W(\text{electrical}) - \Delta W(\text{field}). \qquad (2.14a)$$

In terms of the self-inductances L_s and L_r of the stator and rotor coils, respectively, and the mutual inductance of the system M_{sr}, this equation may be written [13]

$$\Delta W(\text{mechanical}) = \tfrac{1}{2}i_s^2 \, \Delta L_s + \tfrac{1}{2}i_r^2 \, \Delta L_r + i_s i_r \, \Delta M_{sr}, \qquad (2.14b)$$

where i_s and i_r are the currents in the coils. The self-inductance of a coil is numerically equal to the product of the number of turns and the self-generated magnetic flux passing through it, divided by the current flowing through it. Mutual inductance is a measure of the coupling that exists between systems of current-carrying coils. The mutual inductance of a pair of coils is given by the product of the number of turns in the first and the flux passing through it that arises from the second coil divided by the current flowing in the second coil. Both self- and mutual inductances depend on geometry and are affected by the presence of magnetic material that exists in all practical motors.

The torque is given by

$$T_\theta = \frac{\Delta W(\text{mechanical})}{\Delta\theta} = \frac{i_s^2 \, \Delta L_s}{2\Delta\theta} + \frac{i_r^2 \, \Delta L_r}{2\Delta\theta} + i_s i_r \frac{\Delta M_{sr}}{\Delta\theta}. \qquad (2.15)$$

Each of the three terms can produce useful torque, but generally only one term applies in a given machine. With $\theta = \omega t$ the first two reluctance terms represent strictly synchronous operation and give rise to the so-called reluctance motor. The third term is the largest and the one generally exploited in practical designs.

In the structure of Fig. 2.4c the stator and rotor inductances are essentially independent of rotor position. The variation of mutual inductance is approximately linear with angular displacement. As a result higher order harmonics, which produce oscillatory torques, can be generated. They are usually avoided by spacing the windings so that the density of turns varies sinusoidally about the coil axis. In a machine of p coils symmetrically spaced about the axis of rotation (i.e., a p-pole machine) the mutual inductance varies approximately as $\cos(p\theta/2)$ and the synchronous speed is $2\omega/p$ rad/sec, where ω is the angular frequency of the supply.

Most practical motors depend on magnetic material for enhancing the field intensity and on multiturn coils to establish magnitude and direction of the fields. Magnetic torques thus act on sections of magnetic material, or poles, rather than on current loops. The stationary field is usually generated by several poles of number p arranged concentrically around a cylindrical rotor, as shown diagrammatically in Fig. 2.6. The flux paths are completed through the rotor structure, which is also of magnetic material, and, in most motors, through the supporting frame. By compressing rotating coils of the type shown in Fig. 2.4c into slots cut in the armature the mechanical spacing is reduced and the flux density maintained at a high value. There is a number of ways of distributing the armature windings and their connections to multisegment commutators and slip rings. Generally one coil spans $1/p$ of the armature circumference.

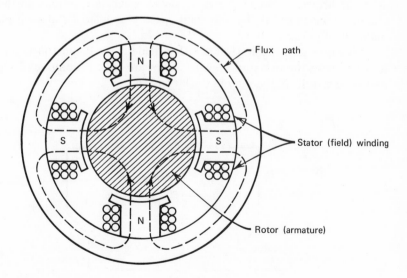

Fig. 2.6 Construction of multipole stator winding.

A complete description of the magnetic-flux fields in any dc motor or generator is complicated by several additional interactions. Current in the armature winding generates a magnetic field, part of which is directly opposed to the stator field and causes demagnetization. It is proportional to the armature current and is compensated for by adding appropriate windings to the field coils. The other component is perpendicular to the direction of field flux and, in motors, results in a concentration of flux in the leading pole tips and a shift in the neutral axis. This effect is also compensated for by suitably placed auxiliary windings. In alternating-current motors, hysteresis effects and eddy currents produce considerable departures from ideal operation considered here.

Direct-Current Motors

SHUNT MOTORS

In shunt-wound motors the field is generated by a high resistance stator winding consisting of a large number of turns. It is connected in parallel with the armature, as shown in Fig. 2.7. At stand still connections may be interchanged for reverse rotation. Since the magnetic flux is essentially independent of the armature current, the speed-versus-torque characteristic is nearly flat, dropping only slightly with increasing torque. Nearly all of the power is applied through the armature and torque is linear with armature current. A speed change of approximately 50% above and below rated speed can be obtained by resistance control of current [14]. Resistance in series with the armature circuit decreases speed, whereas resistance in the field circuit increases speed. The constant speed characteristic at each point is maintained [15], however.

To obtain higher starting torques a few field turns are sometimes connected in series with the armature. Such motors are called "compound motors" and are generally found only in the larger sizes.

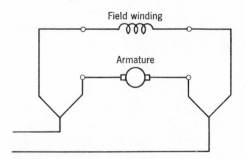

Fig. 2.7   Connection of a shunt wound dc motor.

SERIES MOTORS

Series motors are wound with a smaller number of stator turns which are connected in series with the armature. The flux field thus varies directly with the armature current and torque varies quadratically with current [14]. As in any dc motor, the induced electromotance is low on starting so that the initial current is high and torque is at maximum. As the motor speeds up current and flux drop and the speed increases to a value limited by loading and friction. Speed regulation is generally poor. In large motors rheostats are generally used to limit the starting current. Small motors with light loading attain speed rapidly, however, and the starting rheostat is not necessary.

PERMANENT-MAGNET MOTORS

With the development of new magnetic materials, particularly the low-cost ceramics, dc motors that employ permanent magnets as field sources have become competitive with wound stator types [15]. The elimination of stator windings reduces power input and internal heating and leads to higher efficiency and simpler construction. Since ceramics are not good conductors, eddy current losses are negligible. Speed/torque characteristics are similar to those of shunt motors.

In a newly introduced type of dc motor, called "brushless," commutator problems are eliminated by the use of a permanent magnet rotor. A rotating magnetic field is generated by sequentially switching the current in the windings of a multicoil stator through a transistorized control circuit. Proper sequencing is maintained by means of an optical system consisting of a solid-state light source, rotor-mounted shutter, and photodetector. Through solid-state switching regulated speeds to several thousand revolutions per second are attainable.

Alternating-Current Motors

INDUCTION MOTORS

Most ac motors are of the induction type, so called because currents in the rotor are induced by transformer action from the magnetically coupled field winding. Although wound rotors are sometimes employed, "squirrel-cage" construction is more usual [16]. A set of steel disk-shaped laminations, stacked to form a cylinder coaxial with the motor shaft, is held together by copper bars. The bars are shorted together at both ends of the cylinder and carry the currents induced by alternating currents in the stator winding. The stator fields are stationary in position, but since they alternate in polarity the pulsating flux fields can be considered the equivalent of two oppositely rotating fields of half magnitude. The secondary flux fields generated in the rotor interact with the primary fields to produce a torque on the rotor once

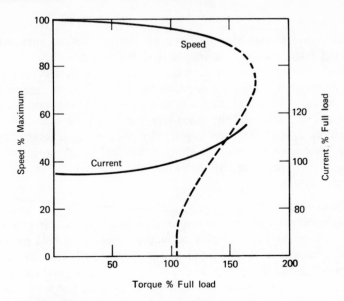

Fig. 2.8   Characteristics of a typical squirrel cage induction motor.

it has been set in motion. Maximum speed is usually somewhat less than synchronous speed. The difference between the two, called the slip speed, is essentially that speed at which just enough torque is produced to overcome the load. Induction motors are reliable and inexpensive but suffer from poor speed control, low starting torque, and high starting current. Typical performance curves are shown in Fig. 2.8.

Simple, single-phase windings, because they produce equal thrusts in opposite directions, do not normally provide self-starting. However, most available motors incorporate an auxiliary stator winding, the current in which is somewhat out of phase with that in the main winding. The effect is to produce a rotating magnetic field that provides sufficient torque to initiate starting. In one version, the split-phase type, the auxiliary winding is disconnected by means of a centrifugal switch after the motor has attained near operating speed.

In so-called capacitor motors a capacitor in series with one winding provides a phase shift, or quadrature excitation. Depending on design, the capacitor may be left in the circuit permanently, completely disconnected as in the split-phase arrangement or reduced to a lower value by removing from the circuit one or more of a parallel set. Starting torques are generally higher than in split-phase operation.

Shaded-pole construction is also used frequently in small-size motors. The auxiliary winding consists of a piece of copper mounted to encircle a portion of a pole face and form what is called a salient pole. Because of induced currents in the short circuit, flux in the encircled portion lags the primary pole field and results in an effective rotation of the field.

REPULSION MOTORS

Repulsion motors represent special designs of the basic dc commutator motor for ac operation. The armature winding is short circuited through the commutator and brushes and power is supplied to the armature by induction, the amount depending on the commutator-brush position. In some versions, referred to as repulsion-induction motors, a centrifugal switch is employed to short circuit the commutator segments and thus converting it to an induction motor at the appropriate speed. It combines the high starting torque of the series motor and the constant-speed characteristic of the induction motor.

SYNCHRONOUS MOTORS

Modern, self-starting synchronous motors are generally of the reluctance or the hysteresis type. Reluctance is a property of magnetic-field paths that corresponds to resistance in electrical circuits. In Fig. 2.6, for example, the dotted lines indicate the direction of magnetic lines of force. Each line is continuous through a closed magnetic circuit consisting of two pole pieces, a portion of the rotor, and two air gaps. Neglecting fringe effects, each section of the path is characterized by a quantity called reluctance, the value of which is given by the length of the section, divided by the product of the cross-sectional area of the path and the magnetic permeability of that section. Reluctances in series are additive and, since the permeability of air is much less than that of iron, any gap in the magnetic structure causes a considerable reduction in the magnetic induction field strength.

One version of the reluctance motor employs a stator winding similar to that of an induction motor and a modified squirrel-cage rotor. The rotor is notched parallel to the axis of rotation and the sections between notches are called salient poles. Magnetization is greatest in the region of the salient poles because of the small air gap between them and the stator poles. The motor operates as an induction motor in starting and accelerating, but at a critical speed the salient poles of the rotor "lock" onto the rotating field produced by the stator and the speed becomes synchronous. One disadvantage of this type is the hunting characteristic of the salient pole rotor. Such motors will operate at less than synchronous speed if overloaded but with poor regulation and low efficiency.

The hysteresis motor is a relatively new type that exploits magnetic hysteresis in one or more rings of hard magnetic material mounted on a non-magnetic arbor. Cylindrical cast alloy rotors are also used. Hysteresis in magnetic materials refers to the failure, usually nonlinear, of the induction-field intensity to follow a change in the magnetizing field strength H. This

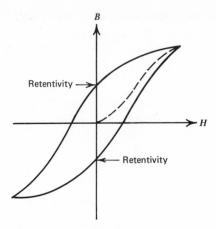

Fig. 2.9 Typical *B-H* magnetization curve of moderately hard iron.

effect is indicated by *B-H* magnetization curves of the type shown in Fig. 2.9. In motors the magnetizing field *H* is produced by current flowing in the stator windings and is proportional to the current and the number of turns in each coil. As the magnetizing field is reduced to zero (i.e., on each half-cycle of alternating current), the rotor tends to remain partially magnetized because the induction is greater than zero. The magnitude of the induction at this point is called the remanance or retentivity. It depends on the type and history of the material. Hard steel has a greater retentivity than soft iron and steel of moderate hardness is used for rotors. In typical hysteresis motors the magnetizing field is provided by stator windings of the split phase or the capacitor type. Thus, since the rotor tends to retain its direction of magnetization as the rotating stator field slips past, the axis of induced magnetization lags the axis of the stator field. The resulting torque causes the rotor to accelerate until it pulls into synchronism with the stator field. At synchronous speed the hysteresis loss theoretically decreases to zero. Because there are no salient poles, noise and hunting are reduced. In some recent designs the geometrical relationship of stator and rotor are inverted without changing their functions. Since the rotor moment of inertia is greater than in conventional design, "flutter" is reduced even further.

Universal Motors

The universal motor is basically a dc series motor with a field-to-armature winding ratio designed for operation on either alternating or direct current [17]. Since currents in the two coils are simultaneously reversed on each half-cycle of supply voltage, the direction of torque remains unchanged throughout each cycle. However, the torque pulsates between zero and approximately twice average value. The winding inductances cause a drop in available voltage so that speed drops as the excitation frequency is increased.

Universal motors are relatively inexpensive; they have the highest power to weight ratio and operate at higher speeds than any other ac motor. Although unloaded speeds to 10,000 rpm and above are common, speed is sensitive to voltage changes and pole flux. As brushes pass over the commutator bars, induced circulating currents that arise in short-circuited coils produce a field tending to reduce the primary field. Arcing reduces commutator and brush life and is also a serious source of radio noise interference.

Servo Devices

SERVO AND CONTROL MOTORS

Servo motors constitute a class of reversible motors specifically designed for mechanically controlling the variable parameter of a system in response to an electrical signal [18]. A block diagram of a simple mechanical servo system is shown in Fig. 2.10. The purpose of this system is to drive an output shaft, usually loaded, so that its angular position corresponds at all times to that of the input shaft. This is accomplished through the "feedback" loop which consists of an error-detecting device and a controller. The output and input shaft positions are compared in the error detector and their difference, or error, is then converted to an electrical signal whose phase and amplitude correspond, respectively, to the direction and degree of error. In the controller the error signal is amplified and used to drive the servo motor in a direction that will reduce the error to zero. Instrument servo mechanisms employ complicated types of motion and more elaborate electromechanical devices than illustrated here, but the basic principles are the same. The required motions are generally limited but inertial and frictional loads may be large so that high torques at low speeds are required. To obtain rapid response

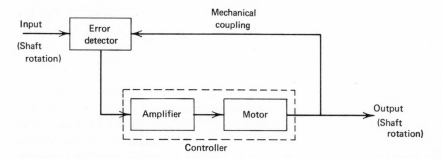

Fig. 2.10   Block diagram of simple mechanical servo system.

with good positional accuracy rotors of low inertia (i.e., small diameter) are employed.

In the design of automatic control systems, especially those of the closed-loop or feedback type, the characteristics of the control motor are specified in terms of over-all system performance. Among several figures of merit commonly used to define motor performance two are of particular importance. First, the theoretical stall acceleration, or torque to inertia ratio, is a measure of the degree to which the motor can follow rapid variations of the input control signal. The consideration includes the maximum duration of stall and the percentage of time the motor is stalled at rated voltage, or duty cycle. On an intermittent basis the stall torque can exceed the nominal rating by many times, provided high peak currents can be handled. This is largely a matter of power dissipation. Second, the time constant is the time required for the motor to attain 63.2% of final speed. It is also defined as the ratio of motor inertia to internal damping. The latter, which is theoretically given by the ratio of stall torque to no-load speed, is a measure of the reduction in torque with increasing speed. Some damping is usually required for stability and in certain motors it is specified in terms of the resistance of the rotor. Viscous and inertial damping mechanisms are also frequently used [19].

Because of the simplicity of the small-diameter squirrel-cage rotor, the two-phase induction type of motor is frequently used in a servo controller in low power applications. Power to the control winding is supplied from an amplifier of low output impedance, as shown in Fig. 2.11a. The phase and voltage depend on the electrical control signal and determine the direction and speed of the output shaft. The other, or main field, winding is operated at rated voltage and is connected through a series capacitor to provide quadrature excitation. In addition, because of inductive reactance, it is generally necessary to "tune" the winding for unity power factor with a shunt capacitor. Correct phase shift may also be achieved directly in the amplifier. This technique has the advantage of better motor damping, but phase variations may develop from impedance variations in the amplifier. The shape of the speed/torque characteristic depends primarily on the rotor resistance. Aluminum rotors have reasonably high resistance, which provides damping and prevents single phasing, a condition in which the motor runs in the absence of a control field.

Direct-current motors inherently provide the negative speed/torque characteristic considered desirable for control motors. For light duty loads two types are frequently employed. In the field controlled arrangement (Fig. 2.11b) the armature is supplied by a constant dc voltage. The field winding is center-tapped to operate from the push-pull output of a direct coupled amplifier. It drives in either direction, depending on which half of the winding

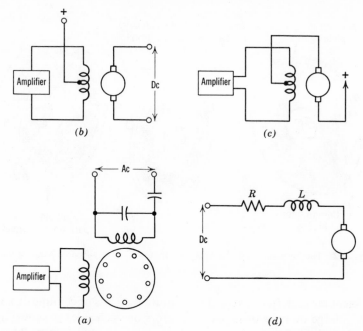

Fig. 2.11   Connections of control motors: (*a*) two-phase ac servo motor; (*b*) field-controlled dc servo motor; (*c*) split field, series-wound universal motor; (*d*) dc moving coil and "printed circuit" motor.

is excited. The split-field, series-wound universal motor, connected as shown in Fig. 2.11*c*, is capable of providing high starting torques. Although dc servo motors suffer from brush noise and arcing, they can deliver several times the power of an ac motor of comparable size. In combination with high power solid-state amplifiers high efficiencies may be obtained.

TORQUE MOTORS

The term "torquer" is used to describe a class of servo actuators designed for producing large forces over short distances or small rotations. The torque is constant and independent of speed. Some recently developed "moving-coil" d-c motors capable of producing extremely high stall torque-to-inertia ratios fall within this category. Since the load can be driven directly without gears, backlash errors are absent. The resulting coupling stiffness leads to a high mechanical resonance frequency necessary for fast response and high resolution. Such features are attractive for servo applications as well as for a wide variety of devices calling for intermittent motion.

Basically the moving-coil motor consists of a wound armature of special design moving in a high-intensity magnetic field produced by a multipole

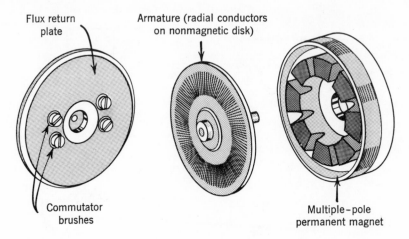

Flux return plate

Armature (radial conductors on nonmagnetic disk)

Commutator brushes

Multiple-pole permanent magnet

Fig. 2.12   The "printed circuit" moving-coil motor (Courtesy Printed Motors, Inc.).

permanent magnet. In one type the armature is a glass or ceramic disk which carries a large number of radial conductors on each side, as shown in Fig. 2.12. Made by printed circuit techniques, or more recently by stamping, corresponding conductors on opposite faces are connected at inner and outer extremes. An equivalent multipole wave winding is achieved by curving the two ends of the conductors in opposite directions. Commutator brushes are supported in an iron flux return plate and bear directly on the bare conductors near the center of rotation.

In another configuration conductors are carried on a hollow nonmagnetic cylinder or "cup" supported at one end and integral with the output shaft. The structure resembles a conventional dc motor in which the armature iron required for flux return remains fixed inside the rotating coil. Because of the smaller diameter, inertia is lower than that of the disk.

Moving-coil motors offer several advantages in many applications. They are essentially low-voltage, high-current machines ideally suited to solid-state drive and control. The electrical time constant is given by the ratio of armature inductance to resistance when driven from a source of near zero impedance. The resistance shown schematically in Fig. 2.11d includes both the conductor and commutator resistance. Since there is no moving iron in the circuit, the inductance and time constant are both very low and commutator arcing is minimal. Torque is directly proportional to current over wide ranges of speed and is limited primarily by duty factor and temperature rise. Cooling by thermal conduction in the integral shaft assembly, however, and the absence of insulation permit relatively high temperature operation. The mechanical time constant, defined as the ratio of armature inertia to damping coefficient, is much shorter than in conventional motors. Eddy-current damping is frequently specified in terms of the resistivity of the armature supporting material. Because there is no rotating iron, the drive is smooth and preferred armature positions are eliminated.

Although torque motors are applicable to start-stop operation, a variety of stepping motors designed for digital positioning systems is also available [20, 21]. One form of so-called "stepper" is a brushless dc motor in which the shaft is rotated through a fixed number of stable incremental steps in each revolution. The stator consists of an even number of wound poles arranged in a structure similar to that in Fig. 2.6. In permanent magnet types the rotor is permanently polarized, usually with several poles, and aligns in the stator field according to which coils are energized. When the stator coils are not energized, the rotor slips into a position where the air gap between stator and rotor poles is a minimum. This amounts to a magnetic detent, or latching action. Variable reluctance type steppers employ rotors of low retentivity. The mechanical construction is such that for a given combination of energized stator coils the rotor can take only one stable position. Higher stepping rates and more steps per revolution can be obtained than with the permanent magnet type. Some types are unidirectional, whereas others run in either direction under a programmed pulse drive. If, however, the pulse rate exceeds the maximum step response in either case the motor slews out of control.

SYNCHRO SYSTEMS

The term "synchro" describes one group of a larger class of motorlike device known generically as rotary inductors, which are widely used in matched pairs to translate angular position to electrical voltages and to convert electrical signals to low torque angular displacements for remote indication and control [22].

The elementary generator (often called a transmitter) consists of a two-pole, single-phase, rotatable primary winding and a three-phase secondary wound on a slotted stator of magnetic material. When the rotor is connected to an ac supply line of constant frequency and amplitude (typically 110 V, 60 ~ or 28 V, 400 ~), a set of three alternating voltages is induced in the secondary windings by transformer action. The respective phases and amplitudes uniquely identify the angular position of the rotor. If the rotor is turned at a constant rate, the three stator voltages, either in phase or in phase opposition with the rotor voltage, are sinusoidally modulated at the rotation frequency.

The synchro motor (frequently called a receiver) is functionally the counterpart of the synchro generator. When voltages produced by the generator are applied to the motor and both rotors are connected to the same line

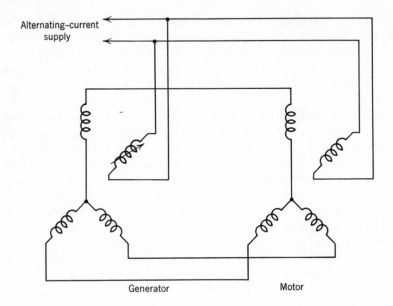

Alternating–current
supply

Generator

Motor

Fig. 2.13   Connection of a three-phase synchro generator and motor.

voltage, as shown in Fig. 2.13, the output shaft of the motor is subjected to a torque. This persists until the relative angular orientation of rotor and stator is the same in the two devices. Construction of the motor is essentially the same as that of the generator to which it is matched. However, to reduce the tendency to overshoot and oscillate with rapid variations of speed, the motor is usually provided with some integral form of mechanical damping. The output torque is low and only very light loads such as indicators can be driven with any degree of accuracy. When large torques are required, the usual practice is to use a control transformer and a servo motor.

Although it is not a true mechanical power device, the synchro-control transformer is included in this category for completeness. It is similar in construction to the simple generator from which its three-phase stator is excited. The single-phase rotor output voltage indicates the angular deviation of the generator rotor from a reference position. Since it is designed for connection to a high impedance, such as a servo amplifier, current flow is negligible and no significant torque is developed.

Differential synchros are used to sense the algebraic difference between two angular positions, as indicated in the block diagram of Fig. 2.14. Construction is substantially the same as in the corresponding simple synchro units except that both rotors and stators have three-phase, distributed windings. The stator of a differential generator is usually excited by the

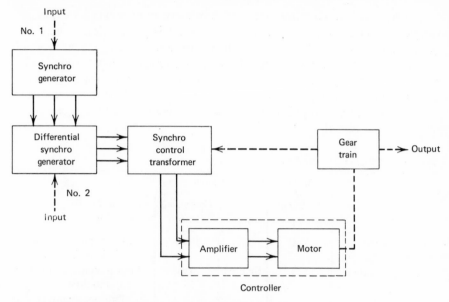

Fig. 2.14 Block diagram of a simple synchro system.

output of a simple synchro generator which may be remotely located. Three voltages appear on the rotor, the phases and amplitudes of which identify the angular position of the remote shaft in relation to that of the local shaft. A differential synchro motor operates from two generators of either type. Thus the angular displacement of the rotor shaft is determined by the algebraic sum of the generator shaft displacements.

Electromagnetic Clutches and Brakes

In modern processing and control systems many situations develop in which direct control of the available source of mechanical power is either not feasible or the degree of control is inadequate. Typical examples include rapid start-stop and reversing operations in tape drives, constant torque loading that occurs in tensioning devices, and variable torque loading that occurs in agitators and centrifugal devices. In such cases an additional degree of control or even complete control can often be obtained by coupling the driven shaft to the prime source through a rotary clutch or brake; for instance, a small, high-speed motor equipped with a large flywheel (i.e., of high inertia) coupled through a suitable clutch can provide large intermittent torques and high accelerations. A clutch needs only to transmit the power applied to it, and the control power required is generally considerably less than that transmitted. The effective power amplification is a useful feature in some types of servomechanism.

As with motors, the important figures of merit in choosing a clutch are torque, inertia, response time, and permissible heat dissipation. When the system includes speed reductions, there appears to be some economic justification for using a small clutch at the higher speed, low-torque shaft. However, increased bearing wear and dissipation, which is proportional to the square of the slip speed, are problems to consider. The latter aspect can be severe in braking applications in which the entire kinetic energy of the driven shaft is absorbed.

Table 2.5   Clutches and Brakes

| | Brake | Clutch | | |
| | Torque at | | Continuous | Typical |
Type	Zero Speed	Slip	Control	Applications
Friction drive	Yes	Poor	Poor	Fail-safe tape transport drives and brakes
Magnetic particle	Yes	Limited	Yes	Film and tape transport capstan drives, vibrators, agitators
Hysteresis	Yes	No	Yes	Variable speed drives
Eddy current	No	Yes	Yes	Servos, oscillation dampers

Some of the more common types of clutch and brake suitable for instrument applications are listed in Table 2.5. Among them, the friction disk is is one of the simplest and most adaptable. As the name implies, it consists of two disks, one of steel and the other usually cork-faced, whose separation is controlled by direct electric solenoid action on one shaft, as indicated in the sketch of Fig. 2.15a. Springs are employed to disengage the disks on removal of control power or conversely to maintain contact in the absence of control. Some models are available for hydraulic or air operation. The latter mode provides faster response and higher rates than either hydraulic or electric control. Large power amplifications are possible but, because of the variability of the surfaces, smooth slip and continuous control with any degree of precision are difficult to achieve. Their chief use is in noncritical and on-off applications.

The operation of magnetic particle devices depends on the high shear strength that exists in a chainlike structure of iron particles under the influence of a magnetic field. Typically, the driving shaft is integrally attached to a drum of magnetic material which rotates within a concentric cylinder attached to the driven shaft as shown in Fig. 2.15b. The space between, called the working gap, is loosely filled with a ferromagnetic powder suspended

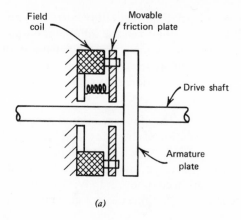

(a)

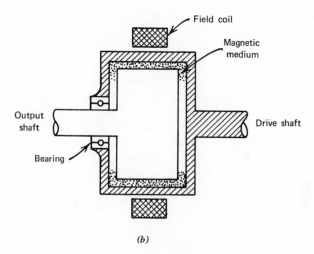

(b)

Fig. 2.15 Typical brake/clutches: (a) electromagnetic friction; (b) magnetic particle.

either in oil or in a dry lubricant. The whole assembly is enclosed in a stator member which contains a stationary field or control coil concentric with the axis of rotation. Slip between the rotating members is smooth and depends on the current in the dc control winding. Transmitted torque, which varies in an approximately linear manner with control current, is independent of speed.

Hysteresis and eddy-current clutches (and brakes) utilize the same principles as electric motors. Except for bearings and slip-ring brushes, there is no mechanical contact between input and output shafts. Torque can be continuously regulated over wide ranges with low control power. The hysteresis type can be driven synchronously or under continuous slip with almost no torque variation. The eddy-current type is speed-sensitive. It requires relative motion between the input and output members to develop a torque that varies approximately as the square of the control current and directly as the speed difference. When built with a permanent magnet, it is frequently used as an oscillation damper.

Air Motors

Even this brief discussion of rotary motion generators would not be complete without some mention of air motors and bearings. Air-driven centrifuges with conventional bearings, which are available in most laboratories, operate at rates up to 500 rps. At the higher speed often used for optical scanning, chopping, and high-speed photography, for example, highly specialized techniques are involved. Turbine designs generally follow those given originally by Beams [23]. However, ordinary bearings develop excessive friction and gas bearings suffer from self-excited instability; that is, the shaft tends to whirl off axis with a frequency that depends on geometry and the spring constant of the gas [24]. Amplitudes build up until the shaft actually makes contact with the bearing sleeve. Lubricating films break down when the linear relative velocity between shaft and bearing approaches 200 fps. In addition, vibration due to imperfect balance causes loading pressures that exceed those allowable for lubricants. High bearing speeds can be attained if oil is supplied under adequate pressure and if the bearing length is limited to a dimension less than the shaft diameter [25]. The bearing is mounted so that it can vibrate longitudinally with the shaft. A rubber "O" ring provides sufficient damping to limit the amplitude.

In applications in which extremely low torques are adequate, as in small-diameter optical chopping wheels, air-driven and supported dental drills can be used at chopping frequencies to 6 kHz [26]. Running without lubricant over periods of hours, stability within 0.5% has been attained. Top speed is limited by aerodynamic drag on the rotor.

Generation of Straight-Line Motion Solenoids

There are relatively few simple "off-the-shelf" devices that can directly generate straight-line motion of any appreciable amplitude. Ironclad electromagnets and solenoids with movable plungers are capable of producing large attractive forces and are available in a wide array of sizes. However, the displacements are generally small and the force/speed as well as force/displacement characteristics are highly nonlinear [27]. When equipped with a return spring, they are useful for on-off, limit, and position control. Low-power versions form the basis of conventional relay actuators.

A large portion of the force exerted on a solenoid plunger is derived from magnetic flux that leaks radially across the coil through the plunger. Flux paths produced by direct current in a long solenoid with the plunger partly

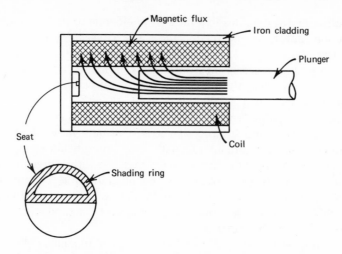

Fig. 2.16   Flux paths in a long solenoid with magnetic cladding.

inserted are somewhat as shown in Fig. 2.16. The net force is a highly complicated function of geometry, position of plunger, and fringing flux field. It is proportional to the product of cross-sectional area and ampere turns and inversely proportional to the length. When the length can be accommodated (i.e., up to a fraction of a meter), relatively large motions can be obtained. The force is small but reasonably constant over the mid-region of the stroke. To enhance the force at the end of the motion, particularly in short-stroke solenoids, the leading end of the plunger is usually tapered. The increased force (called the sealing pull) can cause considerable shock. In small solenoids it is partly absorbed by the return spring.

Solenoids designed for ac operation require laminated structures to reduce eddy-current losses and the equivalent of a shaded pole on the seat to prevent chatter at the end of the stroke. The shaded pole consists of a copper band imbedded in and encircling a portion of the plunger stop somewhat as illustrated in Fig. 2.16. It has the effect of producing a time lag in the magnetic field as the coil current passes through zero twice each cycle. Thus the field in the gap between plunger and stop remains at a reasonably high level throughout each cycle. Because the inductance is low when the plunger is partly withdrawn at the beginning of the stroke, "inrush" currents are high. The effect is to restrict the ac volt-ampere ratings unless auxiliary circuits are provided.

Linear Motors

Many of the drawbacks inherent in solenoids have been overcome by relatively recent innovations in motor design. As the name implies, the linear induction motor operates in a manner analogous to that of a squirrel-cage induction motor. In one version the stator consists of a series of parallel coils arranged along a cylinder, individually separated by spacers of magnetic material and enclosed in an iron housing. With the coils wired in proper sequence to an ac supply, a magnetic field is caused to travel down the axis of the cylinder much as the stator field rotates in an induction motor. Magnetic flux paths are completed through the iron core of a rod-shaped armature free to move along the axis. Currents induced in the copper cladding of the armature interact with the primary field to produce an axial force. The motor operates at essentially high slip with a force that is uniform throughout the stroke. Motion is reversible and limited in amplitude only by mechanical considerations. A similar device has been used as a foil-feed mechanism in which the armature is replaced by a conducting foil. Speeds up to 60 fps have been claimed.

The same basic principle has also been applied to a linear electromagnetic brake [28]. With dc currents in adjacent coils flowing in opposite directions, periodic fields with strong radial components are created along the cylinder axis. The conducting tubular part of the moving element can be considered as a series of short-circuited rings. As in a motor, induced currents react with the fields to produce a force but in a direction opposing motion.

Another version of the linear motor has been applied to a pen recorder [29]. The armature, which is magnetically supported on a three-point ball-bearing suspension carries a set of two-phase windings. The stator in this case consists of a series of short-circuited bars much like the rotor of a conventional two-phase motor. Because there is no gearing, backlash is eliminated.

Mechanical Mechanisms

Innumerable mechanisms have been developed, particularly in the machine-tool industry, for converting the rotary motion of a motor shaft to straight-line motion [30]. These mechanisms include cam followers, bar linkages, slider-cranks, and various types of yoke. All are reciprocating in nature and are generally characterized by limited linearity and amplitude. Some are also subject to shock produced by large decelerating forces. A split nut driven on a precision lead screw and restrained from rotating with the screw is one of the better methods of converting rotary to linear motion in which low speeds are adequate [31]. For light-duty instruments in which power transfer is not a consideration friction and rack and pinion drives are often useful. Both are limited in precision, the former because of backlash and the latter because of slippage. Pulley-driven belts or wires, similar to those used in radio dials, also fall within this category [32]. The timing belt, which consists of a flat belt with a series of evenly spaced teeth on the inside circumference, offers some advantages. It does not slip, backlash is minimal, and noise is low. Special pulleys are required, however.

Air-thrust bearings are capable of extremely precise motions over limited ranges. One device that has been described employs a small ball floating in a pressurized air bearing [33]. Thrust is transmitted through the ball to a smooth-faced member against which it rests. Frictionless movements accurate to 10^{-6} in. over a range of 10^{-3} in. are obtained by varying the air pressure.

Generation of Vibrational Motion

In the majority of cases vibrational motion constitutes a form of energy that is undesirable in a measuring or control instrument. There are some notable exceptions, however, chiefly in optical [34] and electrical choppers and vibrating electrometers, in which low amplitude vibrational motion can be employed to advantage. Even in these cases considerable care is sometimes required to prevent the transmission of energy to other sensitive components. Simple pendulums, violin strings, and tuning forks represent some of the oldest examples of vibrational devices. Acoustic energy is inseparably related to vibration but is more conveniently treated as a separate phenomenon in Chapter V.

Vibration implies periodicity which in mechanical systems can occur only if a force exists that tends to restore a displaced mass to some equilibrium position. On a macroscopic scale mechanical restoring forces are built up from energy stored in compliant members under strain—helical coils, flat leafs, spirals, torsion bars, and variations on each of these. One of the more common design functions of a spring is to give return action to a unidirectional device. In a simple slow-speed cam mechanism, for example, a spring may be used to keep the follower in contact with the cam surface. At high speeds, however, and especially with cams of high eccentricity, resonance becomes important. The spring and its associated mass form a mechanically resonant circuit, and, if the system is lightly damped, it can be shocked into resonant vibrations of large amplitude. To avoid unduly large out-of-phase forces and contact bounce the spring system must be suitably tuned by adjusting the spring constant or the driven mass.

From the standpoint of stability and power consumption mechanical oscillators for use in instrument transducers are usually operated at or near resonance. Two approaches may be taken in designing a resonant spring system. The first makes use of the lumped-parameter equivalent circuit in Fig. 2.3, which is generally valid at low frequencies. In this case it is assumed that the mass of the compliant member is negligible or can be lumped with the driven mass. In the absence of damping solution of the equation of motion for a system with one degree of freedom yields the fundamental vibration

Table 2.6 Typical Mechanical Vibrators

Model		Equation of Motion	Fundamental Angular Frequency
Uniformly loaded cord T: tension m: mass/unit length		$T\dfrac{\partial^2 z}{\partial x^2} - m\dfrac{\partial^2 z}{\partial t^2} = 0$	$\omega_1 = \left(\dfrac{\pi}{l}\right)\left(\dfrac{T}{m}\right)^{1/2}$
Uniform circular membrane T: radial tension m: mass/unit area	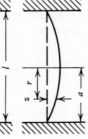	$T\dfrac{1}{r}\dfrac{\partial}{\partial r}\left(r\dfrac{\partial z}{\partial r}\right) - m\dfrac{\partial^2 z}{\partial t^2} = 0$	$\omega_1 = \left(\dfrac{2.4}{a}\right)\left(\dfrac{T}{m}\right)^{1/2}$
Uniformly loaded cantilever Y: Youngs modulus I: cross section moment of inertia m: mass/unit length	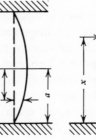	$YI\dfrac{\partial^4 z}{\partial x^4} + m\dfrac{\partial^2 z}{\partial t^2} = 0$	$\omega_1 = \left(\dfrac{3.52}{l^2}\right)\left(\dfrac{YI}{m}\right)^{1/2}$
Cantilever with concentrated load Y: Youngs modulus I: cross section moment of inertia M: mass	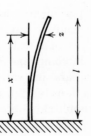	$YI\left(\dfrac{\partial^3 z}{\partial x^3}\right)_{x=l} - M\left(\dfrac{\partial^2 z}{\partial t^2}\right)_{x=l} = 0,$ $M \gg ml$	$\omega_1 = \left(\dfrac{3YI}{l^3 M}\right)^{1/2}$

frequency

$$\omega_0 = \left(\frac{k}{M}\right)^{\frac{1}{2}} \text{rad/sec,} \tag{2.16}$$

where M is the vibrating mass and $k = 1/C_M$ is the spring constant. From the solution of the analogous electrical circuit the displacement of a lumped mass under the action of a sinusoidal driving force of angular frequency ω and amplitude f_0 is given by the sum of (a) an exponentially damped free-vibration term of frequency somewhat less than the natural resonant frequency and (b) a steady-state term. Using the definition of critical damping resistance $R_C = 2\sqrt{kM}$, the second term becomes [35]

$$x = \frac{f_0}{k}\left\{\frac{\cos(\omega t - \theta)}{\{[1 - (\omega^2/\omega_0^2)]^2 + [2(R_M/R_C)(\omega/\omega_0)]^2\}^{\frac{1}{2}}}\right\}, \tag{2.17}$$

where, again from electrical circuit theory, the phase angle $\theta = \tan^{-1} R_M\omega/(k - M\omega^2)$. It is evident that the amplitude of motion becomes infinite when $\omega = \omega_0$ and $R_M = 0$. Invariably there is sufficient residual damping resistance so that this situation cannot develop.

When the mass and the compliant coefficient are distributed through the spring member, a second approach is used for design calculations. Basically it amounts to solving the wave equation, taking into account internal stresses and shear forces. Methods for calculating deflections and resonant frequencies are given in works on the theory of structures and applied mathematics [10]. Some results for typical structures are given in Table 2.6. The spring constants are functions of geometry (length l and moment of inertia about the axis of bending I) and material used in fabrication (Young's modulus Y). Cantilever construction is frequently used in switching and chopping devices. The double cantilever in which the free ends of two vibrating reeds are joined by a rigid member is a convenient method for generating nearly straight-line oscillatory motion. It may be driven magnetically, as indicated in Fig. 2.17, or mechanically with a crank at amplitudes in the neighborhood of 1 cm, depending on the frequency required. Efficiency is high, provided the mechanical circuit is tuned to the drive frequency. Structural members in torsion can also be driven electromagnetically [36].

Descriptions of various types of vibrating mechanisms used in transducers are found in trade journals, and only two are mentioned here to illustrate principles of operation; for example, tuning-fork resonators are available for use as low frequency sources and filters. The fork, a variable reluctance pickup coil, and an electromagnetic drive are incorporated in a closed-loop circuit. Random circuit noise in the drive coil causes the fork to vibrate with low amplitude at its resonant frequency. The signal is detected by the pickup, externally amplified, and fed back to the drive coil. With sufficient gain the

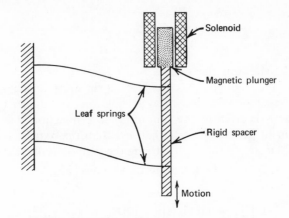

Fig. 2.17 Magnetically driven double cantilever.

action is regenerative and vibrations are sustained at a predetermined amplitude. With temperature compensation accuracies of $\pm 0.01\%$ and better are obtained.

Another more recent device that depends on compliant components is shown in Fig. 2.18. It consists basically of an S-shaped band of preformed spring metal, constrained between two guides, and a pair of rollers that is free to move [37]. The band is held under tension to ensure a tight wrap around the rollers. Since the band and the rollers move at the same speed, there is no slip and almost no friction. Each half of the S tends to unwind,

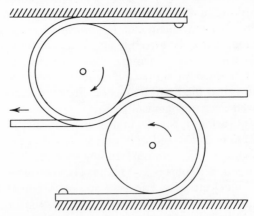

Fig. 2.18 Geometry of a frictionless mechanical mechanism (after Wilkes). (Copyright, 1968, American Society of Mechanical Engineers.)

but in the absence of an external force the balanced spring forces result in an equilibrium position. By suitable design of the spring band, that is, by tapering its width and/or thickness, a variety of force-deflection characteristics can be obtained. Under certain conditions the compliance coefficient (spring constant) can take on negative values, a situation corresponding to positive feedback in an electronic amplifier. Proposed uses include electrical switching, recording, speed and torque changes, sequencing operations, clutching, braking, and viscoelastic damping.

4 PHYSICAL LAYOUT

Figures 1.1 through 1.6 (Chapter I) illustrate the use of block diagrams in the design of a typical laboratory instrument. The blocks, which may represent single components, subassemblies, or even self-contained units, are laid out according to function with signal paths shown by the most direct routing. In a practical instrument the requirements of operational accessibility and, to a greater or lesser extent, isolation from ambient interference impose additional constraints on the physical arrangement and the interconnections of the component parts. The effects of interference are particularly important but usually difficult to predict. Unless adequate precautions are taken in parts layout, however, disturbances of mechanical, thermal, or electromagnetic origin may introduce unwanted signals and couplings between functional components that can seriously affect reliability.

Rack and Enclosure Structures

Aside from purely aesthetic and housekeeping considerations, the chief purpose of an instrument enclosure is to provide an integral framework for mounting the components and in which operating convenience and safety are compatible with satisfactory performance. The choice of a structure is largely a matter of personal preference and depends on the size and weight of the equipment, its purpose, heat dissipation, and the environment in which it is to operate.

For temporary hookups of electronic equipment in preliminary design and experimental stages the standard EIA (Electronic Industries Association) open rack is useful. It consists of a pair of vertical channels, usually of cold rolled steel, attached by bolted gussets to a self-supporting base. Floor-mounted racks stand 76 in. high but shorter units are available for bench-top mounting. Tapped holes are spaced to permit mounting standard 19-in. panels which can be obtained in a wide range of widths. Specialized racks and frames may also be constructed from standard prepunched extrusions and corner castings or welded from structural angles and channels. Chasses on which the circuits are laid out may be bolted to the panel and supported by cantilever action. This is the structure most often used in self-contained commercial equipment. So-called rack adapters are usually supplied by the manufacturer, especially with small units that can be mounted side by side. Alternatively, the chasses may be equipped with flanges for vertical mounting. Needless to say, heavy chasses should be mounted near the bottom of the rack. The open rack allows easy access to the equipment but does not provide shielding to operator or equipment nor does it provide a high degree of mechanical stability. Since parts placement is dictated by considerations of weight, controls and meters are not always at the most convenient location.

For general-purpose commercial and laboratory work the cabinet rack is preferable to the open rack. It consists basically of steel channels welded into a rigid frame. Available in a variety of sizes, desk, bench, or relay-rack heights are common. Removable sides, doors, and tops—with and without louvers—permit complete enclosure when necessary. In a typical unit sides have internal U braces with perforated channels for fastening rails on which shelves, drawers, or chassis slides may be mounted. In some circumstances even the welded frame construction may not provide the required degree of mechanical rigidity. In such cases the frame may be used to support a more rigid member, as shown in the advanced breadboard of Fig. 2.19. Here optical and mechanical components are mounted on a lathe bed and electronics components are conventionally installed. Light-weight parts may also be attached to doors for accessibility.

The enclosed cabinet lends itself to simple safety interlocking methods for the protection of operating personnel. In the simplest type of interlock, commonly used in home radios, the mains supply is wired through a plug and socket arrangement, which is automatically disconnected when the back cover is removed. Such an arrangement is inexpensive and effective if there is no possibility of exposed wiring. A better solution is to use a low voltage relay, the coil of which is energized through mechanical switches incorporated in door latches. The relay itself can be remotely located if desired. High voltages, particularly if they exist across capacitors of large value, present potential shock hazards that can be lethal and additional precautions are mandatory. One method that has proved reliable employs a massive bar of low resistivity material which, in its normal position, short-circuits the capacitor. In the circuit "on" condition the bar is held off the shorting contacts by means of a solenoid that is energized through an interlock. If power is interrupted, the bar drops by its own weight to discharge the capacitor rapidly. A third spring-loaded contact is usually provided so that the stored energy can be partially dissipated through a resistor before actual shorting occurs.

Since enclosed cabinets may present problems in temperature control, the question of anticipated power dissipation merits serious consideration

Fig. 2.19 An enclosed cabinet and frame for electromechanical instrumentation.

before a final selection is made. Air is a poor thermal conductor and heat dissipation from packaged equipment occurs primarily by convection. Radiating sources should be arranged so that natural air currents flow upward to produce a more or less uniform equilibrium distribution of temperature. Normally, the hottest and least sensitive components should be placed near the top of the cabinet to avoid heating more sensitive components that operate at a lower temperature. For natural convection to be effective hot components should present large-area vertical surfaces and flow paths should be unimpeded; for example, circuits using large numbers of thermionic tubes are preferably mounted on vertical chasses whenever possible so that the air flow around the tubes is least restricted. Thermal design by convection is further complicated if forced air cooling is incorporated within packaged units. In this case suitably placed baffles may be used to alter air currents. Usually the problem is one of heat removal. When heat retention is desired in a particular area, foamed plastics and aluminum foil provide good insulating barriers.

The problem of heat removal from enclosures is complicated and seldom amenable to direct calculation with any degree of precision. As circuit complexity increases, the trend is toward the use of packaged units and tightly packed modules. The arrangement best suited to natural convection cooling is often not compatible with functional considerations or, as more frequently happens, with minimum volume. In such cases forced air cooling is usually the most economical method for controlling temperatures. When air is passed through a chamber containing a thermal source, the air temperature increases by an amount that is inversely proportional to the specific heat and mass of the air involved. Since the specific heat is essentially constant, the difference between the exhaust and input temperatures is given by

$$\Delta T = 0.25 \frac{P}{dM/dt} \,^{\circ}\text{C} \qquad [\text{specific heat} = 0.237 \text{ cal/(gm)(}^{\circ}\text{C)}], \quad (2.18)$$

where P is the power absorbed by the air in watts and dM/dt is the air flow in kilograms per minute. Usually the permissible temperature rise is given for a set of components, and it is necessary to select an air mover capable of producing an adequate volume flow rate. The latter may be calculated from

$$\frac{dV}{dt} = 1.76 \frac{P}{\Delta T} \text{ ft}^3/\text{min} \qquad (\text{specific gravity} = 0.075 \text{ lb/ft}^3). \quad (2.19)$$

This latter equation is approximate at best. The energy transfer process depends on the system configuration, the shape of the hot body, the thermal resistance in the laminar layer that exists between the hot element and the air stream, and on the velocity of the air. Heat sinks with plates or fins oriented to present large surface areas and the least turbulence in the air stream are most effective in heat transfer. Low velocities are desirable to reduce turbulence and to allow the maximum contact time. Conversely, a high flow rate creates turbulence and circulates more air through low resistance paths in which it is not needed. In addition, the higher power consumed by the blower motor contributes to the total dissipation. Ducts of small cross section for directing air within an enclosure are also of doubtful value because of high frictional losses.

Air movers are specified by air delivery rate (cubic feet per minute) versus static pressure (inches of water) curves for constant values of impeller speed.

Typically, the flow rate increases in a nonlinear manner as the back pressure is reduced. The back pressure that exists in a system is difficult to calculate. If it differs from atmospheric pressure to any degree, it is most easily determined from empirical measurements of the system impedance, that is, the ratio of pressure to flow rate. Another frequently used specification is static fan efficiency η_S or the ratio of air power output P_a to shaft power input. Since the work done in moving a volume of gas V against a static pressure p_s is equal to product Vp_s,

$$\eta_S = \frac{P_a}{P_i} = \frac{p_s(dV/dt)}{P_i}. \tag{2.20}$$

Unfortunately, awkward units of pressure (inches of water) and volume flow (cubic feet per minute) are normally used by most manufacturers. With P_i (product of electrical input and motor efficiency) expressed in watts the efficiency becomes

$$\eta_S = 0.12 \frac{P_s(dV/dt)}{P_i}. \tag{2.21}$$

The value of this relation is based on the fact that for a given flow rate the efficiency depends on the type of impeller. The least efficient mover is the simple propeller. It can produce high flow rates against low static pressures and is used chiefly for flushing and circulating air within a cabinet. For general-purpose applications the centrifugal type of blower produces low flow rates against moderate pressures. Air movers of this type are available in standard 19-in. panel enclosures for rack mounting. The so-called vane axial blower has the highest efficiency over a wide pressure range but at low flow rates. In a typical unit the impeller rests on the inner race of the motor bearing. Vanes exposed in the air stream serve as radiators to conduct heat away from the motor.

When forced air cooling is used, the cleanliness of the environment and air supply becomes an important consideration. Reactive fumes arising from chemical processes can damage mechanical and electronic components unless they are suitably protected. In addition, accumulations of dust lower heat transfer. Depending on severity, filters at the air intake will generally alleviate the latter problem with some sacrifice in efficiency.

Parts Arrangement

After the decision has been made on the type of device required to perform a desired function the technical aspects of the selection of electrical, mechanical, and other components, their placement, and interconnections must be carefully considered. Virtually all the basic elements that constitute an instrument are obtained from parts manufacturers. Some of the more important ones that are commonly used are listed in Table 2.7. Except for highly

Table 2.7 Instrument Components

Electronic	Electrical	Electromechanical	Hardware	Assembled Products	Miscellaneous
Vacuum tubes	Transformers	Motors	Receptacles	Modules	Optical elements
Transistors	Meters	Relays	Plugs	Printed circuits	Photo detectors
Diodes	Switches	Servomechanisms	Shields	Delay lines	Light sources
Integrated circuits	Fuses	Choppers	Heat sinks	Transducers	Photographic devices
Resistors	Circuit breakers	Fans, blowers	Cables	Power supplies	
Capacitors	Filters	Potentiometers	Waveguides	Electronic counters	
Inductors			Air filters		
			Accessories		

specialized requirements, which cannot be satisfied by available devices, the modern trend is toward the use of packaged units and modules. Thus the major design problem reduces to one of assembling operational units in such a manner that the individual elements are readily accessible and free of ambient disturbances. The question of accessibility cannot be overemphasized, particularly in the design of electronic apparatus. With the increasing use of solid-state components there is a tendency toward miniaturization, even though space is seldom a major factor. As a result, the equipment not only becomes difficult to service but higher thermal densities can lead to increased failure rates which, in turn, demand more service.

Depending on the end use and type of instrument, there are essentially two broad design philosophies. The first is generally followed in situations in which structural rigidity, size, weight, and possible physical abuse are important considerations. Castings or steel angles and channels are useful for mounting electric motors, mechanical movements, and optical elements. Electronic power equipment is usually mounted on chasses of cold rolled steel or aluminum alloy sheet of sufficient thickness to provide the required strength. The chassis may be simply a box, plate, or frame equipped with a flange or other means for securing it as a unit within the instrument structure. Holes and cutouts made for mounting components always reduce the rigidity. When necessary, angles, channels, or deformed surfaces may be employed to obtain added stiffness. Alternatively, certain components may form integral parts of the structure; for example, power transformers are rigid, sturdy, and insensitive to shock and vibration and may be used as corner gussets to join two or more perpendicular surfaces. Other massive parts should be mounted close to structural supports and, insofar as possible, in such a way that weight is uniformly distributed. Low frequency and large amplitude electrical and electronic circuits, such as power supplies and power amplifiers that are themselves insensitive to stray pickup, permit a great deal of latitude in parts placement. However, since high currents over extended lines produce intense electromagnetic fields, the possible effects on other sensitive circuits should be considered.

The second design philosophy, of which printed and integrated circuits are perhaps the most familiar examples, is applicable to low power devices of reasonably small size. Although printed circuits can be made by several techniques, such as printing, spraying, plating, embossing, and stamping, photofabrication techniques produce the most generally satisfactory results [38]. The process consists basically in coating a metal-clad insulating substrate with a light-sensitive plastic coating, photographically exposing it through a suitable transparency, and etching away all but the desired metal. The light-sensitive material, called photo resist, is hardened under the exposed areas so that only the unexposed areas are leached away in photographic processing. The exposed metal is then chemically etched, leaving

Fig. 2.20   Front and rear views of a typical printed circuit card.

the desired pattern. The photofabrication technique is not limited to the manufacture of electronic circuits. Virtually any material that can be chemically dissolved or deposited by electroplating or evaporation can be formed into mechanical parts with planar or surface geometry. In addition to printed circuits, typical applications include slip rings, switch contacts, name plates, engravings, masks, screens, and a variety of mechanical parts in a wide range of thicknesses (0.0005 to 0.125 in.). Selective metal removal and deposition permit design intricacies that would be extremely expensive or even impossible by conventional machining. Resolution is limited only by molecular interactions and depth of etch. Since the master drawing from which the photographic transparency is produced can be many times the size of the final part, extremely high precision can be obtained. Typically, lateral tolerances are about one-tenth of the metal thickness for single-sided etching and half that for double-sided etching. Corners are radiused to somewhat less than the etch depth.

Printed circuits are available in a wide variety of substrate materials. All are relatively fragile, however, and can support reliably only such lightweight components as transistors, diodes, and low-wattage passive elements, which are attached by inserting the leads through eyelets in the card and dip soldering to the printed circuit. Front and rear views of a typical card are shown in Fig. 2.20. Except for the smaller sizes, cards should be supported

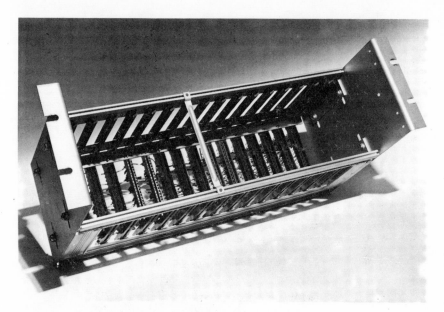

Fig. 2.21 Card rack for mounting printed circuitry.

along at least three edges. The card enclosure frame shown in Fig. 2.21 is a convenient means of mounting multiple circuits. Precision receptacles into which the cards are inserted permit connection between the printed circuitry and conventional wiring. Contacts are usually made directly on the card as part of the circuit. In applications that require interchangeability between cards of varying thicknesses matching plugs may be mechanically attached to the card.

One of the chief disadvantages of printed circuitry for experimental purposes is the difficulty of altering circuits. Components can be changed only by careful and tedious resoldering of delicate connections. Wiring can be changed only by scraping away sections of the printed "wire" and replacing it with conventional wiring. When there is any doubt about a particular circuit, the better procedure is first to construct the circuit on a card of the same dimensions as the final design but with conventional wiring. A variety of cards is available for this purpose, some with prepunched holes for inserting mounting pins and with plugs attached for mounting to printed circuit receptacles. A hand-wired experimental circuit of this type is shown in Fig. 2.22. Except for the difficulty in fabricating exact duplicates and the somewhat clumsy looking appearance, such techniques have considerable merit for laboratory and breadboard work.

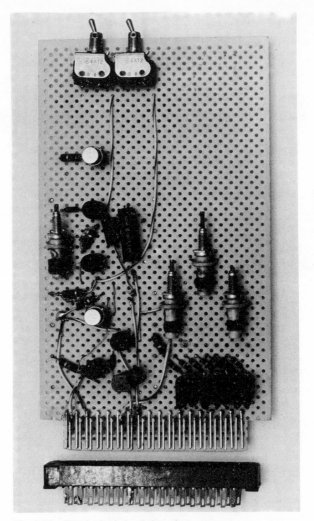

Fig. 2.22   Hand-wired circuit board.

Hardware and Cabling

The number and variety of hardware items used in electronic instruments are so extensive that it would take several volumes to enumerate them. Except in special cases, the manufacturers' recommendations for mounting components generally should be followed. Since the descriptions and ratings of the familiar items listed in parts catalogs are self-explanatory, only a few of those most subject to maintenance problems are mentioned here.

Fig. 2.23   Typical transistor sockets.

In mass-produced printed circuit boards low-power diodes and transistors are usually soldered directly into the circuit. Mounting pads, through which the leads are inserted, serve to relieve the leads of stress and provide a longer lead length and some heat-dissipating air space. With proper equipment this technique produces a highly reliable connection. For experimental and breadboard purposes pin sockets such as those shown in Fig. 2.23 are generally quite adequate. Most are made with gold-plated, spring-temper, beryllium copper contacts with chamfered entrances for easy insertion. Contact resistance is nominally less than 0.01 Ω. These boards are available with as many as 12 leads for TO-style integrated circuit packages and with either long or short lead solder terminals. The header, or body, is available in a range of low-loss dielectric materials which are resistant to normal reagents and solvents. Module test connectors, consisting of a matrix of contacts with 0.1 to 0.2 in. grid spacings are also available. For the flat-package integrated circuit and similar components the standard socket consists essentially of a molded rectangular cavity into which the element is placed. Barriers on both the hinged lid and the body of the socket provide positive lead separation. As the lid is closed, the leads are depressed against the contacts in a wiping action to ensure a low resistance connection. Terminals are brought out to the underside of the socket. In another version the socket is mounted on a standard 15-lead circuit board with the leads wired to the connector.

For setting up systems with a higher order of complexity a so-called "universal chassis" has recently become available. It consists of a printed circuit card incorporating 16 integrated circuit sockets. Depending on the model, it can accommodate TO-style, flat, or in-line packages. Input and output connections are made through an edge connector or through coaxial connectors which may also be used for monitoring and measurement. Circuit interconnections are made by inserting 22-gage solid wires into pin jacks, two of which are connected by printed wiring to each socket pin. Provision is made for distributing three supply voltages to each integrated circuit.

The various electromechanical functional units that make up a complete instrument are interconnected by means of cables and/or wiring harnesses of a complexity that depends on the signal flow path—coaxial cables, multiconductor cables, open transmission lines, or bundled wires—and on the arrangement of the units. Fortunately faults are rare in properly installed cables, the majority of failures occurring by fracture at the end fittings. Engineering guide lines are simple: avoidance of unnecessary flexing, kinks, and long unsupported runs; cleating at suitably spaced intervals to avoid catching; use of stranded conductors when possible; and adequate clamping at the ends so that tension is transferred to the strongest part. Failure to observe this last rule is the single most frequent cause of cabling difficulties.

Flat ribbon cables are relatively recent innovations that offer the advantages of flexibility and long flexlife, ease of installation, and controlled spacing of conductors within one harness. The two types currently being manufactured, flat strip and round conductor, are essentially electrical transmission lines with parallel conductors embedded in an insulator. They can be obtained with almost any combination of wire sizes with shielded and unshielded wires mixed in the same cable. Because all conductors lie in one plane, resistance to bending is low and sharp bends at hinges and retractable drawers are permitted.

The internal distribution of power-supply voltages to multiple circuits within a unit is conventionally made with bundled wire harnesses. Although somewhat bulky and time-consuming to install, these harnesses are adequate when the number of circuits is small. For completely engineered data processing and repetitive circuits the custom-made laminated bus offers several advantages. It consists of the requisite number of flat conductors, insulated from each other and molded into a completely sealed multiconductor element. Exact locations of solder, wire wrap, spade, and other types of terminal can be specified. Resistance and inductance, which are governed by the conductor width and spacing can be reduced to low values.

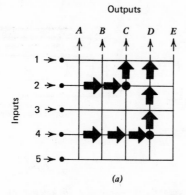

(a)

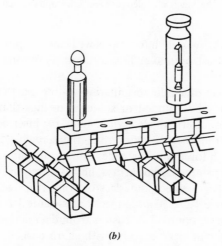

(b)

Fig. 2.24 Pin connections in an *X-Y* program matrix: (*a*) shorting type; (*b*) component connectors. (Sealectroboard, courtesy Selectro Corp.)

Another device that is applicable to programmed electronic control and instrument systems is the patchboard. Similar to a telephone switchboard, it permits switching and interconnecting input-output circuits of many types. One novel version consists of the *X-Y* matrix of buses shown in Fig. 2.24. Two or more parallel contact decks, insulated from one another, are sand-wiched between nonconducting boards. The top board, or front panel, has insertion holes at each *X-Y* intersection. Insertion of a shorting pin connects the upper and lower decks at a particular coordinate point; insertion of a component holder, containing a diode, for example, connects that component between the *X* and *Y* buses at the selected coordinate. Other models provide

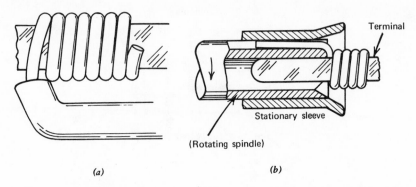

Fig. 2.25 Solderless connections: (*a*) the wirewrap tool; (*b*) a wired connection (after Mallina [39]). (Copyright, 1953, The American Telephone and Telegraph Co., reprinted by permission.)

single-pole–single-throw switch functions with captive pins at each intersection, single-contact test points, or bussed contacts on one board with individual contacts on the other.

The simplest type of cable termination is the barrier terminal strip. Individual wires may be crimped or soldered to lugs that are fastened by machine screws or, alternatively, wires may be inserted directly under screwheads. Since the wire is softer than the screwhead, it is elastically deformed under high forces and provides a mechanically stable connection. Matrix boards and printed circuit arrays, however, require large numbers of connections and the so-called solderless or wire-wrap technique is finding increasing acceptance [39]. The connection is made by wrapping several turns of soft wire under controlled tension around a relatively hard terminal, normally rectangular in cross section, with sharp corners as shown in Fig. 2.25*a*. The wrapping tension is large enough to crush the oxide films on the wire and terminal to form a "gastight" contact. Tapered stiffness near the end of the wrap alleviates local stresses that occur in solder and screw-type terminals. In its simplest form the wrapping tool (Fig. 2.25*b*) consists of a steel rod with an axial hole in which the terminal is inserted and an offset axial hole from which the wire is fed. The wires may be stripped off the terminal with a similarly simple tool.

Finally there is the question of selecting suitable cable connectors. In many cases what appears to be a clear choice is clouded by confusion between military specifications and performance ratings. A connector is as much a part of an instrument as any other component and quality should not be sacrificed. On the other hand, specification to higher standards than necessary often results in needless cost and complexity. Multiple pin connectors in round or rectangular pin arrangements, as shown in Fig. 2.26, are adequate for

Fig. 2.26   Typical multicontact connectors.

most purposes. They are available in a wide range of sizes, number of conductors, and ratings for applications listed by the manufacturer—rack and
panel, printed circuit, power supply, and communications. Good design
practice dictates casing and clamping the free end except for plug-in type
modules that are otherwise protected. Some models can be potted or
hermetically sealed for protection against extreme ambients.

The coaxial cable is generally used for radio and higher frequencies and
for many test instruments that require wide bandpass and short rise-time
characteristics. It consists basically of a center conductor embedded in a
dielectric covered with a braided outer conductor which in turn is protected
by an outer jacket. The important properties are impedance (50–100 Ω),
capacitance (10–30 pF/ft), and attenuation. Several types of connector have
been designed to match particular characteristics to prevent reflections and
consequent loss of power. Of the two types in common use—the so-called
UHF and BNC shown in Fig. 2.27—the BNC type has several advantages.
The capacitance is lower, it requires less panel space, and the quick disconnect
bayonet-locking coupling makes it easy to use. The shell should make good
electrical connection to the cable shield, preferably by soldering, and be
clamped to the outer jacket. A high-voltage series is rated to 5000 V. Adapters
may be had for coupling the various types of both styles.

Fig. 2.27   High-frequency connectors: (*a*) UHF; (*b*) BNC.

Thermal Considerations

One of the major design aims in laying out an instrument is to ensure that each component is in a thermal environment compatible with its operating limits. Over-all ambient conditions are not difficult to control by the methods outlined in Section 4, but localized temperatures in dissipative and active elements, largely self-generated, can exceed safe limits unless suitable precautions are taken. Heat generated in components with large surface areas, such as electric motors and power resistors, is effectively dissipated by thermal conduction to metallic bases and by convection air currents; for example, as much as half the heat developed in a typical carbon resistor is conducted away through the leads. Thermionic vacuum tubes are another major source of heat in electronic equipment. In typical radio-type tubes dissipation takes place chiefly by convection and to some extent by radiation. (Some high-power installations require liquid cooling. The equipment is specialized and recommendations of the manufacturer should be followed closely.) Design practice calls for adequate spacing of components to permit convection currents to flow and good metal-to-metal bonds to provide conduction paths of low thermal resistance. The latter implies short leads of adequate size and good solder joints. Finally temperatures at questionable points can be determined with reasonable accuracy by means of special paints and waxes. Reacting by color changes over a range from 45 to 1100°C, they may be applied as small dots, several of different ratings, to localized areas.

Fortunately most components can tolerate severe overloads of short duration, though at some sacrifice to life expectancy and stability, but solid-state devices, such as transistors and diodes, are extremely vulnerable to high-temperature operation. If power dissipation is allowed to exceed the rated maximum, permanent changes in gain, open or short circuits, or even complete destruction of the junction are almost certain to follow. One of the most effective methods of controlling junction temperatures involves increasing the effective surface area by means of heat sinks in good thermal contact with the device enclosure. Although any metal plate of sufficient area will serve the purpose, many different geometries have been designed for specific applications. A few of the commoner ones are shown in Fig. 2.28. Thermal resistivities of devices and sinks are given by the manufacturer. From a knowledge of the anticipated ambient temperature and power to be dissipated it is a simple matter to calculate the required size of sink (see Section 2). Some power transistors and diodes operate with their case or mounting studs at circuit potential and must be electrically insulated from the heat sink. The usual practice is to use washers of anodized aluminum, mica, or Teflon—listed in order of increasing thermal resistivity—coated on both sides with a thin layer of Silicone grease. Anodized aluminum is subject to scratching and consequent electrical shorting; mica is subject to flaking and cracking. On the other hand, the thermal resistivity of Teflon is more than twice that of aluminum. In extreme cases forced air is frequently used to increase the effective thermal gradient between sink and ambient, with a consequent reduction in volume.

Thermoelectric coolers [40] based on the Peltier effect have also proved effective in controlling temperatures of small components and for spot cooling larger assemblies [41, 42]. Electric current flowing in a series circuit composed of two different conducting materials produces heating or cooling at the junction, depending on the direction of current flow. Commercial devices employ P- and N-type bismuth telluride alloy couples that are arranged electrically in series but thermally in parallel, as indicated in Fig. 2.29. Although capable of withstanding temperatures to 300°C, they are typically rated at a hot junction temperature of 100°C. The design variables are the temperature difference between hot and cold junctions, input current, and the thermal load in watts. Typical characteristics are shown in Fig. 2.30. Depending on thermal ambients, temperatures can be controlled to 0.1°C. By cascading units, that is, by using a second stage to cool the hot junction

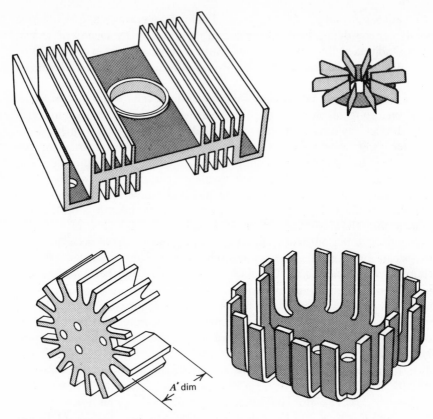

Fig. 2.28 Typical heat sinks: (a) high power; (b) low power.

of the first, a wider range of temperature difference can be obtained. The coefficient of performance, defined as the ratio of thermal power absorbed at the cold junction to electrical input power, is in the neighborhood of 0.5 and nearly independent of thermal capacity. Since currents are relatively high, some care must be exercised to limit magnetic fields in sensitive apparatus.

It is common practice to cool photodetectors and preamplifiers for thermal noise reduction. An element of small-size, such as an infrared detector, for example, can be effectively cooled by mounting it on a thermally conducting rod immersed in liquid nitrogen [43]. Nitrogen gas has also been used for cooling photomultiplier tubes [44]. Gas cooled by passing through a coil of copper tubing immersed in liquid nitrogen is introduced into the base of the housing and allowed to escape near the top. Before cooling the gas is dried at room temperature and passed through a chamber formed of two

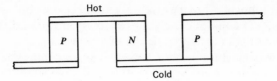

Fig. 2.29   The *P-N* thermoelectric (Peltier) temperature controller.

glass plates positioned over the end of the tube. The latter step is necessary to prevent frosting and accumulation of water on the phototube window. For large scale apparatus the closed-cycle refrigeration system is considerably more efficient than any of the other methods [45].

Electromagnetic Shielding and Grounding

Standard practice calls for grounding electrical appliances and instrument enclosures for the protection of operating personnel. The term "grounding" in this sense connotes an electrical connection to an equipotential plane (usually earth or building frame) through a path of sufficiently low impedance to prevent the existence of hazardous potentials. It is also commonly recognized that sensitive circuits should be grounded and possibly shielded as well. To avoid the confusion that attends any discussion of grounding procedures safety and system grounds should be considered as completely

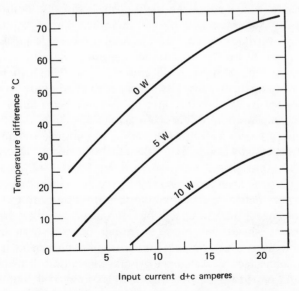

Fig. 2.30   Characteristics of a typical thermoelectric element.

independent equipotential planes that are connected at one and only one point. Shielding is a concept closely related to system grounding and merits careful consideration in the initial design of any instrument.

To protect personnel from shock hazards any apparatus containing electrical elements should be enclosed if the operating potentials are more than a few volts. Metal cabinets or rugged framed screens, which are preferred, should be connected to one another and through a reliable connection to the safety ground. In present-day construction, this is normally wired through the alternating current mains from an earth connection near the power transformer. All modern electrical equipment conforms to national safety codes and is supplied with three-wire power cables and three-prong plugs that automatically connect the cabinet, and usually, the circuit as well, to the safety ground. With some sensitive devices this procedure cannot be followed because of disturbances on a common ground line that supplies several different installations. In such cases the circuit connection can sometimes be removed from the cabinet and earthed through separate wiring.

Shields are employed to attenuate or reduce the intensity of electromagnetic fields that would otherwise disturb the motion of charge carriers which constitutes the signal current in an electric circuit. The optimum structure for a given application assumes one of three basic forms, depending on whether the interfering field is primarily electrostatic, magnetostatic, or a radiation field. Also, depending on the nature of the disturbance, shielding may be applied to the source or the receiver; for example, radiation at radio frequencies is restricted by Federal law to given levels and must be attenuated at the generator by suitable screening. On the other hand, radiation fields at machine and power-line frequencies are seldom controllable and screening from their effects must be carried out at the instrument. In passing, it should be mentioned that truly static electric and magnetic fields can be offset by equal and opposing local fields. The danger in this technique is that both fields are influenced by the position and motion of objects in the vicinity so that reliable compensation is difficult to maintain.

In its elementary form an electrostatic shield is a completely closed box constructed of electrically conducting material [46]. Any of the common metals, such as copper, brass, aluminum, or steel, have sufficiently high conductivities to satisfy most requirements. By the definition of a conductor the metal boundary defines a closed equipotential surface and the interior is effectively screened from the effects of external fields. These boxes are known as Faraday shields or cages. Potentials may exist on insulated conductors within the enclosure so that the interior is not in general field-free. If the shield is connected to a reference ground plane, no free charges can exist on the surface, and the exterior region is also screened from internal fields.

A practical circuit requires at least three terminals—signal input, signal output, and a terminal that ordinarily shares a common current path with the other two. The latter is called the zero-signal reference or system ground. When such a circuit is placed within a shield, potential differences appear across the capacitances that exist between each signal terminal and the shield. Depending on the geometry, the mutual capacitances may form a feedback path around the circuit from output to input. This effect can be avoided by proper placement and spacing of the components. A more reliable technique eliminates the capacitance between the common terminal of the circuit and the shield by a direct connection to the shield.

The signal source in an instrument, for example, a transducer, is usually located at some distance from the rest of the circuit, say an amplifier. It is connected to the circuit by a cable, the shield of which forms an extension of the circuit enclosure. Since the transducer output is defined with respect to an external reference point, that point becomes the zero-signal reference. This reference should be ohmically continuous through the entire circuit and contained within, but insulated from, the shield except for the one connection at the signal source. A typical circuit configuration that follows these dictates is shown in the block diagram of Fig. 2.31.

Although it is usually accepted that signal leads should be short, a physical instrument of any size occupies enough space to encompass regions of varying potential. Since these potentials may be capacitively (sometimes ohmically) connected to the various segments of the shielding, potential gradients may be produced and, as a result, cause parasitic currents to circulate through the shield. In Fig. 2.31 these currents are restricted to the shield without influencing circuit performance and constitute what is frequently called the shield drain. However, if the system ground is connected to the shield at more than one point it is evident that extraneous currents can flow in ground loops to produce "pickup." From the same line of

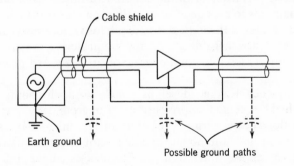

Fig. 2.31 Electrostatic shielding of instrument electronic circuits (after Morrison [46]).

reasoning it is evident that the shield should never be used for the system ground return. In more complex systems separate ground planes are frequently used for each subsystem and connected by the shortest route to the main system ground.

Many portable instruments operate from batteries enclosed within the shield. The majority of instruments operate on direct current derived from rectifier supplies which must be connected to the circuit through ports in the shield. Because of the greater than zero impedance of even well-regulated supplies, coupling may occur between various subsystems connected to a common power supply. As design guides, low- and high-frequency circuits, as well as low- and high-level stages, are preferably powered individually, each with a separate ground connection. Alternating-current power may be supplied through transformers that incorporate electrostatic shields. In the usual design the shield consists of one or more copper foils surrounding the primary winding. The foils are made long enough to permit a lap joint and are insulated at the joint to prevent forming a short-circuited turn. At low frequencies pairs of wires carrying equal currents in opposite directions, as used in radio tube filament connections, are twisted together to minimize radiation.

The most effective shielding material at radio frequencies has low electrical resistivity. The magnetic component of radiation incident on the shield induces potential gradients which give rise to eddy currents. Since the induced currents are in a direction that will produce a reaction opposing the incident field, penetration of the incident radiation is limited. The skin depth δ, or depth at which the field is reduced to 37% of its surface intensity, is given by [47]

$$\delta = \left(\frac{2\rho}{\omega\mu}\right)^{\frac{1}{2}}, \tag{2.22}$$

where ω is the angular frequency of the radiation, ρ is the resistivity, and μ is the magnetic permeability of the material; u ranges from unity for non-magnetic materials to a value of several thousand for some magnetic alloys. Some typical values of theoretical skin depth for various materials at several frequencies are listed in Table 2.8. At high frequencies it is evident that eddy currents in any reasonably good conductor are restricted primarily to the surface.

Radio frequency leakage develops chiefly from discontinuities in the enclosure shield, antennalike protrusions of ungrounded components, and conduction along power wiring. The latter can be eliminated by using suitable line filters. As a rule of thumb any openings should be less than one quarter wavelength in largest dimension. At frequencies above 150 kHz mesh screening performs almost as well as solid sheet, provided the seams make

Table 2.8 Skin Depth in Shielding Materials

Material	δ (mm)			
	60 Hz	1 kHz	1 MHz	3×10^9 MHz
Brass	16.3	4.0	0.13	2.3×10^{-3}
Aluminum	11.0	2.7	0.08	1.6×10^{-3}
Copper	8.5	2.1	0.07	1.2×10^{-3}
Iron	1.4	0.35	0.01	0.20×10^{-3}
Magnetic iron alloy	0.37	0.09	0.002	0.05×10^{-3}

good metal to metal contact with sufficient overlap. Metal gaskets with spring fingers are widely used on flat surfaces for sealing lids and doors. Another type of gasket is made of knitted wire mesh that can be formed around openings. Surfaces on which the gaskets bear must, of course, be free of paint and other insulating films. A typical application is shown in Fig. 2.32. The gasket is compressed when the lid is closed to form a joint that is almost radiation proof.

As the frequency of the radiation field is decreased the skin depth becomes greater and the magnetic permeability of the shield material takes on more importance. Shielding action occurs not only through the generation of eddy currents but also through the short-circuiting of magnetic flux through the material. Concentric shields of alternating layers of good conductors and materials of high permeability are highly effective in the low-frequency region. Finally, at power line frequencies and below, the effectiveness of a shield depends almost entirely on its thickness and permeability. Alloys of iron, nickel, and cobalt have permeabilities as high as 10^5. Even with these materials, however, poor magnetic joints and air gaps add reluctance to the flux path and must be avoided. Dividing a given thickness of material into

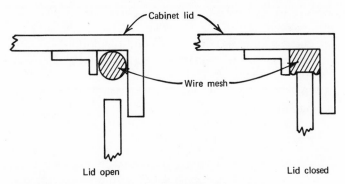

Fig. 2.32 Radiofrequency shielding with wire-mesh gaskets.

two or more concentric layers with staggered joints increases the degree of shielding somewhat.

Vibration Isolation

Vibration in its simplest mode is a periodic motion that occurs in an elastic system subjected to a disturbing force. Even a simple instrument contains many compliant elements, each of which may be considered as part of al elementary mechanical circuit with its own fundamental mode. If the disturbance has a frequency content near the natural resonant frequency of any of the elementary circuits, it can be magnified by a means analogous to the build-up of voltage in a resonant electrical circuit The net result of even moderate amplitudes may appear as a decreased signal-to-noise ratio in delicate transducers and in the extreme may lead to malfunctioning and failure.

As with any extraneous disturbance, the most effective point to reduce mechanical noise is at the source. There are several obvious design precautions that apply to mechanical devices incorporated within the instrument: (a) avoidance of the heavy impacts that frequently occur in solenoids and relays, (b) substitution of uniform rotation for oscillating motion whenever possible, (c) reduction of the mass of oscillating members, (d) counterbalancing eccentric loads in rotating parts, (e) reduction of acceleration components in cyclic motions, and (f) mounting arrangements such that the center of gravity is midway between both horizontal and vertical supports.

In many situations the measures just enumerated are inadequate to reduce vibration to a sufficiently low level. More frequently the sources (building and auxiliary machines) are beyond control of the designer. In such cases the only resort is to some form of mechanical isolation. A mechanical system has six degrees of freedom—three each in translation and rotation—and an associated resonant frequency for each one. A general analysis of all possible modes in a real system is extremely difficult. However, since the resultant motion obeys vector-field relations, some insight can be gained by considering each mode separately. In particular, that motion in the direction of the principal disturbing force is ordinarily the most important.

The mechanical circuit with one degree of motion (Fig. 2.3) may be used as a filter in the same manner as the analogous electrical circuit. Displacement x as a function of time t and angular drive frequency ω is given by (2.17). The amplitude of the force transmitted by the system is the vector sum of the forces transmitted through the spring deflection kx and by the damping element $R_M(dx/dt)$; that is [35],

$$f_T = \left[(kx)^2 + \left(R_M \frac{dx}{dt} \right)^2 \right]^{\frac{1}{2}}. \tag{2.23}$$

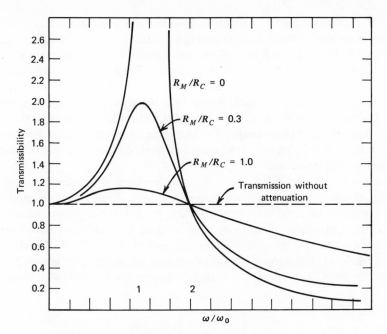

Fig. 2.33 Transmissibility of a mechanical circuit.

The transmissibility T of the system is defined as the fractional force that is transmitted or the ratio of transmitted to applied forces. It is a straightforward calculation to show from (2.17) or from the equivalent electrical circuit that

$$T = \left\{ \frac{1 + [2(R_M/R_C)(\omega/\omega_0)]^2}{[1 - (\omega^2/\omega_0^2)]^2 + [2(R_M/R_C)(\omega/\omega_0)]^2} \right\}^{1/2}, \tag{2.24}$$

where, as before, ω_0 is the resonant angular frequency and R_C is the critical damping resistance. Transmissibility is plotted as a function of ω/ω_0 for three values of the ratio R_M/R_C in Fig. 2.33. Several features of this plot merit careful scrutiny. First, when the ratio of drive-to-resonant frequencies $\omega/\omega_0 = \sqrt{2}$, the applied force is transmitted without attenuation, regardless of the value of mechanical resistance. Second, when $\omega/\omega_0 > \sqrt{2}$, the greatest *attenuation* of transmitted force occurs in the absence of resistance. Third, when $\omega/\omega_0 < \sqrt{2}$, the applied force is *amplified* in transmission and, for low values of resistance, can attain a very large amplitude indeed at $\omega = \omega_0$. Since it is impossible to contrive mechanical systems with no resistance whatever, the infinite transmissibility predicted by theory is never attained in practice. In this low-frequency region damping is highly desirable.

It is obvious that indiscriminate use of so-called shock mounts and resilient dampers is seldom of value in attenuating vibrations. In fact, without a full knowledge of the frequencies involved and a suitable choice of mounting the amplitude of vibration may even be increased. The basic principle underlying effective vibration control requires the system mass to be mounted on a compliant structure in such a way that the natural frequency of the system (including mount) in the direction of the disturbance is several times smaller than the disturbing frequency. Damping dissipates energy by converting it to heat. It is an effective control element only at frequencies near and much below resonance.

Metal springs exhibit stable coefficients within their elastic limit and are only slightly affected by temperature and humidity. Since metal transmits sound, a resilient material such as rubber, felt, or cork is frequently installed between the spring and its support. One method that has been described for isolating a sensitive infrared detector cell operating at 13 Hz is illustrated in Fig. 2.34a [48]. The natural period of rotation of the platform is stated to be approximately $\frac{1}{3}$ sec. Another technique is shown in Fig. 2.34b [49]. Wood

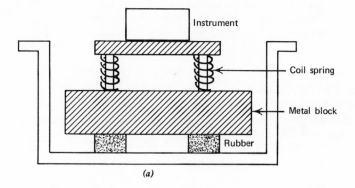

(a)

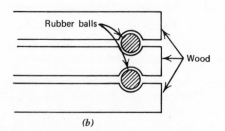

(b)

Fig. 2.34 Vibration isolators: (a) spring mounts; (b) air mounts.

supports are separated and retained in position by balls at each corner. The upper set is of hard rubber; those in the lower set are tennis balls which provide a compliant coefficient through the air contained within them.

Numerous types of vibration isolator are commercially available [50]. Some use helical coil springs in conjunction with some form of damping. Viscous damping has already been considered in the mechanical circuit of Fig. 2.3. The damping force is proportional to the rate of displacement and is a function of the exciting frequency. It is useful for optical installations and inertial platforms subject to shock and when return to equilibrium position is required. Friction damping is always present to some extent. It is independent of displacement and velocity but limits the minimum transmissibility that can be attained. Hysteretic damping is typical of most elastometric materials. The damping force is proportional to displacement but in phase with the velocity. Response characteristics are similar to those found in viscous dampers but independent of applied frequency. Other types of isolator employ compressed air as the compliant member. For certain applications they offer the advantages of low internal friction and adjustability of the spring constants. In closing this section it is emphasized once again that vibration is a complex phenomenon that can exist in many modes. Effective application of any isolating device demands that it be designed to handle the specific frequencies of the disturbance.

References

1. G. W. A. Dummer, C. Brunetti, and L. K. Lee, *Electronic Equipment Design and Construction*, McGraw-Hill, New York, 1961.
2. G. Shiers, *Design and Construction of Electronic Equipment*, Prentice-Hall, Englewood Cliffs, N.J., 1966.
3. R. H. Myers, K. L. Wong, and H. M. Gordy, *Reliability Engineering for Electronic Systems*, Wiley, New York, 1964.
4. G. W. A. Dummer and N. B. Griffin, *Environmental Testing Techniques for Electronics and Materials*, Macmillan, New York, 1962.
5. G. W. A. Dummer and N. B. Griffin, *Electronic Equipment Reliability*, Wiley, New York, 1960.
6. D. C. Greenwood, *Manual of Electromechanical Devices*, McGraw-Hill, New York, 1965.
7. H. K. P. Neubert, *Instrument Transducers*, Clarendon, Oxford, 1963.
8. H. F. Olson, *Acoustical Engineering*, Van Nostrand, Princeton, N.J., 1957.
9. F. A. Fischer (trans. S. Ehrlich, F. Pordes), *Fundamentals of Electroacoustics*, Interscience, New York, 1955.
10. L. A. Pipes, *Applied Mathematics for Engineers and Physicists*, McGraw-Hill, New York, 1958.

11. *NEMA Motor Standards*, Publication No. MG1-1967, NEMA, New York.
12. R. W. Mathews, *Machine Design*, **40**, 58 (March 21, 1968).
13. G. R. Slemon, *Magnetoelectric Devices*, Wiley, New York, 1966.
14. J. R. Wickey, *Machine Design*, **36**, 20 (March 19, 1964).
15. J. R. Ireland, *Electro-technol.*, **71**, 86 (March, 1963).
16. W. A. Anderson, *Machine Design*, **36**, 4 (March 19, 1964).
17. A. L. Sebok and L. H. Easton, *Machine Design*, **36**, 60 (March 19, 1964).
18. S. A. Davis, *Electromechanical Design*, **12**, 109 (April, 1968).
19. A. Diamond, *Electrotechnology*, **76**, 28 (July 1965).
20. G. Baty, *Electromechanical Design*, **10**, 55 (July, 1966).
21. T. R. Fredrikson, *Electro-Technol.*, **80**, 36 (November, 1967).
22. J. B. Ayer, *Inst. and Control Sys.*, **40**, 121 (June, 1967); **40**, 110 (July, 1967).
23. J. W. Beams, F. W. Linke, and P. Sommer, *Rev. Sci. Instr.*, **9**, 248 (1938).
24. S. Gray, *Machine Design*, **40**, 142 (April 25, 1968).
25. B. Brixner, *Rev. Sci. Instr.*, **30**, 1041 (1959); **36**, 1297 (1965).
26. P. Lena, *Appl. Opt.*, **7**, 716 (1968).
27. H. C. Roters, *Electromagnetic Devices*, Wiley, New York, 1941.
28. F. Deutch, *Rev. Sci. Instr.*, **36**, 849 (1965).
29. G. Ehrenberg, *Inst. and Control Sys.*, **40**, 109 (March, 1967).
30. F. D. Jones, Ed., *Ingenious Mechanisms for Designers and Inventors*, Vols. I–IV, Industrial, New York, 1957.
31. H. Bairnsfather, *J. Sci. Instr.*, **44**, 59 (1967).
32. P. H. Sydenham, *J. Sci. Instr.*, **44**, 465 (1967).
33. P. J. Sim, J. B. Weir, *J. Sci. Instr.*, **44**, 934 (1967).
34. H. G. Lipson and J. R. Littler, *Appl. Opt.*, **5**, 472 (1966).
35. C. R. Freberg, E. N. Kemler, *Elements of Mechanical Vibrations*, Wiley, New York, 1957.
36. J. L. Engle and J. J. Freed, *Rev. Sci. Instr.*, **39**, 307 (1968).
37. D. F. Wilkes, *Mech. Eng.*, **90**, 12 (April, 1968).
38. H. B. Lovering, *Solid State Tech.*, **11**, 39 (July, 1968).
39. R. F. Mallina, *Bell Sys. Tech. J.*, **32**, 525 (1953).
40. S. E. Rea, *Inst. and Control Sys.*, **40**, 99 (January, 1967).
41. H. P. Beerman and G. C. Rozett, *Rev. Sci. Instr.*, **36**, 1258 (1965).
42. J. P. Paris and V. F. Damme, *Rev. Sci. Instr.*, **36**, 1058 (1965).
43. S. Abramowitz, A. M. Bass, and A. E. Ledford, Jr., *Appl. Opt.*, **4**, 255 (1965).
44. A. R. Franklin, W. W. Holloway, Jr., and D. H. McMahon, *Rev. Sci. Instr.*, **36**, 232 (1965).
45. A. L. Broadfoot, *Appl. Opt.*, **5**, 1259 (1966).
46. R. Morrison, *Grounding and Shielding Techniques in Instrumentation*, Wiley, New York, 1967.
47. D. R. Corson and P. Lorraine, *Introduction to Electromagnetic Fields and Waves*, Freeman, San Francisco, 1962.
48. D. E. Collins, *Rev. Sci. Instr.*, **36**, 850 (1965).
49. B. Arnovich, I. Galperin, and S. Carangelo, *Rev. Sci. Instr.*, **37**, 125 (1966).
50. *Airmount Design Manual*, Firestone Industrial Products Co., Noblesville, Ind., 1966.

Chapter **III**

BASIC ELECTRICAL PRINCIPLES
Leon F. Phillips

1   RESISTANCE, INDUCTANCE, AND CAPACITANCE

Resistance

On the basis of the ease with which they can be made to carry an electric current materials may be classified as either conductors or insulators, with the reservation that the category of insulators includes the special class of materials known as semiconductors. We have something to say about the properties of semiconductors in Chapter IV; our present discussion deals only with conductors, which for most practical purposes can be taken to mean metals. The distinguishing characteristic of a metallic solid is that it contains delocalized electrons that can travel through the crystal lattice under the influence of an externally applied electric field. Thus a source of steady field, for example, a chemical battery, is able to drive a current of electrons around a closed circuit of conducting material, as in Fig. 3.1. The

79

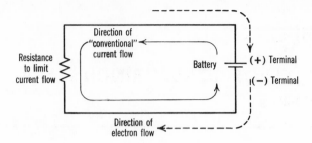

Fig. 3.1   Elements of a simple circuit.

flow of electrons leaves the negative terminal of the battery and returns through the positive terminal. It is somewhat unfortunate that this model of the conduction process was developed after it had been decided that the "conventional current," in terms of which the behavior of circuits is analyzed, consists of a flow of *positive* charge from the positive battery terminal through the external circuit and back to the negative terminal. However, provided we are careful to be sure in any particular instance whether it is the conventional current or the electron current that is being considered, this can lead to no confusion.

The amount of current that a battery can drive through a conductor is given by Ohm's law,

$$E = IR, \tag{3.1}$$

where E is the electromotive force (emf) of the battery measured in volts, I is the current flowing measured in amperes (A), and the constant R, known as the resistance of the conductor, is measured in ohms. A current of one ampere corresponds to the flow of one coulomb (C) of charge per second through the conductor. The basic unit here was formerly the international ampere, defined in terms of the mass of silver deposited by electrolysis when the current passes through a silver coulometer. The international ohm was similarly defined in terms of the resistance of a column of pure mercury under standard conditions, and the international volt was the electromotive force required to drive a current of one international ampere through a resistance of one international ohm. These units are about 0.05% larger than the more fundamental meter-kilogram-second-ampere (mksa) units, which are defined in terms of the magnetic forces between current-carrying wires and which do not depend on the properties of any particular material such as silver or mercury.

The reciprocal of resistance is termed conductance and is measured in ohm^{-1}, sometimes written mho. When several conductors are connected in series, the total resistance is the sum of the separate resistances; when they

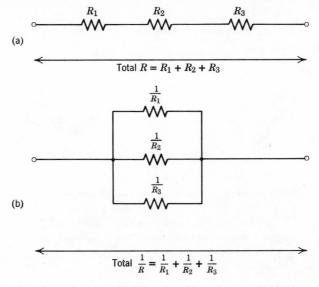

Fig. 3.2 (*a*) Resistances added in series; (*b*) conductances added in parallel.

are connected in parallel the total conductance is the sum of the separate conductances (Fig. 3.2).

In comparing different materials it is usual to describe their conducting ability in terms of specific conductance (κ) or specific resistance (ρ), also called resistivity. These quantities are defined as the conductance and resistance, respectively, between opposite faces of a 1 cm cube of material. For a sample of length l and uniform cross section A we would have

$$R = \frac{\rho l}{A} \tag{3.2}$$

or

$$R^{-1} = \frac{\kappa A}{l} \tag{3.3}$$

so that the units of ρ and κ are ohm.cm and ohm^{-1}cm^{-1}, respectively.

When a current is driven through a conductor some work must be done against the internal resistance of the material; the power that is dissipated in this way appears as heat. The rate at which work is converted to heat, that is, the power dissipation in watts (W) is given by

$$W = EI = \frac{E^2}{R} = I^2R. \tag{3.4}$$

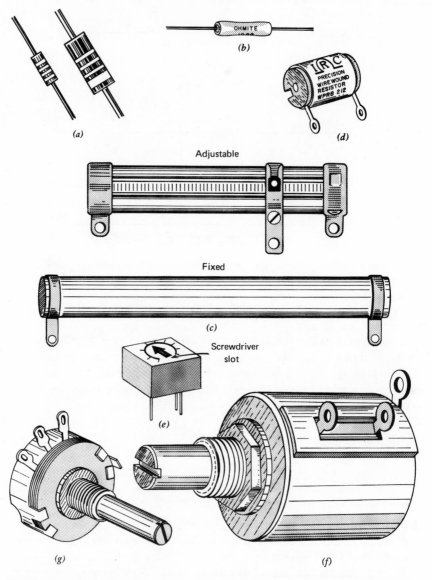

Fig. 3.3 Some fixed and variable resistors: (*a*) typical $\frac{1}{2}$- and 1-W carbon resistors, 5 or 10% tolerance; (*b*) wire-wound resistor, 2 or 5% tolerance; (*c*) adjustable and fixed power resistors, 25 and 40 W, 10% tolerance; (*d*) wire-wound resistor, tolerance 0.1 or 0.5%; (*e*) subminature potentiometer for mounting on printed circuit board; (*f*) 10-turn wire-wound potentiometer; (*g*) 2-W carbon potentiometer.

Practical resistors, which are widely used to dissipate power, limit current flow, or provide controlled voltage steps, typically have values in the range of about one ohm (1 Ω) through one thousand ohms (one kilohm = 1 K), up to a few times 10 million ohms (10 megohms = 10 M). For special purposes it is possible to obtain glass-encapsulated resistors, such as those made by Victoreen or Welwyn in the United States and Britain respectively, having values up to 10^{12} Ω. Unless special precautions are taken the insulation resistance in a practical circuit is likely to be around 10^{10} or 10^{11} Ω. At the other end of the scale the resistance of a short piece of copper wire to which good contacts have been made is typically a few thousandths of an ohm. The resistance of the human body is of the order of 100 K.

The physical size of a resistor is directly related to the amount of power it is able to dissipate without over-heating; the resistors most commonly found in the signal circuits of electronic instruments have $\frac{1}{4}$-W or $\frac{1}{2}$-W ratings. For noncritical parts of the circuit they are usually solid "composition" resistors of 5 or 10% tolerance. When accuracy, stability, or low noise is important, they may be wire-wound or of a type made by depositing a thin film of metal or carbon on a cylindrical insulator. In circuits carrying a lot of power resistors may be found in the ratings of 5, 10, 25, or 50 W; these are almost exclusively wire-wound. All resistors have temperature coefficients whose sign and magnitude depends on the type of material used in their construction. With wire-wound resistors the value of the resistance invariably increases with increasing temperature, whereas with carbon and composition resistors the reverse is true. The temperature coefficient is put to practical use in the *thermistor*, in which a bead of fused metal oxides serves as a resistive element with a very large negative temperature coefficient.

Variable resistors are known as rheostats if the purpose of the variation is to control a flow of current and as potentiometers (commonly abbreviated to "pots") if the purpose of the variation is to select a desired voltage from along the length of the resistor. A rheostat is invariably wire-wound; a potentiometer may be wire-wound or built around a conducting film. In either case a spring-loaded wiper is used to select the point at which the variable contact is made. Typically, the sliding contact can be adjusted by rotating a shaft over a range of about 270°, but when very fine control is called for a 10- or 15-turn potentiometer, such as a Beckman Helipot, can be used. A selection of typical fixed and variable resistors is illustrated in Fig. 3.3.

So far we have considered the behavior of resistance only in relation to the direct current (dc) which flows in a circuit containing a battery or other dc generator. In order to deal with electrical *signals* we also have to consider the circuit behavior when current and voltage are changing rapidly. Since any complex signal can be synthesized by adding various sine and cosine

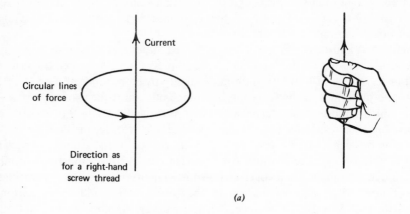

(a)

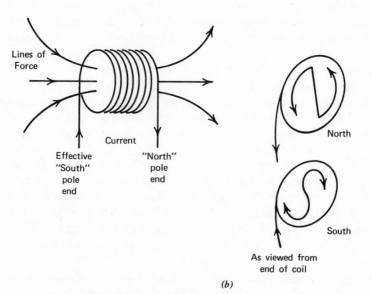

(b)

Fig. 3.4 Directions of magnetic fields for (*a*) straight wire and (*b*) coil or solenoid.

terms together (cf. Fourier synthesis), it will be sufficient to consider the effect of an alternating current (ac) of circular frequency ω radians per second, where ω can take any value we choose. The voltage and current will then obey the equations

$$E = E_0 \sin \omega t, \tag{3.5}$$

$$I = I_0 \sin (\omega t + \delta), \tag{3.6}$$

where δ is the angular phase difference, or phase-shift, between the applied ac voltage and the ac current. Here E_0 and I_0 are the *amplitudes* of the voltage and current signals, the quantities $2E_0$ and $2I_0$ are the *peak-to-peak amplitudes* of voltage and current, and the quantities $0.707E_0$ and $0.707I_0$ are the *root-mean-square* (rms) values of voltage and current. When power output is most important, as with the ac mains supply, it is normally the rms value of voltage that is stated. Electrical signals, on the other hand, are usually quoted as so many volts peak-to-peak. Equations 3.5 and 3.6 may also be expressed in terms of the frequency f in cycles per second (cps) or hertz (Hz) by substituting

$$\omega = 2\pi f. \tag{3.7}$$

The information content of an ac signal is usually present in the form of time-dependent variations in the amplitudes E and I at a constant "carrier" frequency ω. The signal is then said to be *amplitude modulated* (am). Most of the signals encountered in scientific instruments are of this type. Sometimes, however, it is convenient to let the amplitudes remain constant and to express the information in the form of variations in the angular frequency ω. The signal is then said to be *frequency modulated* (fm), and the carrier frequency is the value of ω when no modulation is present.

In a purely resistive circuit (i.e., one in which capacitance and inductance play no part) the voltage and current are always related to one another by (3.1). Hence in (3.6) we must have $\delta = 0$, and the current and voltage are exactly in phase with one another. The only effect of frequency in this case, when stray capacitance and inductance are negligible, is that at very high frequencies (above about 10 Mc = 10^7 Hz) current tends to travel over the surface of a conductor rather than through the interior and the effective value of R increases.

Inductance

The association of a steady magnetic field with a conductor carrying a steady electric current is well known through its practical application to the electromagnet. The direction of the magnetic field, that is, the direction in which the north-seeking pole of a bar magnet would tend to move, is shown in Fig. 3.4 in relation to the current flow, both for a straight wire and for a coil or solenoid. Since the field of a solenoid is not fundamentally

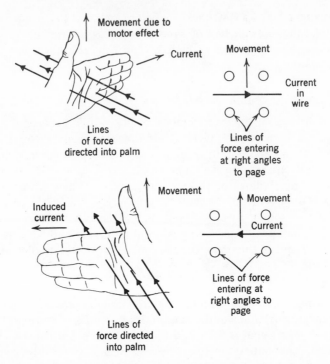

Fig. 3.5 (*a*) The left-hand rule for motors; (*b*) the right-hand rule for dynamos.

different from that of a bar magnet, it is to be expected that a solenoid and a bar magnet will interact, just as two bar magnets interact, to attract or repel one another. If we now confine our attention to a small segment of the wire forming the coil, we can conclude that any current-carrying wire placed in a steady magnetic field experiences a force. The direction of this force acting on the wire is found by experiment to be given by the left-hand or "motor" rule, which is illustrated in Fig. 3.5*a*.

This interaction also occurs in reverse, that is, an emf is generated or "induced" between the ends of a wire which moves through a magnetic field in a direction at right angles to the lines of force. (If the motion is not exactly at right angles to the field, it is only the vector component in this direction that is effective.) The practical application of the effect to generators depends on the fact that the emf can cause a current to flow through an external circuit and thus be made to do work or produce heat. Unless we are planning to violate the first law of thermodynamics we must therefore expect to be called on to provide this work when we cause the wire to move. Thus the wire must experience a force *due to the flow of current*, in a direction that opposes the original motion, and it follows that the directions of the motion and the induced current must be related by the right-hand or "dynamo" rule* of Fig. 3.5*b*. The statement that the direction of the current always opposes the motion that produces it is known as Lenz's law. An example of a practical application of this law is the standard practice of protecting a sensitive moving-coil meter from damage during transit by closing the circuit between the meter terminals with a piece of wire.

So far we have considered the motion produced by a current through a wire in a stationary field and the current induced by moving a wire through a stationary field. There is yet a third way to combine these factors, namely to consider the effect of a varying magnetic field on a stationary wire. This could be observed in practice by using a solenoid to vary the field. Since the lines of force change position as the field strength varies we once again have them cutting the wire at right angles and an emf is thereby induced. This is the operating principle of the transformer, in which no mechanical movement is involved. The quantity that governs the magnitude of the emf induced in one conductor by the changing current through another is called the *mutual inductance* (*M*) of the two and is defined by the equation

$$E = -M \frac{dI}{dt}. \tag{3.8}$$

Here *E* is the induced emf, the negative sign is an expression of Lenz's law, *M* is the mutual inductance, and dI/dt is the rate of change of the primary current. The induced current in a transformer is called the secondary current; in an ideal transformer the ratio of the ac voltages across the primary and secondary windings is the same as the ratio of the numbers of turns in the windings. A conductor may also interact with the changing magnetic field due to its own current variation, in which case we speak of *self-inductance* (*L*). Self-inductance is also described by (3.8), with *L* replacing *M*.

The unit of inductance is the henry (H), which is an inductance such that an emf of 1 V is induced by a current that changes at a rate of 1 A/sec. Inductance, like resistance, is a property of any conductor, but the term *inductor* is normally reserved for a multiturn coil with some specified value of self-inductance, the value typically being measured in millihenries (mH). An inductor used to smooth out or limit current variations in a circuit is generally called a "choke." If the choke coil has an iron core to increase the magnetic coupling between the turns, an inductance of 10 H can be obtained in quite a small space without using extremely thin wire. Some practical inductors are illustrated in Fig. 3.6.

Let us calculate the current that flows through an inductor when an ac voltage is applied. The inductor impedes the flow of current through the

---

* As an aid to remembering which rule is which there is a simple mnemonic: "Dad's a dynamo and dad's always right," which should preferably be memorized early in life.

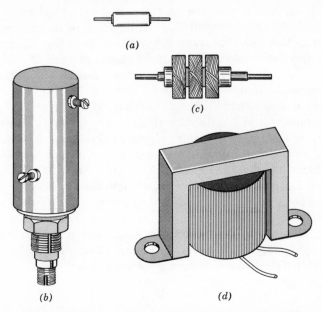

Fig. 3.6 (a) Minature ferrite-bead choke for removing unwanted radiofrequency signals; (b) adjustable encapsulated radiofrequency (rf) coil; (c) rf choke; (d) iron-cored choke for smoothing mains ripple in a dc power supply.

action of the induced emf, which opposes the external emf that is tending to increase the current I. Thus the external voltage at any instant must be equal and opposite to the induced emf, and if the meaning of the symbol E is changed so that it now represents an externally applied ac voltage, as in Fig. 3.7a, we have instead of (3.8)

$$E = \frac{L\,dI}{dt} \tag{3.8a}$$

$$= E_0 \sin \omega t. \tag{3.5}$$

We expect an alternating current of the form

$$I = I_0 \sin(\omega t + \delta). \tag{3.6}$$

Hence

$$E_0 \sin \omega t = \omega L I_0 \cos(\omega t + \delta), \tag{3.9}$$

and if we put $t = 0$ we see that δ must be some odd multiple of $\pi/2$ in order to satisfy (3.9). However, in order for E to be positive when dI/dt is positive, as in Fig. 3.7b, the voltage must *lead* the current by 90°; that is, $\delta = -\pi/2$.

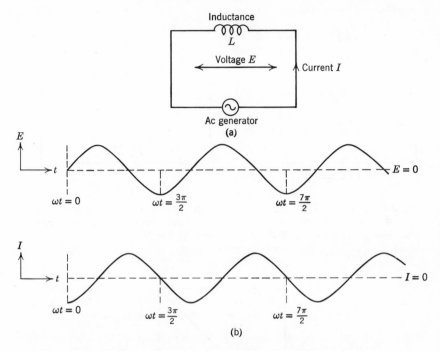

Fig. 3.7 Current and voltage waveforms for an inductor: (*a*) circuit diagram; (*b*) waveforms.

Now if we insert $\omega t = \pi/2$ in (3.9) we obtain

$$E_0 = \omega L I_0, \tag{3.10}$$

and the peak current is seen to be the same as would flow through a resistance of ωL ohms. Because the current and voltage are exactly 90° out of phase, the power supplied by the generator is alternately positive and negative and the average power dissipated in the inductor, neglecting its residual ohmic resistance, is zero. In this situation we speak of a pure *reactance X* of ωL ohms, where the use of X for reactance is analogous to the use of R for resistance. The corresponding quantity in the general case, in which the phase difference is not exactly 90°, is termed *impedance*, with the symbol Z. The reciprocal of impedance, measured in mhos, is termed *admittance* (Y).

In a circuit that contains both resistance and inductance, such as those in Figs. 3.8 and 3.9, we need to take account of the fact that in one of the circuit elements the current and voltage are in phase and in the other they are 90° out of phase. The natural way to proceed in this situation is to draw vector diagrams, such as those in Fig. 3.10*a* and *b*, whose significance should be self-evident. A convenient alternative is to write the reactance of the inductor

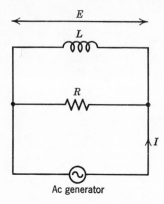

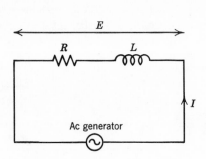

Fig. 3.8 Circuit with inductance and resistance in parallel; E has the same phase across both R and L.

Fig. 3.9 Circuit with inductance and resistance in series; I has the same phase in both R and L.

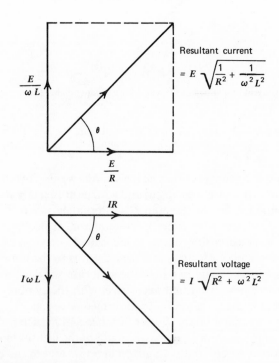

Fig. 3.10 (*a*) Addition of current vectors for R and L in parallel. The resultant current lags behind the voltage by an angle $\theta = \tan^{-1}(R/\omega L)$. (*b*) Addition of voltage vectors for R and L in series. The resultant voltage leads the current by an angle $\theta = \tan^{-1}(\omega L/R)$.

as $j\omega L$, where j is the square root of -1, used here in the sense of an operator that rotates a polar vector anticlockwise through 90°. (We use j instead of i to avoid confusion with the symbol for current.) The resultant admittance vector in the parallel circuit is then given by

$$Y = \frac{1}{R} + \frac{1}{j\omega L} \tag{3.11}$$

$$= Y_1 + Y_2 \tag{3.12}$$

and the magnitude of Y in mhos is given by the length of the resultant vector, that is,

$$|Y| = (|Y_1|^2 + |Y_2|^2)^{1/2} \tag{3.13}$$

$$= \left(\frac{1}{R^2} + \frac{1}{\omega^2 L^2}\right)^{1/2} \tag{3.13a}$$

Similarly, the resultant impedance vector in the series circuit is given by

$$Z = R + j\omega L \tag{3.14}$$

$$= Z_1 + Z_2, \tag{3.15}$$

where the magnitude of Z in ohms is given by

$$|Z| = (|Z_1|^2 + |Z_2|^2)^{1/2} \tag{3.16}$$

$$= (R^2 + \omega^2 L^2)^{1/2} \tag{3.16a}$$

Some typical transformers are illustrated in Fig. 3.11. A power transformer, which usually provides several secondary voltages for different purposes, is an essential component of any mains-operated instrument. Since the effects of mutual inductance depend on *changing* primary current, it is obvious that transformers are not useful for direct current; the low-frequency response of a transformer is usually a reflection of its physical size, best response to slowly changing currents being obtained with a massive iron core and many turns of wire. Radiofrequency transformers are commonly air-cored or have a more or less rudimentary core of a low-conductance material such as ferrite. The variable transformer, or autotransformer, one example of which is given in Fig. 3.11, is a convenient source of a variable ac voltage for supplying heaters and filament lamps. Another useful form is the self-regulating transformer in which the primary current is, at peak, sufficient to produce saturation of the flux in the iron core. Thus the maximum field cut by the secondary windings is almost independent of the input voltage. The result is a somewhat distorted secondary waveform whose amplitude is almost independent of variations in the primary voltage. A self-regulating transformer is commonly used as the first stage of voltage regulation in an instrument whose power supplies are operated from the ac mains.

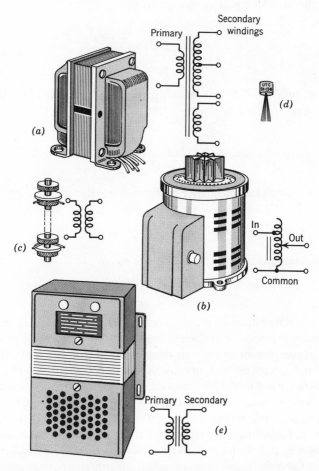

Fig. 3.11 Some practical transformers: (*a*) power transformer for mains input to a power supply, with circuit symbol showing center-tapped secondary winding and low-voltage filament winding; (*b*) variable autotransformer ("variac" or "powerstat") with circuit symbol; (*c*) coreless radiofrequency transformer and circuit symbol; (*d*) subminature transformer for interstage coupling in a transistor amplifier; (*e*) self-regulating transformer for reducing mains-voltage fluctuations and circuit symbol.

Capacitance

The capacitance of an object is a measure of the amount of charge that must be placed on it to raise its electrical potential by a fixed amount. In the cgs electrostatic system of units this definition leads to the simple result that the capacitance of a conducting sphere is equal to its radius in centimeters. The fundamental unit of capacitance is the farad (F), which is the capacitance of a body such that the addition of 1 C of charge raises its potential by 1 V. This turns out to be an inconveniently large unit (the equivalent conducting sphere would be somewhat larger than the earth), and the capacitors normally encountered in electrical circuits have values measured in microfarads (μF $= 10^{-6}$ F) or picofarads (pF $= 10^{-12}$ F). The basic capacitor law is

$$q = CV, \tag{3.17}$$

where q is the charge in coulombs required to raise the potential of a capacitance of C farads by an amount V volts.

Practical capacitors are normally a version of the parallel plate capacitor (Fig. 3.12a) in which V is the voltage between the plates and q is the charge on one plate, the other plate being held at a fixed potential. The plates usually consist of sheets of metal foil, spaced by a thin insulating *dielectric* which may be impregnated paper, polystyrene, polyester, or other plastic. The whole assembly is rolled into a tight cylinder or folded into a slab to conserve space. When high voltage differences are to be withstood or only small values of capacitance are required, the plates are usually in the form of a metal film deposited on opposite sides of a glass or ceramic wafer. Capacitors of this type are available in values ranging from about 10 pF to 10 μF and have no preferred polarity; that is, either plate can be at a positive potential with respect to the other. Larger values of capacitance, from about 0.5 to 10,000 μF, are available in the form of *electrolytic* capacitors, in which the dielectric consists of the thin oxide film formed between a sheet of aluminum or tantalum and a solution of electrolyte when the metal is held at a negative potential with respect to the solution. The metal sheet, which usually forms the outer case of the capacitor, must always be at a negative potential. If there is an inverse potential greater than about 1 V an explosion may occur because of the pressure of gas released by electrolysis inside the case. The most common type of variable capacitor, or "tuning" capacitor, has two sets of parallel plates in air, one set fixed and the other able to rotate on a shaft so that the area of overlap of the plates can be varied continuously. The difference between maximum and minimum capacitance is typically a factor of 10, with the maximum in the range 50 to 1000 pF. Several identical capacitors are often controlled by rotating the same shaft (they are then said to be "ganged") to obtain higher total capacitance or to allow the capacitance in

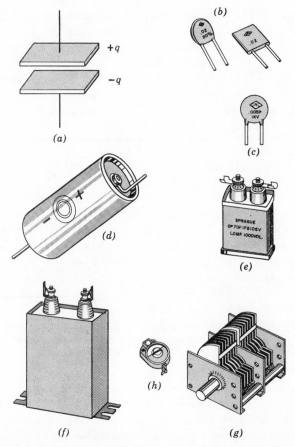

Fig. 3.12 Capacitors: (*a*) principle of parallel-plate capacitor. A charge $+q$ placed on the top plate induces an equal opposite change on the lower plate, so that a current effectively flows *through* the capacitor; (*b*) low-voltage capacitors with plastic dielectric; (*c*) high voltage, ceramic-disk type; (*d*) electrolytic type, high capacitance, low voltage; (*e*) oil-impregnated paper, high voltage; (*f*) oil and plastic, very high voltage (~ 10 kV); (*g*) two-gang variable tuning capacitor; (*h*) minature variable "trimming" capacitor, range 4.5 to 25 pF.

several associated circuits to be varied simultaneously. A selection of fixed and variable capacitors is illustrated in Fig. 3.12b–h.

Consider the effect of applying an alternating voltage to a capacitor C, as in Fig. 3.13a. The voltage difference between the plates is described by

$$E = E_0 \sin \omega t, \tag{3.5}$$

where

$$E = \frac{q}{C}, \tag{3.18}$$

and we expect an ac current of the form

$$I = I_0 \sin (\omega t + \delta), \tag{3.6}$$

where now

$$I = \frac{dq}{dt} \tag{3.19}$$

$$= C \frac{dE}{dt}$$

$$= C\omega E_0 \cos \omega t$$

$$= \omega C E_0 \sin \left(\omega t + \frac{\pi}{2} \right) \tag{3.20}$$

and

$$I_0 = \omega C E_0. \tag{3.21}$$

The particular choice of $\delta = +\pi/2$, illustrated by the waveforms of Fig. 3.13b, is made on the basis of the requirement that the maximum voltage between the plates occurs when the current is just about to change from positive to negative, that is, from charging to discharging the capacitor. Thus a capacitor C has a reactance of $1/\omega C$ ohms, with the current leading the voltage by 90°

Circuits with resistance and capacitance connected in parallel and in series are illustrated in Figs. 3.14 and 3.15, respectively. Once again we can calculate the unknown current or voltage with the aid of vector diagrams, as shown in Fig. 3.16, or else we can write the reactance of the capacitor as $-j/\omega C$. Using the second method, the resultant admittance vector of the parallel circuit is

$$Y = Y_1 + Y_2 \tag{3.12}$$

$$= \frac{1}{R} + j\omega C, \tag{3.22}$$

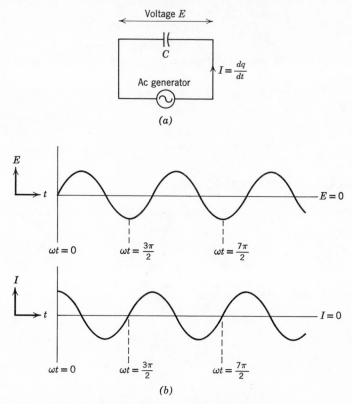

Fig. 3.13 Current and voltage waveforms for a capacitor: (a) circuit diagram; (b) waveforms.

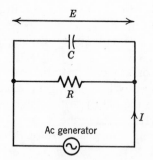

Fig. 3.14 Circuit with capacitance and resistance in parallel; E has the same phase across both R and C.

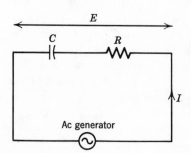

Fig. 3.15 Circuit with capacitance and resistance in series; I has the same phase in both R and C.

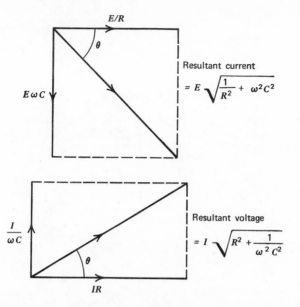

Fig. 3.16 (a) Addition of current vectors for R and C in parallel. The resultant current leads the voltage by an angle $\theta = \tan^{-1}(\omega CR)$. (b) Addition of voltage vectors for R and C in series. The resultant voltage lags behind the current by an angle $\theta = \tan^{-1}(1/\omega CR)$.

where the magnitude of Y in mhos is given by

$$|Y| = (|Y_1|^2 + |Y_2|^2)^{1/2} \tag{3.13}$$

$$= \left(\frac{1}{R^2} + \omega^2 C^2\right)^{1/2}. \tag{3.13b}$$

Similarly, the resultant impedance vector of the series circuit is given by

$$Z = Z_1 + Z_2 \tag{3.15}$$

$$= R - \frac{j}{\omega C} \tag{3.23}$$

where the magnitude of Z in ohms is given by

$$|Z| = (|Z_1|^2 + |Z_2|^2)^{1/2} \tag{3.16}$$

$$= \left(R^2 + \frac{1}{\omega^2 C^2}\right)^{1/2}. \tag{3.16b}$$

The main advantage of the vector diagram is that it makes it easy to see how to calculate the final phase difference between current and voltage.

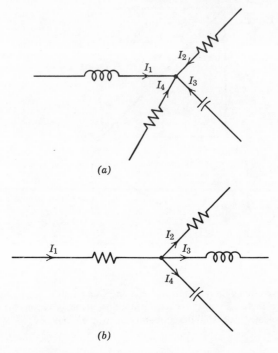

(a)

(b)

Fig. 3.17 Illustrations of Kirchhoff's first law: (a) $(I_1 + I_2 + I_3 + I_4) = O$; (b) $I_1 = (I_2 + I_3 + I_4)$.

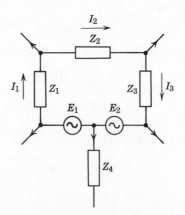

Fig. 3.18 Illustration of Kirchhoff's second law: $E_1 + E_2 = I_1Z_1 + I_2Z_2 + I_3Z_3$.

2 NETWORKS CONTAINING *R, L,* AND *C*

Kirchhoff's Laws

In this section we consider the relationships between currents and voltages in *passive networks*. A passive network is one in which the relationships between input and output currents and voltages are always linear, the coefficients of the linear equations being functions of the impedances and admittances in the network. An active network, containing tubes, transistors, or diodes in addition to *R, L,* and *C,* is described by linear equations over only a limited current or voltage range. Passive networks are important constituents of nearly all measuring instruments. Sometimes they are used merely to fix the voltage and current levels so that a tube or transistor is operating in its linear range or to condition a signal so that it is suitable for acceptance by an active network. At other times, as in a conductance bridge, they constitute virtually the whole instrument.

In the last section we encountered two basic laws for combinations of circuit elements; namely, for elements in series the total impedance is the (vector) sum of the individual impedances and for elements in parallel the total admittance is the sum of the individual admittances. There are two further laws, known as Kirchhoff's laws, that we shall often use. The first is the following:

The algebraic sum of the currents entering and leaving at any point in a steady current network is zero.

This statement, which can be regarded either as a consequence of the requirement that electric charge be conserved or as a definition of a steady current network, is illustrated in Fig. 3.17. The second law is the following:

The sum of the products of current and impedance around any closed loop in a steady current network is equal to the sum of the emfs of any generators included in the closed loop.

This statement is illustrated in Fig. 3.18. There are certain restrictions on the manner in which these laws can be used, especially the second law. The first restriction is that ac and dc currents, when both are present, should always be dealt with separately. With direct current there is no need to consider effects of phase angle; a capacitor can be regarded as essentially an infinite resistance and an inductor as a very low resistance. The second restriction is that when more than one ac generator is involved we must take account of any phase or frequency difference between the ac signals that they produce. In practice it may be easiest to analyze the network for each generator separately and to obtain the final current or voltage at any point by superposition of the separate sine-wave contributions from all generators.

Applications of Kirchhoff's Laws to Simple Networks

Figure 3.19 shows one section of a ladder network in which it is not specified whether the impedances are R, L, or C. This is a four-terminal network with two input and two output terminals and corresponding input and output voltages. From the first law we obtain

$$I_1 = I_2 + I_3 \tag{3.24}$$

and from the second law

$$E_1 = I_1 Z_1 + I_2 Z_2 \tag{3.25}$$

we also see that

$$E_2 = I_2 Z_2. \tag{3.26}$$

We can eliminate I_2 from these equations and rearrange the two equations into the forms

$$E_1 = \frac{Z_1 + Z_2}{Z_2} E_2 + Z_1 I_3 \tag{3.27}$$

$$I_1 = \frac{1}{Z_2} E_2 + I_3, \tag{3.28}$$

which relate the input voltage and current to the output voltage and current and the circuit impedances. Equations 3.27 and 3.28 are conveniently combined in the matrix expression

$$\begin{pmatrix} E_1 \\ I_1 \end{pmatrix} = \begin{pmatrix} \dfrac{Z_1 + Z_2}{Z_2} & Z_1 \\ \dfrac{1}{Z_2} & 1 \end{pmatrix} \times \begin{pmatrix} E_2 \\ I_3 \end{pmatrix}. \tag{3.29}$$

The main advantage of this formalism is that if we have several networks in series, as in Fig. 3.20, the matrix relating the input voltage and current to the

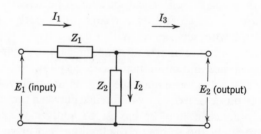

Fig. 3.19   Simple four-terminal network.

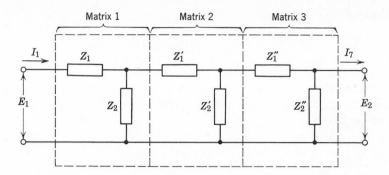

Fig. 3.20 Three simple networks cascaded.

output voltage and current for the whole system is simply the product of the individual matrices for the separate network sections. For the sake of review the method of forming the product of two 2×2 matrices is shown in (3.30):

$$\begin{pmatrix} a_1 & a_2 \\ a_3 & a_4 \end{pmatrix} \times \begin{pmatrix} b_1 & b_2 \\ b_3 & b_4 \end{pmatrix} = \begin{pmatrix} a_1b_1 + a_2b_3 & a_1b_2 + a_2b_4 \\ a_3b_1 + a_4b_3 & a_3b_2 + a_4b_4 \end{pmatrix}. \tag{3.30}$$

We note that the product is also a 2×2 matrix whose elements are linear combinations of products of the elements of the separate matrices. In an alternative notation (3.30) could be written

$$\begin{pmatrix} a_{11} & a_{12} \\ a_{21} & a_{22} \end{pmatrix} \times \begin{pmatrix} b_{11} & b_{12} \\ b_{21} & b_{22} \end{pmatrix} = \begin{pmatrix} a_{11}b_{11} + a_{12}b_{21} & a_{11}b_{12} + a_{12}b_{22} \\ a_{21}b_{11} + a_{22}b_{21} & a_{21}b_{12} + a_{22}b_{22} \end{pmatrix},$$

$$\tag{3.31}$$

which would enable us to write for the matrix C, given by

$$A \times B = C, \tag{3.32}$$

the standard result

$$c_{ij} = \sum_k a_{ik}b_{kj}. \tag{3.33}$$

The matrix equation (3.32) can be rearranged into the form

$$B = A^{-1} \cdot C \tag{3.34}$$

since

$$A^{-1} \cdot A \cdot B = A^{-1} \cdot C, \tag{3.35}$$

where A^{-1} is a matrix defined as the reciprocal of A. [Note that the order of factors in (3.34) is important.] Any square matrix for which the corresponding determinant is nonzero can be shown to have a reciprocal which is given by

$$(a_{ij})^{-1} = \left(\frac{\hat{A}_{ij}}{\text{Det } A} \right). \tag{3.36}$$

Here $(a_{ij})^{-1}$ is the element corresponding to a_{ij} in the reciprocal matrix, $\hat{A}_{ij}$ is the cofactor of a_{ji} (not of a_{ij}) in the determinant corresponding to the original matrix (a_{ij}), and Det A is this determinant. For our present 2×2 matrix we have

$$\text{Det } A = \begin{vmatrix} a_{11} & a_{12} \\ a_{21} & a_{22} \end{vmatrix} = a_{11}a_{22} - a_{12}a_{21}. \tag{3.37}$$

The cofactor of an element a_{ji} in the determinant is $(-1)^{i+j}$ times the part remaining when row j and column i containing the element are crossed out. Hence, for example,

$$\hat{A}_{12} = \text{cofactor of } a_{21} = -a_{12} \tag{3.38}$$

$$\hat{A}_{22} = \text{cofactor of } a_{22} = +a_{11} \tag{3.39}$$

and

$$A^{-1} = \begin{pmatrix} \dfrac{a_{22}}{\text{Det } A} & \dfrac{-a_{12}}{\text{Det } A} \\[2ex] \dfrac{-a_{21}}{\text{Det } A} & \dfrac{a_{11}}{\text{Det } A} \end{pmatrix}. \tag{3.40}$$

The formula for the reciprocal matrix (3.36) can be obtained in a straightforward way by solving the simultaneous equations corresponding to (3.32) when B and C are column matrices. With the aid of this formula it is a simple matter to transform (3.29) into an equation giving E_2 and I_3 explicitly in terms of E_1 and I_1. The result is

$$\begin{pmatrix} \dfrac{Z_1 + Z_2}{Z_2} & -Z_1 \\[2ex] \dfrac{-1}{Z_2} & 1 \end{pmatrix} \times \begin{pmatrix} E_1 \\ I_1 \end{pmatrix} = \begin{pmatrix} E_2 \\ I_3 \end{pmatrix}. \tag{3.41}$$

Another situation in which the matrix notation is particularly advantageous occurs when networks are connected in parallel. In this case we arrange the equations connecting input and output voltages and currents for the individual networks in the form

$$I = Y \times E, \tag{3.42}$$

where I is the column matrix of the input and output currents, E is the corresponding matrix for voltages, and Y is a 2×2 matrix whose coefficients are functions of the admittances in the network. When the networks are connected in parallel, they must all have the same input and output voltages

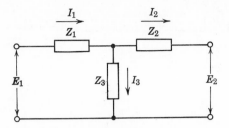

Fig. 3.21 Single-*T* network.

but the total input and output currents are the sums of the contributions from each network. Thus we can write

$$(I + I' + I'' + \cdots) = (Y + Y' + Y'' + \cdots) \times E, \tag{3.43}$$

where the addition rule for the matrices I and Y is simply

$$\begin{pmatrix} y_{11} & y_{12} \\ y_{21} & y_{22} \end{pmatrix} + \begin{pmatrix} y'_{11} & y'_{12} \\ y'_{21} & y'_{22} \end{pmatrix} = \begin{pmatrix} y_{11} + y'_{11} & y_{12} + y'_{12} \\ y_{21} + y'_{21} & y_{22} + y'_{22} \end{pmatrix}. \tag{3.44}$$

It should be recalled that two matrices can form a sum only if they have the same number of rows and the same number of columns and can form a product only if the number of columns of the first is the same as the number of rows of the second.

To illustrate the use of (3.43) we consider the *T*-network of Fig. 3.21. Kirchhoff's laws give

$$I_1 = I_2 + I_3 \tag{3.45}$$

and

$$E_1 = I_1 Z_1 + I_3 Z_3, \tag{3.46}$$

$$E_2 = I_3 Z_3 - I_2 Z_2. \tag{3.47}$$

Eliminating I_3 and rearranging, we obtain

$$I_1 = \frac{Z_2 + Z_3}{Z} \cdot E_1 - \frac{1}{Z} \cdot E_2,$$

$$I_2 = \frac{Z_3}{Z} \cdot E_1 - \frac{Z_1 + Z_3}{Z} \cdot E_2,$$

which in matrix form is

$$\begin{pmatrix} I_1 \\ I_2 \end{pmatrix} = \begin{pmatrix} \dfrac{Z_2 + Z_3}{Z} & -\dfrac{1}{Z} \\ \dfrac{Z_3}{Z} & -\dfrac{Z_1 + Z_3}{Z} \end{pmatrix} \times \begin{pmatrix} E_1 \\ E_2 \end{pmatrix}. \tag{3.48}$$

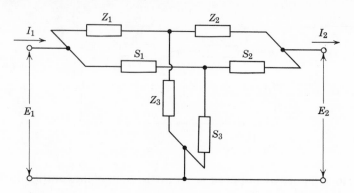

Fig. 3.22 *T* networks in parallel.

Here we have written Z as an abbreviation for $(Z_1 Z_2 + Z_2 Z_3 + Z_3 Z_1)$. We now have the equation corresponding to (3.42). Therefore, with two such networks in parallel, as in Fig. 3.22, we can immediately write

$$\begin{pmatrix} I_1 \\ I_2 \end{pmatrix} = \begin{pmatrix} \dfrac{(Z_2 + Z_3)S + (S_2 + S_3)Z}{SZ} & -\dfrac{S + Z}{SZ} \\ \dfrac{Z_3 S + S_3 Z}{SZ} & -\dfrac{(Z_1 + Z_3)S + (S_1 + S_3)Z}{SZ} \end{pmatrix} \times \begin{pmatrix} E_1 \\ E_2 \end{pmatrix}$$

(3.49)

where we have used S in place of Z for the second network to avoid possible confusion between primed and unprimed quantities.

More elaborate networks can be built up from series and parallel combinations of those we have considered. In the next part of this section we consider some networks of practical importance, with specified circuit elements in place of the general impedances Z.

Some Practical Networks

Consider the *integrating network* of Fig. 3.23. Here we must use (3.29),

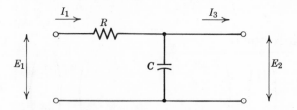

Fig. 3.23 Integrating network.

with $Z_1 = R$ and $Z_2 = 1/j\omega C$. The 2×2 matrix therefore becomes

$$\begin{pmatrix} 1 + Rj\omega C & R \\ j\omega C & 1 \end{pmatrix},$$ (3.50)

which enables us to relate E_1, I_1 to E_2, I_3 in the general case. To determine the reason for the name "integrating network" let us suppose that E_2 is measured with a device which has a very high input impedance, that is, which draws a negligible current from the output terminals. A cathode-ray oscilloscope would be the ideal choice. We now have $I_3 = 0$, so that the top line of the matrix equation reduces to

$$E_1 = E_2(1 + Rj\omega C)$$ (3.51)

$$= E_2 Rj\omega C,$$ (3.52)

when ω is large, that is, at high frequencies. Now

$$E_1 = E_1^\circ \sin \omega t$$ (3.5)

so

$$\int_{\pi/2\omega}^{t} E_1 \, dt = -\frac{E_1^\circ}{\omega} \cdot \cos \omega t.$$ (3.53)

(Here the lower limit of the integral was chosen to eliminate an inconvenient constant term which would result from starting the integration at $t = 0$.) On the right-hand side of 3.53 we can replace $\cos \omega t$ by $j \cdot \sin \omega t$ and the integral becomes

$$\frac{-jE_1}{\omega} = E_2 RC.$$ (3.54)

Putting this result in words, the output voltage of the integrating network is equal to $1/RC$ times the time-integrated value of the input voltage, provided $R\omega C$ is much greater than unity. We also note that when ω is very small compared with $1/RC$ we have

$$E_1 = E_2,$$ (3.55)

so that as the frequency is increased gradually from zero the output-voltage signal changes from being exactly in phase with the input to being $90°$ out of phase, lagging behind the input. The changeover occurs, as can be seen in Fig. 3.25, in a relatively narrow band of frequencies near $\omega = 1/RC$.

Next consider the *differentiating network* of Fig. 3.24. We again use (3.29), in this case with $Z_1 = 1/j\omega C$ and $Z_2 = R$, and the 2×2 matrix becomes

$$\begin{pmatrix} 1 + \dfrac{1}{jR\omega C} & \dfrac{1}{j\omega C} \\ \dfrac{1}{R} & 1 \end{pmatrix}.$$ (3.56)

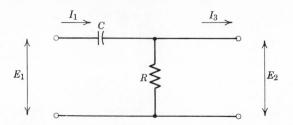

Fig. 3.24 Differentiating network.

Once more we let $I_3 = 0$ and the top line of the matrix equation yields

$$E_1 = E_2\left(1 - \frac{j}{R\omega C}\right),$$ (3.57)

so in this case

$$E_1 = E_2,$$ (3.58)

when ω is large compared with $1/RC$, whereas when ω is small compared with $1/RC$ we have

$$E_1 = \frac{-jE_2}{R\omega C}.$$ (3.59)

The changeover from the output leading the input by 90° to the output being in phase with the input occurs near $\omega = 1/RC$ and is also shown in Fig. 3.25. To see the reason for the name "differentiating network" we differentiate both sides of (3.5) and obtain

$$\frac{dE_1}{dt} = \omega E_1^\circ \cos \omega t$$ (3.60)

$$= j\omega E_1^\circ \sin \omega t$$ (3.61)

$$= j\omega E_1$$ (3.62)

$$= \frac{E_2}{RC},$$ (3.63)

when ω is small compared with $1/RC$. In words, the result is that the output voltage of the differentiating network is RC times the time-derivative of the input voltage, provided $R\omega C$ is much less than unity.

Next we consider some simple RC networks whose practical utility depends on the existence of a frequency at which the j-component of the output signal is zero; that is, the output is either exactly in phase or 180° out of phase with the input. Such *phase-shift networks* are widely used to control the frequency of the output from audiofrequency oscillators; some examples of this application are given in Chapter IV.

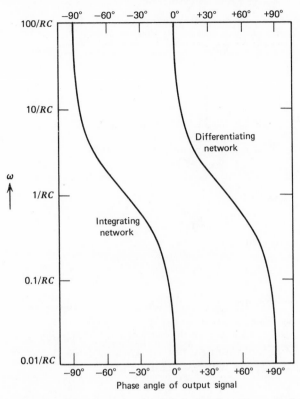

Fig. 3.25   Relative phase of output signal as a function of $\omega = 2\pi f$ for integrating and differentiating networks.

The zero phase-shift network of Fig. 3.26 consists of two sections in series, the first having the matrix (3.50) and the second, the matrix (3.56). The product of the two matrices is found to be

$$\begin{pmatrix} 3 + jR\omega C - \dfrac{j}{R\omega C} & 2R - \dfrac{j}{\omega C} \\[2mm] \dfrac{2}{R} + j\omega C & 2 \end{pmatrix}, \tag{3.64}$$

so that if the output voltage is measured without drawing any appreciable current, for example, by using an oscilloscope, the top line of the matrix equation reduces to

$$E_1 = E_2 \left(3 + jR\omega C - \dfrac{j}{R\omega C} \right), \tag{3.65}$$

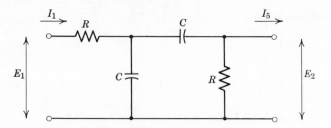

Fig. 3.26   Zero phase-shift network for voltage signals.

which further reduces to

$$E_1 = 3E_2 \tag{3.66}$$

at the frequency given by

$$\omega = \frac{1}{RC}, \tag{3.67}$$

at which frequency the input and output are exactly in phase and the input signal is attenuated by a factor of 3.

It is also interesting to connect the network in reverse, as in Fig. 3.27, and to compare the input and output *currents*. The matrix we require is now the reciprocal of (3.64), which is readily found to be

$$
\begin{pmatrix}
2 & \dfrac{j}{\omega C} - 2R \\[3mm]
-j\omega C - \dfrac{2}{R} & 3 + jR\omega C - \dfrac{j}{R\omega C}
\end{pmatrix} = (Z), \tag{3.68}
$$

where now

$$(Z) \times \begin{pmatrix} E_1 \\ I_1 \end{pmatrix} = \begin{pmatrix} E_2 \\ I_5 \end{pmatrix}. \tag{3.69}$$

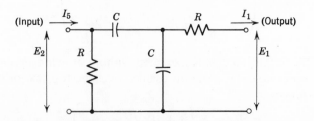

Fig. 3.27   Zero phase-shift network for current signals.

Hence, if the output current I_1 is measured with a very low impedance instrument (an ordinary ac ammeter is a good approximation to this) so that the output voltage is zero, the bottom line of the matrix equation reduces to

$$I_1\left(3 + jR\omega C - \frac{j}{R\omega C}\right) = I_5. \tag{3.70}$$

In this case the input and output currents are exactly in phase at $\omega = 1/RC$, when

$$I_5 = 3I_1. \tag{3.71}$$

The reader may have noticed that the symmetry of the results for the voltage and current networks stems from the fact that the determinants of the matrices (3.50) and (3.56) have the value unity [the same is true of (3.41), (3.64), and (3.68)]. Whenever the determinant is unity, we have from (3.40) the result

$$(a_{11})^{-1} = a_{22}, \tag{3.72}$$

so that a relationship which holds between the input and output voltages of a network when the output current is zero must also hold between the input and output currents when the same network is connected in reverse and the output voltage is zero.

The networks of Figs. 3.26 and 3.27 work on the principle that the phase shift produced by the first combination of R and C is exactly reversed by the second and a zero phase shift results. To achieve a phase shift of 180° in this way we combine three sections, each giving a shift of 60°, as in Fig. 3.28. However, we cannot simply use three sections chosen to give a 60° phase shift on the basis of Fig. 3.25 because the first two sections will not be operating into a high impedance. For network (a) it is necessary to multiply together three matrices similar to (3.50) and for network (b), three matrices

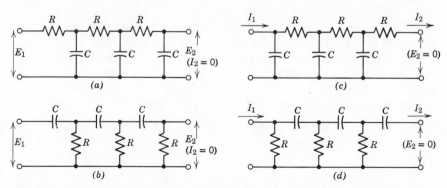

Fig. 3.28   180° phase-shift networks; (a) and (b) for voltage signals, (c) and (d) for current signals.

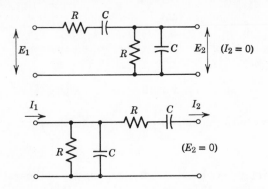

Fig. 3.29 Wien bridge zero phase-shift networks for voltage and current signals.

similar to (3.56). The results for networks (c) and (d) will then follow immediately because the relevant determinants are unity. It is left as an exercise for the reader to show that the 180° phase shift occurs at $\omega = 1/RC\sqrt{6}$ and that the input signal is attenuated by a factor of 29 at this frequency.

One further network of this type that we should consider is the *Wien bridge* network of Fig. 3.29, which is used to produce a zero phase shift. For the voltage signal case we use (3.29), with $Z_1 = R + 1/j\omega C$ and $1/Z_2 = 1/R + j\omega C$. The resulting matrix is

$$\begin{pmatrix} 3 + jR\omega C - \dfrac{j}{R\omega C} & R + \dfrac{1}{j\omega C} \\[4mm] \dfrac{1}{R} + j\omega C & 1 \end{pmatrix}, \tag{3.73}$$

which leads to the same frequency of zero phase shift and attenuation factor that were found for the network in Fig. 3.26.

The *twin T-network* of Fig. 3.30 has the useful property that there is one particular frequency at which the attenuation factor becomes infinite, that is, signals of this frequency are excluded from the output signal. The matrix equation in this case is (3.49), with $Z_1 = Z_2 = R, Z_3 = 1/2j\omega C, S_1 = S_2 = 1/j\omega C$, and $S_3 = R/2$. If the network works into a high impedance, that is, $I_2 = 0$, the bottom line of the matrix equation yields

$$\frac{E_1(Z_3 S + S_3 Z)}{SZ} = \frac{E_2(Z_1 S + Z_3 S + S_1 Z + S_3 Z)}{SZ}, \tag{3.74}$$

where

$$S = S_1 S_2 + S_2 S_3 + S_3 S_1 = \frac{-(1 + j\omega CR)}{\omega^2 C^2} \tag{3.75}$$

and

$$Z = Z_1Z_2 + Z_2Z_3 + Z_3Z_1 = \frac{R(1 + j\omega CR)}{j\omega C}.$$ (3.76)

The condition $E_2/E_1 = 0$ thus reduces to

$$0 = Z_3S + S_3Z$$

$$= \frac{(1 + j\omega CR)(R^2\omega^2C^2 - 1)}{2j\omega^3C^3};$$

that is,

$$\omega = \frac{1}{RC} = 2\pi f$$ (3.77)

which gives the frequency at which the input signal is completely attenuated. The value of E_1/E_2 and the phase shift at any other frequency can be calculated from the formula

$$\frac{E_1}{E_2} = \frac{1 + 4jR\omega C}{R^2\omega^2C^2 - 1},$$ (3.78)

which is obtained by substituting the values of S and Z in (3.74).

So far we have considered only networks containing resistance and capacitance, that is, RC networks. Networks containing resistance and inductance can be treated in an analogous way and it is possible to devise RL networks to replace any of the RC networks we have considered. However, because of the valuable ability of a capacitor to isolate the dc voltage levels on its terminals from one another and because of the relative ease of fabrication of capacitors having any desired value of capacitance over a very wide range, the capabilities of RL networks are not often exploited. Inductors find their greatest application in LC networks, especially in the resonant circuits which are discussed in the next part of this section.

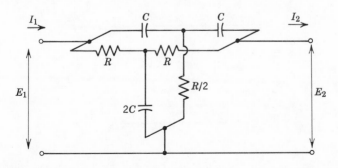

Fig. 3.30   Twin-T network.

Resonant Circuits

Two possible configurations for an LC resonant circuit are shown in Fig. 3.31, in which the residual resistance of the coil of wire that makes up the inductor L is shown as a separate resistor r. For the series circuit (a) we have

$$Z = r + j\omega L - \frac{j}{\omega C}, \tag{3.79}$$

and we observe that at the frequency

$$\omega = (LC)^{-\frac{1}{2}} \tag{3.80}$$

we have simply

$$Z = r.$$

and the voltage and current signals are exactly in phase, with

$$E_0 = I_0 r \tag{3.81}$$

At any other frequency the magnitude of Z in ohms is given by

$$|Z|^2 = r^2 + \left(\omega L - \frac{1}{\omega C}\right)^2, \tag{3.82}$$

so that the current which flows at the *resonant frequency* given by (3.80) is the maximum current for a particular value of E_0. At the resonant frequency

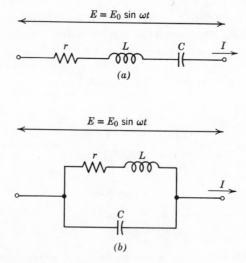

Fig. 3.31 (a) Series resonant circuit; (b) parallel resonant circuit. The residual resistance of the inductor is indicated by the small resistor r.

the voltage across either the inductor or the capacitor separately is equal to $I\omega L$, which can be very much greater than the voltage Ir across the whole circuit. In effect the circuit behaves in the same manner as a pendulum which is set into oscillation by a series of correctly timed gentle impulses; the final amplitude of the oscillation is limited only by the amount of damping, which in the pendulum case is made up of air resistance and friction and in the coil is due to the unwanted resistance r. The applications of resonant circuits exploit the voltage magnification that occurs at the resonance frequency, and it is usually desirable that this magnification be as large as possible. Thus the ratio of the voltages, which is given by

$$Q = \frac{\omega L}{r} = \left(\frac{L}{r^2 C}\right)^{1/2},$$ (3.83)

is widely used as a figure of merit for such circuits. A typical coil with an inductance of 2.0 mH, and resistance of 200 Ω, would have a Q of 628 in a circuit for which the resonant frequency $f\,(= \omega/2\pi)$ was 10 MHz.

For the parallel resonant circuit of Fig. 3.31*b* we have

$$Y = j\omega C + \frac{1}{r + j\omega L},$$ (3.84)

which is best rearranged into the form

$$Y = \frac{r + j(\omega C r^2 + \omega^3 L^2 C - \omega L)}{(r^2 + \omega^2 L^2)}.$$ (3.85)

If we neglect $\omega C r^2$ in comparison with $\omega^3 L^2 C$ in the numerator, we find that the condition for the voltage and current signals to be in phase is simply $\omega^2 LC = 1$; that is, the resonant frequency is also given by (3.80) in this case. At the resonant frequency (3.85) reduces to

$$Y = \frac{1 + j/Q}{r(1 + 1/Q^2)}$$

$$= \frac{1}{r}$$

to a good approximation. This is a minimum value of Y, so that at resonance the current flowing through the circuit is also a minimum.

It is interesting to consider the amount of energy that is stored in a resonant circuit as a result of excitation by a small current i at the resonant frequency. Physically it is easy to see that the energy is transferred back and forth between the inductor and the capacitor twice during each cycle, whereas the total amount of stored energy remains constant. Thus we have only to consider the peak amount of energy associated either with the fully charged capacitor or with the field of the inductor when the current is at its maximum. The work done in building up the current in an inductor to a value I is the integral of $LI\,dI$, or $\frac{1}{2}LI^2$, which is the energy stored in the magnetic field at the end of the process; similarly the stored energy in a capacitor is the integral of $V\,dq = CV\,dV$, or $\frac{1}{2}CV^2$. For the present purpose we use, for the small current whose peak value is i_0, the formula

$$\text{energy stored} = \tfrac{1}{2}Li_0{}^2. \tag{3.87}$$

Now let us compare this with the total energy dissipated in one cycle in the resistance r. The instantaneous dissipation is

$$w(t) = ri_0{}^2 \sin^2 \omega t, \tag{3.88}$$

so that, since the average value of $\sin^2 \omega t$ is $\frac{1}{2}$, the energy dissipated in one cycle is given by

$$\text{energy dissipated} = \tfrac{1}{2}ri_0{}^2, \tag{3.89}$$

and by comparison of (3.87), (3.89), and (3.83) we obtain

$$Q = \frac{\omega \times \text{energy stored}}{\text{energy dissipated per cycle}}. \tag{3.90}$$

This provides an alternative definition of Q which is applicable to electrical systems in which the quantities appearing in (3.83) are difficult to evaluate, for example, to the case of a microwave cavity resonator, and even to resonance in nonelectrical systems such as pendulums and organ pipes.

If we plot $1/|Z|$ for the series circuit against ω, we obtain a graph that shows how the voltage developed across the capacitor or inductor varies with frequency. The result is a resonance curve, of which several examples are shown in Fig. 3.32. It is apparent that a high value of Q corresponds to a tall and narrow resonance peak, with the current falling off very rapidly as ω varies from the resonant frequency. If we define the "half-power points" as the values of frequency at which the current, or $1/|Z|$, has fallen to 0.707 of its peak value, the *bandwidth* of the resonant circuit is defined as the difference between the frequencies at the half-power points. It can be shown that Q is equal to the ratio of the resonance frequency to the bandwidth; that is,

$$Q = \frac{\omega_0}{\Delta\omega} = \frac{f_0}{\Delta f}. \tag{3.91}$$

[To obtain this result note that at the half-power points $|Z|^2 = 2r^2$ and solve the two quadratic equations in ω that result from substituting this value of $|Z|^2$ in (3.82).] Equation 3.91 enables Q to be determined experimentally from the shape of a measured resonance peak.

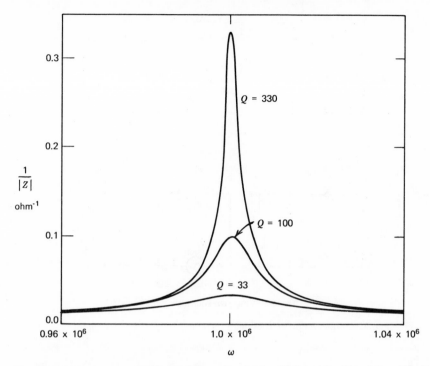

Fig. 3.32   Resonance curves calculated for series circuit with $L = 1.0$ mH and $C = 10^3$ pF; with $Q = 330, 100,$ and 33, corresponding to $r = 3\Omega, 10\Omega,$ and 30Ω.

Thevenin's and Norton's Theorems

It often happens in practice that we have a relatively large and complicated network whose detailed internal behavior does not have to be known, since only the currents and voltages at specified pairs of terminals are required. We suppose here that the network is a passive one or that we are in a range in which linear equations hold if active circuit elements such as transistors and tubes are present. According to *Thevenin's theorem*, the voltage signal delivered at a pair of output terminals is then completely equivalent to that of an output voltage generator, with a signal E_{out} in series with an output impedance Z_{out}. This is illustrated in Fig. 3.33, in which we have assumed a load Z_L across the output terminals and in which we have also included a pair of input terminals and an external signal generator with an input voltage E_{in}. The voltage signal generators are assumed to have negligible internal resistance. The input terminals are identical with the output terminals, except that no signal voltage exists between them in the absence of the external generator and we are left with just an input impedance Z_{in}.

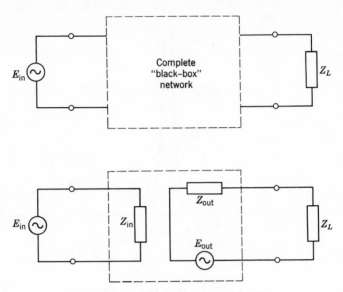

Thevenin's theorem equivalent circuit

Fig. 3.33 Illustration of Thevenin's theorem.

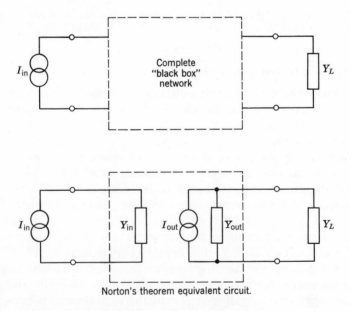

Norton's theorem equivalent circuit.

Fig. 3.34 Norton's theorem equivalent circuit.

For any pair of terminals the corresponding impedance is to be found by measuring the impedance between the terminals when all *independent* voltage sources are removed, that is, when there is no other signal input to the network. Thus for the present four-terminal network

$$Z_{\text{out}} = \left(\frac{\partial E_{\text{out}}}{\partial I_{\text{out}}}\right)_{E_{\text{in}}} \tag{3.92}$$

and

$$Z_{\text{in}} = \left(\frac{\partial E_{\text{in}}}{\partial I_{\text{in}}}\right)_{E_{\text{ext}}}, \tag{3.93}$$

where E_{ext} is any external signal source that might be in series with Z_L. The voltage signal E_{out} is to be found by measuring the voltage between the terminals when they are open-circuited; that is, when Z_L is infinite.

The alternative representation, according to *Norton's theorem*, is illustrated in Fig. 3.34. Here we have an external current generator I_{in} of very high internal resistance and an external load admittance Y_L, and the network is now represented at the output by a similar current generator I_{out} in parallel with an output admittance Y_{out}. The admittances of the equivalent network in this case are simply the reciprocals of the impedances found in the application of Thevenin's theorem; that is,

$$Y_{\text{out}} = \frac{1}{Z_{\text{out}}}, \tag{3.94}$$

$$Y_{\text{in}} = \frac{1}{Z_{\text{in}}}, \tag{3.95}$$

The current signal I_{out} is to be found by measuring the current that flows between the output terminals when they are short-circuited, that is, when Y_L is infinite. It follows, from Fig. 3.33, that

$$E_{\text{out}} = I_{\text{out}} Z_{\text{out}}. \tag{3.96}$$

With the aid of the last three equations we can change from the Thevenin representation to the Norton, or vice-versa, according to which is more convenient for the purpose at hand. This conversion is referred to as a *source transformation*. It is important to note that the two forms of equivalent circuit yield identical results only at the terminals under consideration and not at other points in the network. Thus, for example, when Z_L is infinite the power dissipated in Z_{out} in Fig. 3.33 is zero, but in the circuit of Fig. 3.34 with the terminals open-circuited the current generator still dissipates power in the shunt impedance Y_{out}. Some important source transformations, and the relationships between the corresponding voltage and current generators in the equivalent circuits, are given in Fig. 3.35.

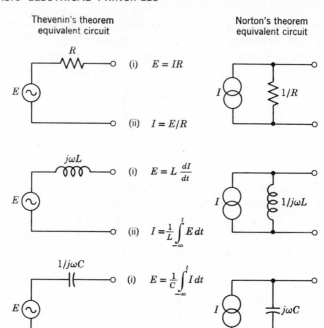

Fig. 3.35 Source transformations for resistance, inductance, and capacitance.

3   ELECTRICAL MEASUREMENTS

Direct-Current Measurements

The measurable quantities encountered so far in this chapter fall naturally into three groups: dc voltage and current; ac voltage, current, frequency, and phase angle; and resistance (or conductance), inductance, capacitance, and resultant impedance for their various combinations. We discuss methods of measurement for each of these groups in turn. A fourth group of measurable quantities related to signals in the form of short pulses, constituting pulse height, pulse width, rise and delay time, and repetition rate, is considered in Chapter IV.

The fundamental measurement of direct current involves the measurement of the force between two current-carrying wires in some form of current balance. This type of measurement, however, is usually confined to national laboratories concerned with the maintenance of primary and secondary standards. For precise current measurements in a research laboratory it is customary to measure the voltage drop produced when the current flows through a standard resistor or, rarely, the integrated current over a period of time by weighing the silver deposited in a silver coulometer. A somewhat less precise measurement involves the determination of the amount of iodine liberated when the current is passed between platinum electrodes immersed in a solution of potassium iodide, that is, through an iodine coulometer. The most convenient method of detecting or measuring direct current when the accuracy is not required to be better than about 0.1 % is to use a galvanometer or a moving-coil meter, of which many varieties exist. Since the moving coil meter is the most often encountered device for measuring current, we consider it first.

The operating principle of a typical moving-coil meter is illustrated in Fig. 3.36. Most of the panel meters used in scientific instruments are of this type. The torque produced by the interaction of the current in the coil with the field of the permanent magnet is just counteracted by the restoring force due to the small coiled spring. The zero reading of the meter can be adjusted by altering the position of the fixed end of the restoring spring. Depending on the thickness of the wire used in the coil, the strength of the restoring

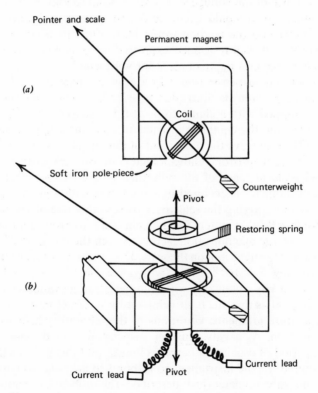

Fig. 3.36 Diagram of construction of a moving-coil ammeter: (a) plan; (b) perspective.

spring, and the delicacy of the suspension, the full-scale reading of the meter may range from tens of amperes to about 10 μA (10^{-5} A). The more sensitive meters sometimes have an external *clamp* lever, by which the coil can be immobilized when the meter is not in use. When this is not present, it is advisable to short-circuit the terminals with a piece of wire so that the pointer will not oscillate excessively while the meter is being moved about (cf. Lenz's law). The current range of the meter can always be extended by adding a *shunt* resistor in parallel with the coil; if R is the resistance of the shunt and r, that of the coil, the current required for a full-scale reading is multiplied by a factor $(1 + r/R)$. Alternatively, a sensitive meter can be used as a *voltmeter* if a large resistance is placed in series with the coil; for example, a meter reading 50 μA full scale and a series resistor of 1 M together constitute a voltmeter reading 50 V full scale. Ideally a voltmeter should draw no current at all; that is, it should have an infinite internal resistance, since the reading given by the meter is always too low by an amount equal to the current flowing multiplied by the internal resistance of the voltage source. If the internal resistance of the voltage source were equal to that of the voltmeter, half the voltage drop would occur across the source resistance and half across the meter and the reading would be too low by a factor of 2. The reciprocal of the internal resistance, expressed as so many *amperes-per-volt*, is commonly stated as a figure of merit for voltmeters.

The type of coil suspension used in a sensitive reflecting galvanometer (D'Arsonval suspension) is illustrated in Fig. 3.37. These instruments are invariably equipped with a clamp to protect the suspension when it is not in use. In addition, the complete instrument contains a light source and a scale on which to observe the movement of the reflected beam and, usually, a selection of shunt resistors. Galvanometers of low sensitivity may have a pointer and scale in place of the reflecting system. A convenient type of sensitive galvanometer is enclosed in a small box with a glass scale on the front, a switch for varying the sensitivity by selecting one of several shunts, and a multiple-reflection system for the light beam to provide a long *optical lever*, that is, a large magnification factor between the mirror deflection and the movement of the light spot on the scale. The sensitivity of such an arrangement is typically 5×10^{-9} A/mm, with an optical lever 1 m long. The maximum sensitivity obtainable with a moving coil galvanometer is about 500 times as good as this, the limit being set by such factors as the effects of small temperature gradients, vibrations of the laboratory as a whole, and Brownian motion. As a galvanometer suspension is made more delicate, its natural period of oscillation becomes longer, and this governs the length of time required for the instrument to respond to a change in current. For the box-type galvanometer just described the oscillation period would typically be 2 to 3 sec; for an extremely sensitive galvanometer suspension

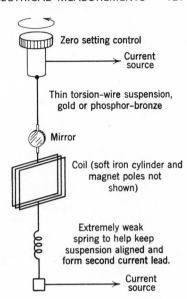

Zero setting control

Current source

Thin torsion-wire suspension, gold or phosphor-bronze

Mirror

Coil (soft iron cylinder and magnet poles not shown)

Extremely weak spring to help keep suspension aligned and form second current lead.

Current source

Fig. 3.37 Typical construction of a sensitive D'Arsonval galvanometer suspension.

it might be 30 sec or more. If the terminals of a galvanometer are short-circuited, the coil is hardly able to move because of the induced current and Lenz's law, whereas if the terminals are open-circuited the coil is likely to oscillate about its final position for a long time before settling down. Intermediate between these two situations is a *critical damping resistance* such that, when the external resistance across the galvanometer terminals has this value, the speed at which the coil approaches its final resting position is optimized. The value of the critical damping resistance, which is commonly 5 to 50 times the coil resistance, should be specified by the manufacturer of the instrument. The term *ballistic galvanometer* is usually applied to an instrument whose response time is so long that the final reading is proportional to the amount of charge that has passed through the coil, that is, to the integrated value of the current. If the duration of the current flow is short compared with the natural period of the suspension, any galvanometer will respond in such a manner.

Before leaving the moving-coil meter two other refinements of the basic device need to be mentioned, namely the multimeter (VOM = volt-ohm-meter) and the vacuum-tube voltmeter (VTVM), which are extremely useful and versatile test instruments, able to measure resistance as well as voltage or current. The AVO-meter is a type of multimeter which has provision for measuring a wide range of ac and dc voltages and currents, as well as resistance.

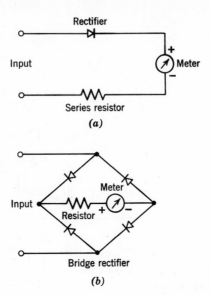

Fig. 3.38   Circuits for use with an ac voltmeter: (*a*) with half-wave rectifier; (*b*) with full-wave rectifier.

Two basic circuits for converting a dc voltmeter for use with alternating current are given in Fig. 3.38. Both employ the ability of a *rectifier* or *diode* to conduct electricity only in one direction and not in the reverse direction. We have more to say about diodes and rectifiers in Chapter IV. The essential difference between the two circuits of Fig. 3.38 is that in (*a*) the current is able to flow through the meter only during half of each cycle (the arrow in the rectifier symbol gives the direction of preferred flow for the conventional positive current), and in (*b*) the bridge arrangement of four half-wave rectifiers allows current to flow in the same direction through the meter on both halves of each cycle. Germanium diodes usually require a forward voltage drop of around 0.2 V before they conduct appreciably and do not work properly with very low currents; therefore it is difficult to make very sensitive meters for alternating current. (An alternative type of meter, which uses a fixed coil to attract a piece of soft iron fixed to the pointer, does not encounter this difficulty, but unfortunately such "moving-vane" meters are inherently insensitive.) Another use for a diode is shown in the circuit of Fig. 3.39 in which a diode is used to protect a delicate meter against overloading. When the voltage drop across the meter exceeds 0.2 V, or 0.5 V in the case of a silicon diode, the current begins to be shunted through the parallel diode.

Alternating-current meters that use rectifiers respond to *average* input voltage, which is 0.638 times the peak voltage of a pure sine wave. Their

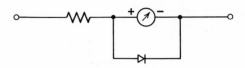

Fig. 3.39   Use of a shunt diode to prevent overloading a sensitive meter.

scales, however, are calibrated to read rms (root-mean-square) voltage, which is 0.707 of the peak value of a pure sine wave. These ratios do not hold if there are two or more frequencies present or if the wave is distorted. In this case an average-reading meter, or a peak-reading meter, will not give an accurate reading of the rms value. The significance of the rms voltage is that it is the value of the dc voltage that results in the same power dissipation across a resistor as the given ac voltage, regardless of the ac waveform. Meters that actually respond to rms voltage are always so specified by the manufacturer. If the meter type is not specified, it may be assumed to be average-reading, except in the case of one popular inexpensive VTVM, the Heathkit, which indicates peak-to-peak voltage.

The different voltage ranges of a multimeter can be obtained simply by selecting suitable series resistors for the meter itself, which usually has a sensitivity of about 50 μA full scale. The different current ranges are generally selected by means of an *Ayrton shunt*, as shown schematically in Fig. 3.40. The advantage of this arrangement is that resistors to the left of the selector switch setting add themselves to the meter resistance, whereas the current divides itself between the meter and the resistors to the right of the switch

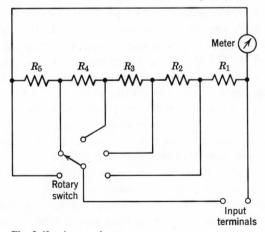

Fig. 3.40   Ayrton shunt.

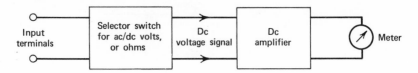

Fig. 3.41 Block diagram of a vacuum-tube voltmeter.

setting, with the result that it is not necessary to use extremely low resistance shunts to obtain full-scale readings from currents of several amperes.

To measure resistance the multimeter incorporates a battery and allows a portion of the current that the battery can drive through the external resistance to flow through the meter. The battery emf is usually 1.5 V, although some multimeters also contain a second battery with an emf of around 22 V for use with very high resistances. Even the output of the 1.5-V battery may be great enough to destroy the delicate wires required in some types of potentiometer, and the higher voltage used on high-resistance ranges can produce temporary or permanent breakdown of the active junctions in semiconductor devices such as transistors. It follows that a resistance meter, that is, the "ohms" range of a multimeter or VTVM, should be applied with caution to unfamiliar equipment, but with this restriction the ohmmeter is one of the most useful test instruments.

The main difference between a multimeter and a vacuum-tube voltmeter is that the latter incorporates a dc amplifier between the input and the meter. A block diagram of a VTVM is given in Fig. 3.41. A dc amplifier is simply an electrical circuit for magnifying changes of dc-voltage levels; the manner in which such an amplifier works is described in Chapter IV. The main advantage of the VTVM over the multimeter stems from the fact that the input impedance of the dc amplifier can be very high—up to 10^{15} Ω if special tubes are used (see Chapter IV)—and is maintained even when small voltages are being measured. A VTVM with very high input impedance is usually called an electrometer. With a VTVM it is therefore possible to measure a voltage from a high resistance source, to measure a very small current by observing the voltage drop produced across a very high resistance, and to measure a very high resistance. For these specialized measurements several precautions must be taken; we return to this topic in Chapter IV when we can give some consideration to the details of the circuitry involved.

The next instrument to be considered under the heading of d-c measurements is one that allows precise measurement of voltage under conditions in which no current is drawn from the source and of current under the same conditions by measuring the voltage drop across a precision resistor. This is the slide-wire *potentiometer*, whose basic principle is illustrated in Fig.

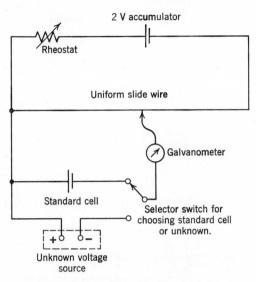

Fig. 3.42 Principle of the slide-wire potentiometer.

3.42; a circuit diagram for a typical commercial instrument is given in Fig. 3.43. The measurement involves a comparison of the voltage to be measured with the voltage drop produced by a fixed current along a uniform wire. The position of the sliding contact is adjusted until the sensitive galvanometer shows no deflection, at which point the unknown voltage and the potential drop along the wire must be equal. The wire is calibrated by measuring the fraction of its length which is sufficient to balance the emf of the standard cell; the rheostat may be used to set this fraction at some convenient value. The precision and accuracy of the measurement are governed by the uniformity of the wire, the accuracy with which the emf of the standard cell is known, the sensitivity of the galvanometer, and the precision with which the position of the sliding contact can be determined. There are other sources of error in the measurement, notably thermal emf's when dissimilar wires are present in the circuit and care is not taken to keep the instrument at a uniform temperature, errors due to drifts in the current delivered by the battery or accumulator, and changes in the standard cell emf due to temperature variation or to an accidental flow of current—the safe upper limit of current for most standard cells is about 100 μA. The errors listed in this last sentence, however, can all be avoided by careful procedure. Among other errors, those due to nonuniformity of the wire and lack of precision in locating the sliding contact are not at present limiting factors. Commercial general-purpose potentiometers normally have

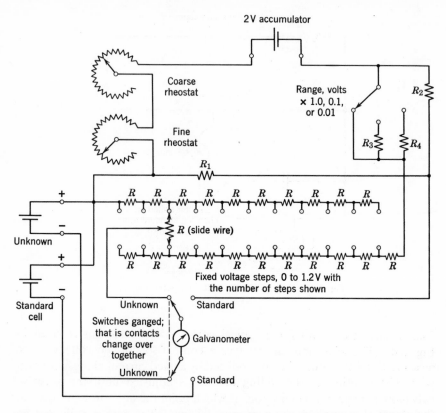

Fig. 3.43 Type of circuit used in a commercial potentiometer. The rheostats are used to set the midpoint of R_1, R_2 at 1.0186 V during standardization. The ends of the slide wire are moved by a rotary switch so that the slide wire covers any desired 0.1 V range; R_3 and R_4 alter this range to 0.01 and 0.001 V, respectively.

a range of about 0 to 2 V, and the voltage can usually be read to within 0.02 mV or better. Some expensive instruments are built to allow measurements to be made with an accuracy of better than ± 1 μV, but elaborate precautions are required in order to exploit this precision.

The usual laboratory voltage standard is the Weston normal cadmium cell. It has an emf, that is, an open circuit output voltage, of 1.018636 V at 20°C and a temperature coefficient of 41 μV/°C at this temperature. The unsaturated Weston cell, which has an emf between 1.0183 and 1.0190 V, can be calibrated precisely by comparison with the saturated normal cell and is to be preferred for many purposes because its temperature coefficient is only -10 μV per degree. When measurements are made with a Weston cell that is uncalibrated, or of uncertain history, it is reasonably safe to assume

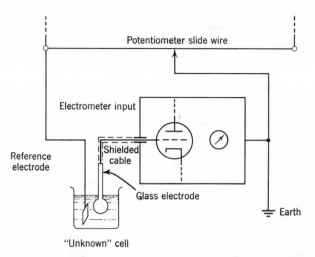

Fig. 3.44   Electrometer used in place of galvanometer for measuring the emf of a cell with very high internal resistance.

that the emf is 1.0186 ± 0.0005 V in the vicinity of 20°C. The best type of standard cell for potentiometric work has a built-in protective resistor in series with the cell. The resistor can be removed from the circuit by holding down a button when the final stage of balancing the potentiometer is reached.

The other factor that may limit the accuracy of a potentiometric voltage measurement is the sensitivity of the galvanometer. The most sensitive range of the usual box-type galvanometer is such that a current of 10^{-9} A, corresponding to a deflection of 0.2 mm with a 1-m optical lever, can just be detected. Thus, if a potential difference near 0.1 V is to be measured with an accuracy of 1 part in 10^4, that is, within 10^{-5} V, the resistance in series with the galvanometer must be no greater than 10^4 Ω. This is often a serious limitation. As an extreme case we can consider the measurement of the emf of a cell that contains a glass electrode, as used in the estimation of hydrogen, sodium, or calcium ions. The internal resistance of a cell containing a glass electrode is of the order of 10^8 Ω, and therefore a potentiometer equipped with the common type of galvanometer could do no better than ± 0.1 V when measuring the emf of such a cell. The way out of this difficulty is to use an *electrometer*, that is, a vacuum-tube voltmeter of very high input impedance, as shown in Fig. 3.44. With this arrangement the accuracy of measurement is usually limited by electrical noise to about ± 50 μV.

An arrangement for using a potentiometer in combination with a precision resistor to measure current is shown in Fig. 3.45. Precision resistance standards are available in decade values (i.e., integral values of 1 to 10 times

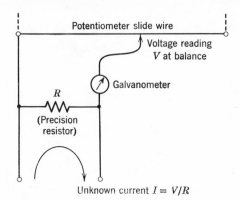

Fig. 3.45   Current measurement with a potentiometer.

some power of 10) over the range of 10^{-3} to 10^6 Ω. Typical good-quality decade resistance boxes for general laboratory use have an accuracy of around $\pm 0.05\%$, are virtually free of inductive and capacitive effects at frequencies below about 10 KHz, and have a temperature coefficient of about $+3$ ppm/°C near 20°C. The rotary switch contacts used in the selection of the desired resistance value have to be cleaned regularly if accuracy is to be maintained, and it is vital that chemical liquids and vapors be kept away at all times. With the higher valued resistors the wire used is so thin that serious corrosion problems can result from the prolonged action of traces of soldering flux. For maximum stability wire-wound resistors are annealed to remove mechanical stress and then sealed in vacuum. With all precision resistors it is essential not to exceed the specified maximum allowable power dissipation, which is normally marked on the case of a decade resistance box. High voltages can be measured with a potentiometer in combination with a potential divider built of precision resistors, as shown in Fig. 3.46.

A widely used refinement of the ordinary potentiometer is the *potentiometric recorder*, in which a *servomechanism*, taking the place of the galvanometer, responds to the out-of-balance current by adjusting the position of the sliding contact so that this current is made smaller than some threshold value and at the same time adjusts the position of a pen which shows the instantaneous value of the measured voltage on a moving chart. Thus a continuous record of the measured voltage is obtained. The accuracy of the measurement is not better than about $\pm 0.1\%$, but it is sufficient for many purposes. The voltage standard of a recording potentiometer can be a Weston cell or a circuit that employs zener diodes; the latter are among the semiconductor devices discussed in Chapter IV. A full account of recording potentiometers, recording galvanometers, and related devices is given in Chapter VII.

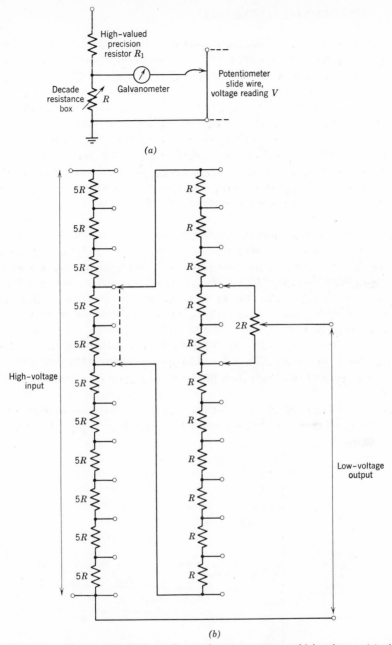

Fig. 3.46 Use of a potential divider and potentiometer to measure high voltages: (*a*) with a simple potential divider; (*b*) Kelvin-Varley potentiometer, used as a precise potential divider, provides a constant load for the input voltage. The paired contacts move together and so always remain the same distance apart.

In this subsection it remains to consider electrostatic, electrodynamic, thermal, and digital instruments. The electrostatic voltmeter consists simply of two conductors between which a force develops as a result of electrostatic attraction or repulsion. The restoring force is usually provided by gravity. Such an instrument is useful for approximate measurements of voltages up to 100 kV. The quadrant electrometer is a delicate instrument that operates on the same principle but in which the restoring torque is provided by a fine quartz fiber. With a quadrant electrometer it is possible to measure currents as small as 10^{-16} A by observing the potential drop across a high resistance or the rate of voltage rise during charging of a small capacitance. Only the best of the electrometers based on dc amplifiers can duplicate this performance.

Electrodynamic ammeters, voltmeters, and wattmeters are of similar construction to the D'Arsonval type of moving-coil meter already described, except that an electromagnet, air-cored in high-precision meters, replaces the permanent magnet. These instruments are normally used only for ac measurements. When the current through the coil reverses its direction, the magnet current also does so, and the direction of the force exerted against the restoring spring does not change. Electrodynamic instruments are generally not very sensitive, are affected by the ambient magnetic field, and are liable to considerable error at high frequencies. They are, however, capable of greater precision than meters that depend on rectifiers ($\pm 0.1\%$ versus $\pm 1\%$).

The operating principle of a thermal meter for current measurements is illustrated in Fig. 3.47. The current to be determined is passed through a

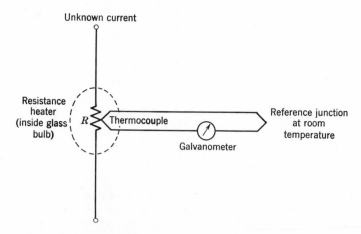

Fig. 3.47 Thermocouple meter.

small heating coil in contact with a thermocouple inside an evacuated glass bulb and the output from the thermocouple is measured with a galvanometer or moving-coil meter. The heat generated, and thus the galvanometer deflection, is proportional to the square of the true rms current. If the heater is in the form of a straight thin wire, so that inductive and capacitative effects are negligible, such an instrument retains its accuracy up to frequencies of the order of a megacycle (10^6 Hz).

A digital instrument is one that displays the result of a measurement in the form of a set of digits, or numbers, rather than as the position of an indicator on a scale. This type of instrument often has facilities for feeding the output data to a tape printer or other storage system for further processing by computer. Digital instruments are expensive, especially if five or more significant figures are required in the final data, but the additional expense is likely to be outweighed by the gain in efficiency and convenience when large numbers of precise measurements have to be made in a short time. At present digital meters are readily available for the measurement of time, the total number and the repetition frequency of fast pulses, the frequency of ac signals, and voltage, current, capacitance, and resistance as well as their various combinations. They are sophisticated instruments, and digital instrumentation is a rapidly advancing field. Therefore the only way to be reasonably sure of obtaining the best instrument for a particular purpose is to compare specifications and prices in as many different manufacturer's catalogs as possible or to seek the advice of someone who has recently done so. Even the principle of operation for an instrument as basic as a digital voltmeter is not standardized: in one type of instrument the unknown dc input is compared with an internal reference voltage, as in a potentiometer, and the resulting potential difference is converted to a pulse signal that is used to drive stepping switches which control both the digital display and a set of precision resistors, the latter forming in effect the slide-wire of a digital potentiometer. In a second type of instrument the input is fed directly to a dc-to-frequency converter, which produces pulses at a rate proportional to the input voltage. The pulse repetition frequency is then read directly with a digital counter. In yet a third type of instrument the difference between the dc input and an internal reference voltage forms an error signal that is converted to pulses and used to set the state of a digital register (basically an electrical circuit for storing numbers in the form of a binary code). The output of the digital register also provides a dc voltage, and it is the difference between this voltage and the input signal that is set to zero when the voltmeter attains a steady reading. A number of circuits used in digital instruments are discussed in Chapter IV. As far as direct current and voltage measurements are concerned it is probably true to say that anything that can be done with a digital instrument can be done more accurately with a potentiometer, but the time required for the potentiometric measurement will inevitably be greater by several orders of magnitude.

Alternating-Current Measurements: The Oscilloscope

Alternating-current voltage and current measurements are often most conveniently made with the help of a moving-coil meter, as described in the first part of this section. The disadvantage of this type of measurement is that it provides no information about the frequency or the phase, relative to some standard signal, of the current or voltage that is being measured. In many situations, however, this lack is of no consequence.

The instrument that is normally used when frequency and phase are important is the cathode-ray *oscilloscope*, which is also the most useful instrument in the entire field of electronics. The principle of operation of the oscilloscope is illustrated in Figs. 3.48*a* and 3.48*b*. Electrons from a hot filament are accelerated by a high voltage (typically 4 to 10 kV) applied to the electrodes of the "electron gun," and the resulting beam is focused to give a bright spot on the phosphorescent screen. The spot on the screen can be moved about by the application of electrical signals to the deflecting plates, and if these signals are repetitive a steady display is produced on the screen. A rapidly changing signal can be photographed, usually with "Polaroid" film if the results are required to be visible almost immediately, or, in the case of a *storage oscilloscope* such as the Tektronix model 564, can be made to persist on the screen for a period as long as an hour for observation and measurement at leisure.

The simplest application of an oscilloscope is the direct comparison of frequency, phase, and amplitude of two sinusoidal signals by means of *Lissajous figures*. In this application one of the signals is used to deflect the spot on the screen vertically while the other deflects it horizontally. If the signals are of identical amplitude and frequency and just 90° out of phase, the resulting pattern on the screen is a circle, but if the signals have the same frequency but differ in amplitude, or if the phase difference is not 90°, the result is an ellipse that may degenerate into a line. Provided the two frequencies remain equal, the circular or elliptical display remains stationary on the screen, but if they differ slightly a stationary display cannot be obtained. Instead the ellipse appears to rotate. Then, as the frequency difference is steadily increased, the figure on the screen passes through a variety of intermediate stages until the frequencies differ by exactly a factor of 2 and a steady display with a single node, that is, in the form of a figure "8," is obtained. If the frequency difference is increased further, the figure undergoes various gyrations until a steady display with two nodes is obtained at the point at which the frequencies differ by a factor of 3. The various,

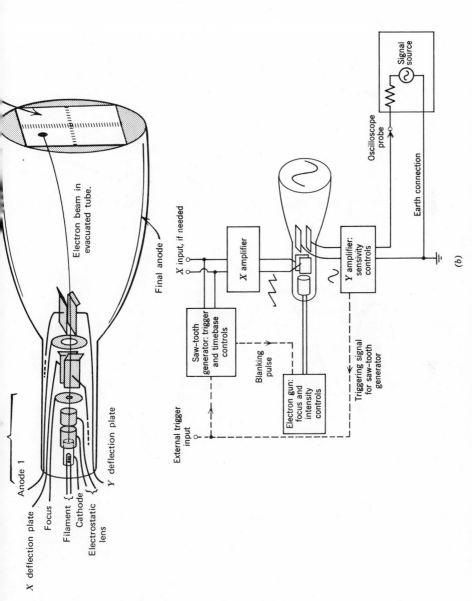

Fig. 3.48 Principle of an oscilloscope: (*a*) construction of the cathode-ray tube. The heated cathode emits electrons that are accelerated and focused to form a bright spot on the phosphorescent screen. The position of the spot is controlled by the potentias of the X and Y deflection plates. (*b*) Block diagram of connections to the cathode-ray tube.

133

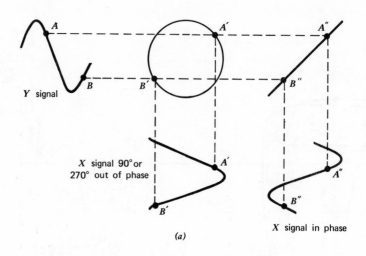

Y signal

X signal 90° or
270° out of phase

X signal in phase

(a)

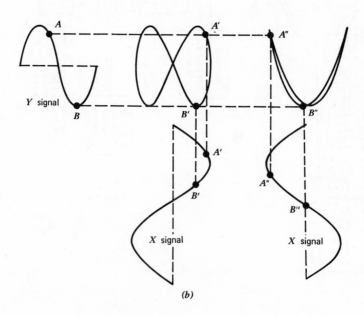

Y signal

X signal

X signal

(b)

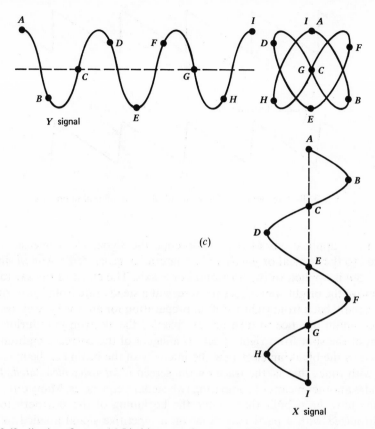

Fig. 3.49 lissajous figures: (*a*) Limiting cases for equal amplitude and frequency; (*b*) figures for equal amplitude and 2:1 frequency ratio; (*c*) figure for equal amplitudes and 3:2 frequency ratio.

more or less complicated patterns that are made to appear during this process are known as Lissajous figures; some examples are given in Fig. 3.49. In general, when two signals differ in amplitude, the relative amplitudes are given by the ratio of the height to width of the Lissajous figures, whereas the ratio of frequencies of vertically and horizontally applied signals is equal to m/n, where m is the number of times the signal trace crosses the horizontal axis and n is the number of times it crosses the vertical axis. The phase difference between the signals is related to the angle by which the Lissajous figure appears to be rotated about a vertical axis in three dimensions, in a way that can most readily be appreciated by constructing a matching diagram after the manner of Fig. 3.49*b*.

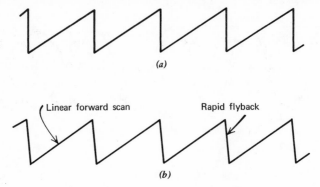

Fig. 3.50 Sawtooth waveforms: (*a*) ideal; (*b*) as realized in practice.

In most applications of the oscilloscope the signal to be measured is applied to the vertical or *y*-axis and an internally generated *sawtooth* signal (Fig. 3.50) is applied to the horizontal or *x*-axis. The effect of the sawtooth is to move the bright spot across the screen at a steady rate from left to right, then rapidly back from right to left in preparation for another steady sweep. It is common practice to turn off, or "blank," the electron gun during the return of the spot from right to left. If a signal of the correct amplitude is applied to the blanking electrode, the intensity of the beam can be made to vary with time; that is, the trace on the screen is *intensity modulated*. This provides another means of comparing two signal frequencies. Many different circuits have been built that enable the beginning of the sawtooth to be synchronized with a particular point on a repetitive signal applied to the *y*-axis and thus allow the vertical input signal to appear as a steady display on the screen. With a steady oscilloscope display the following measurements become possible:

1. The amplitude of the signal in volts can be determined by measuring the size of the signal trace on the screen, typically to within $\pm 3\%$ with a good-quality instrument. To facilitate this measurement the signal is normally applied by way of an amplifier with variable gain, the gain positions being calibrated in terms of volts of input signal per centimeter of deflection of the trace. Good-quality instruments also possess an internal calibration signal that can be used to check the response of the system to a known voltage.

2. The time interval between known points on the signal waveform, and thus the repetition frequency of the signal, can be determined by measuring the corresponding distance along the *x*-axis, again to within a typical uncertainty of $\pm 3\%$. In some instruments the specifications call for this degree of accuracy to be maintained indefinitely by the "time-base" circuits which

control the sawtooth waveform, without regular checking by the operator; in others the reference signal used to check the amplifier gain is derived from the ac mains supply, and the constant mains frequency then provides a standard of comparison for the time base. With common types of oscilloscope it is possible to measure times in the range of 10 to 10^{-6} sec within the specified accuracy.

3. The phase difference between two signals of the same frequency can be measured if a *dual beam* or *dual trace* oscilloscope is available. In a dual beam instrument the cathode-ray tube contains two independent electron guns, each with its own intensity and focus controls and independent triggering of the time bases. In a dual trace instrument the electron beam is made to respond alternately to each of two input signal channels; at high frequencies this is best accomplished by letting the inputs from the two channels control alternate sweeps of the electron beam, whereas at low frequencies the best mode of operation is to switch the beam control back and forth between each signal input at such a high rate that the breaks in the two signal traces are too close together to be seen. The first of these is usually termed the *alternate* mode, and the second the *chopped* mode. Whichever type of instrument is used, it is important in a phase comparison to ensure that both traces are triggered by the same input signal (this may involve using the *external trigger* facility of the oscilloscope for one or both signal channels). When this is so, the phase difference is obtained simply by measuring the distance on the screen between corresponding parts of the two signal waveforms and comparing it with the distance occupied by a complete cycle. Many good-quality oscilloscopes possess the facility for delayed triggering of the time base combined with greater sweep speed following the delay. This facility permits a selected small portion of a waveform to be spread across the full width of the screen so that precise time and phase comparisons become possible.

4. The repetition frequencies of two signals can be compared either by applying them to different channels of a dual-beam oscilloscope or, more precisely, by mixing the two signals together and measuring the difference or "beat" frequency with a calibrated oscilloscope. The principle of the heterodyne beat method is discussed more fully at the end of this chapter in connection with a form of capacitance measurement. If one of the two signals is derived from a stable source, such as a crystal-controlled oscillator, or from a broadcast frequency standard, then the frequency of the other signal can be determined with an accuracy of better than 1 part in 10^6. For best precision the frequencies to be compared should be as similar as possible; for this reason it is often convenient to compare known harmonics of the two frequencies. Suitable harmonics can be generated by passing the original sinusoidal signal through a very nonlinear circuit (e.g., a Class C amplifier

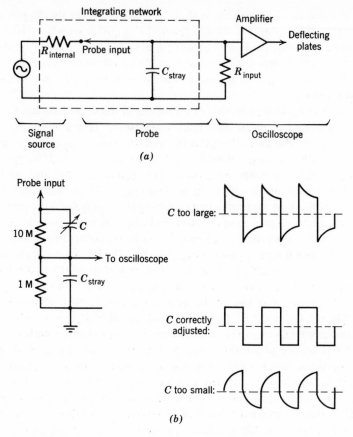

Fig. 3.51*a, b*   Uncompensated and compensated oscilloscope probes.

or a varactor diode; see Chapter IV) and extracting the desired high-frequency component of the resulting distorted signal with a tuned circuit.

The main limitation of an oscilloscope is usually the high-frequency limitation of the probe and amplifier system that intervenes between the signal source and the deflector plates. The upper frequency limit, or *bandwidth*, can be as low as 100 kHz or as high as 250 MHz, depending on the type of circuit used. There is an inverse relationship between gain and bandwidth such that for a particular type of circuit the gain-bandwidth product is approximately constant. The bandwidth for repetitive signals can be effectively increased by a factor of the order of 100 by using a sampling procedure. In a *sampling oscilloscope* a small portion of the waveform is selected from each of a number of repetitions of the signal, and the picture on the screen is built up as a series of dots, one from each sample. For this purpose the bandwidth of the amplifier need be only as great as the frequency of repetition of the whole signal, and the performance of the instrument depends on the circuits that select the short "window" in time when the signal is sampled.

Apart from the bandwidth of the amplifier, another important parameter of the oscilloscope's input system is the stray capacitance between input and earth. As shown in Fig. 3.51a, the probe with its stray capacitance constitutes an integrating circuit, or *low-pass filter*, that diverts high-frequency signals away from the amplifier. A method of overcoming this effect is to use a compensated attenuator probe, as illustrated in Fig. 3.51b. With this type of probe the compensating capacitor is adjusted empirically to give a perfect square-wave output from the instrument's internal calibration signal. With correct adjustment the integrating effect of the input capacitance is removed, whereas the input impedance of the probe and amplifier system, which at high frequencies is mainly the reactance of the input capacitors in series, is multiplied by the attenuation factor of the probe. The attenuation factor is typically 10 but may be higher.

A more elaborate method of reducing the effect of stray capacitance is to use a probe with a "driven shield," as illustrated in Fig. 3.51c. In a simple probe the signal is taken to the amplifier by way of a shielded coaxial cable in which the shield layer of braided wire is held at earth potential and serves

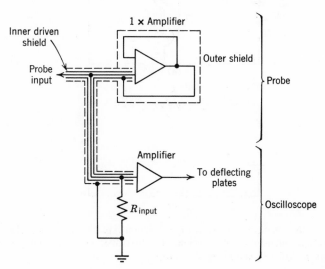

Fig. 3.51c Oscilloscope probe with driven shield to reduce effects of stray capacitance on a rapidly changing input signal.

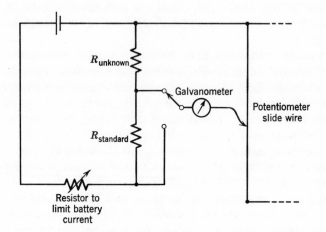

Fig. 3.52 Comparison of an unknown resistor with resistance standard.

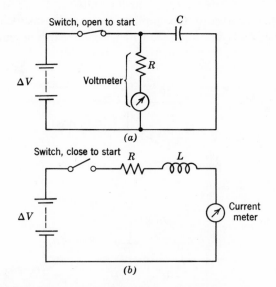

Fig. 3.53 (*a*) Measurement of capacitance by observation of the time taken to discharge from a voltage ΔV; (*b*) measurement of self-inductance by observation of the time taken to build up to a current $\Delta V/R$. (Here V_0 and I_0 are both zero.)

to screen the signal-carrying wire from undesirable signals due to "pickup," that is, unintended inductive coupling with ac mains, local radio stations, electrical machinery, and so on. The capacitance between the signal lead and the shield makes up a large part of the stray capacitance compensated for in an attenuator probe. In the probe of Fig. 3.51c there are two shield layers; the inner shield is driven by an auxiliary unity-gain amplifier of high input impedance and low output impedance (usually a cathode-follower; see Chapter IV) so that its potential accurately follows that of the signal lead. There is then no potential drop across the stray capacitance within the cable and consequently none of the signal current is diverted away from the main amplifier.

Besides the oscilloscope there are various types of commercial "black box" available for measuring frequency or phase, including the digital frequency meters already mentioned. There is little to be gained from discussing these instruments without first considering some aspects of their circuitry. Therefore we shall be content to note that such things exist and to warn that whenever the output of such an instrument is of prime importance it is advisable to monitor the input continuously with an oscilloscope.

Measurement of Resistance, Inductance, and Capacitance

The simplest method of measuring an unknown resistance is to determine the current that a known emf will drive through it, as can be done with an ohmmeter, that is, the "ohms" range of a multimeter. If the resistance value is very large, it may be necessary to measure the current with an electrometer, but the principle remains the same. The same approach can be used for rough measurements of impedance or reactance, given a signal source of known frequency and amplitude and an ac meter.

For moderately precise measurements of resistance the comparison method of Fig. 3.52 is very convenient. In this method the unknown resistor is placed in series with a known standard resistor of approximately the same resistance, and a steady voltage source is used to drive a small current through both. The voltage drop across each resistor is then measured with a potentiometer, and the ratio of the resistances is found as the ratio of the voltages. This method is less convenient with inductance or capacitance because of the complications introduced by differences of phase between current and voltage, and it becomes simpler to make the comparison in an electrical bridge, as described later.

A rather fundamental approach to the measurement of either self-inductance or capacitance is shown in Fig. 3.53. A step voltage signal is applied between the terminals of the inductor or capacitor, which is in series with a known resistance R. (In the case of the inductor the resistance R includes the residual resistance r of the coil.) The value of inductance or capacitance

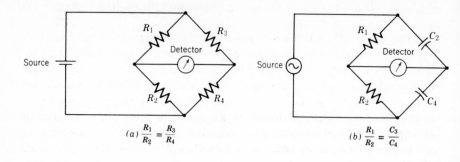

(a) $\dfrac{R_1}{R_2} = \dfrac{R_3}{R_4}$

(b) $\dfrac{R_1}{R_2} = \dfrac{C_3}{C_4}$

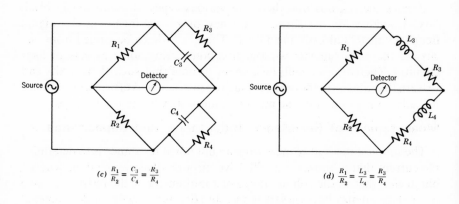

(c) $\dfrac{R_1}{R_2} = \dfrac{C_3}{C_4} = \dfrac{R_3}{R_4}$

(d) $\dfrac{R_1}{R_2} = \dfrac{L_3}{L_4} = \dfrac{R_3}{R_4}$

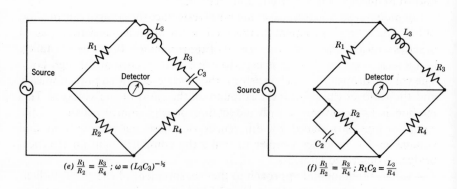

(e) $\dfrac{R_1}{R_2} = \dfrac{R_3}{R_4}$; $\omega = (L_3 C_3)^{-\frac{1}{2}}$

(f) $\dfrac{R_1}{R_2} = \dfrac{R_3}{R_4}$; $R_1 C_2 = \dfrac{L_3}{R_4}$

Fig. 3.54 Balancing conditions for some different types of four-arm bridge.

142

is then calculated from the observed variation with time of the current through the inductor, or the voltage across the capacitor, using one of the equations

$$I = I_0 + \Delta I(1 - e^{-Lt/R}), \tag{3.97}$$

$$V = V_0 + \Delta V(1 - e^{-t/RC}), \tag{3.98}$$

where $\Delta I = \Delta V/R$ is the current change that results from the known voltage change ΔV and I_0 and V_0 are the current or voltage before the change. This method of measurement is very useful for large values of L or C, the time t being measured with a stop watch, and can be extended to small values and correspondingly short times if an oscilloscope is used to follow the current or voltage change.

The most precise measurements of resistance or reactance depend on the comparison of the unknown with a precise standard in a four-arm bridge circuit, of which the Wheatstone bridge of Fig. 3.54a is the most familiar example. The Wheatstone bridge is usually operated from a dc source such as a lead accumulator, with a D'Arsonval galvanometer as the detector of off-balance current. With this arrangement it is easy to see that at balance, that is, with no current flowing through the detector, we must have

$$\frac{R_1}{R_2} = \frac{R_3}{R_4} \tag{3.99}$$

For optimum sensitivity the four arms of the bridge should be of approximately equal resistance and the internal resistance of the detector should be similar to the resistance of one arm.

Other variants of the four-arm bridge are shown in Figs. 3.54b–h, together with equations expressing the conditions that must be fulfilled to obtain zero current through the detector. Since these bridges contain reactive elements, it is necessary to use an ac signal source of some known frequency and to equalize the amplitude and phase of the signals that arrive at opposite sides of the detector. The necessity of adjusting both the amplitude and the phase will in general result in the imposition of *two* conditions for obtaining a balance. The detector may be an oscilloscope or an amplifier in combination with some sort of output device, such as a pair of earphones if the signal is in the audiofrequency range (roughly 20 cycles to 20 kc/sec) or an ac meter. Bridges of type (b) and (c) can be used to compare an unknown capacitance with a standard of capacitance; (c) can be regarded as a precise representation of (b), in which the resistors R_3 and R_4 correspond to the leakage resistances of the capacitors plus whatever parallel resistance is needed to satisfy the balancing conditions. Similarly, bridge (d) can be used to compare two inductances, and the resistances R_3 and R_4 here include the residual resistances of the inductors. Bridges (e) and (f) can be used to compare an inductance with a capacitance; with bridge (e) the frequency ω must be known

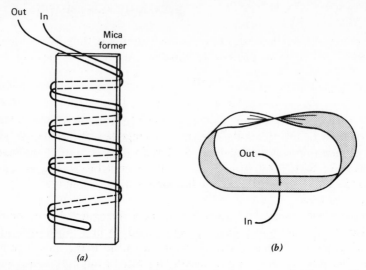

Fig. 3.55 Noninductive resistors: (*a*) doubled wire wound on mica former; (*b*) thin film deposited on surface of Möbius strip.

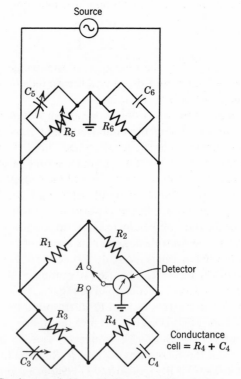

Fig. 3.56 Conductance bridge with Wagner earthing device.

precisely and the output of the signal generator must be a pure sine wave, with no harmonics present. Bridge (*e*) can also be used to measure frequency in terms of known inductance and capacitance. The *Wien bridge* (*g*) can be used either to compare a resistance with a capacitance or to measure frequency. Since the capacitance of a properly constructed parallel-plate capacitor can be calculated from its dimensions, this type of bridge can provide an absolute measurement of resistance if a precise frequency standard is available. Like bridges (*b*) and (*c*), bridge (*h*) can be used to compare resistance and capacitance without the need of a precisely known signal frequency.

Many varieties of four-arm bridge can be obtained commercially for measuring properties such as the conductance of electrolyte solutions, the deformation of the wires in a strain gauge, or the pressure of the gas surrounding the heated wire in a Pirani gauge. It is also easy to assemble a bridge in the laboratory from readily available signal generators, detectors, and decade resistance, inductance, or capacitance boxes. In bridges to be used with ac signals it is essential that resistors be as free as possible of parasitic inductance. Two types of *noninductive resistor* are shown in Fig. 3.55. In the original version each wire is folded double before being wound on a former so that the field produced by the current traveling one way is canceled by the field produced when it comes back. In a more recent type the resistor takes the form of a film deposited on both sides of a thin insulating ribbon bent into a Möbius strip so that the forward and backward currents are always separated only by the thickness of the ribbon. The Möbius resistor has definite advantages at very high frequencies but is unlikely to supersede the older type for general laboratory work.

An interesting development of the four-arm bridge is the *Wagner earthing device*, which is recommended for precise measurements of electrolytic conductance. Because of polarization effects at the electrodes, it is necessary to use an ac signal generator in a conductance bridge, but this introduces the complication of having to balance the capacitance as well as the resistance of the conductance cell. Most of this capacitance probably develops from the presence of the Helmholtz double layer on the surface of the electrodes so that the equivalent electrical circuit of the cell is approximately a series combination of capacitance + resistance + capacitance. However, for most purposes the conductance cell can be treated as just a resistance and a capacitance in parallel, and the simplest type of conductance bridge therefore has the configuration of Fig. 3.54*c*. This simple configuration is not particularly sensitive because of the stray capacitance between the conductance cell and earth. A simple means of overcoming the signal-diverting effect of the stray capacitance is to arrange for the detector itself to be at earth potential, as shown in Fig. 3.56. Here, with the detector switched to *A*, the bridge

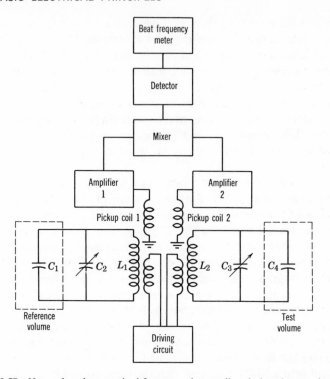

Fig. 3.57 Heterodyne beat method for measuring small variations in capacitance.

is balanced as well as possible by adjusting arms 5 and 6, with resistors and capacitors R_5, R_6, C_5, and C_6. In this way point A is brought to earth potential. Then, with the detector switched to B, corresponding adjustments are made in arms 3 and 4 to bring B to earth potential. The detector is then switched to A for further slight adjustments, then back to B, and so on, until both A and B are at earth potential, and arms 1, 2, 3, and 4 constitute a balanced bridge similar to Fig. 3.54c.

To conclude this section we consider a method of measuring extremely small differences in capacitance that might occur when the dielectric of a parallel-plate capacitor is changed from pure air to air plus a trace of, say, methanol vapor. This is the *heterodyne beat method*, which depends on the detection of small departures from equality in the resonant frequencies of two tuned circuits. A block diagram of the basic apparatus is given in Fig. 3.57. The two identical resonant circuits L_1, C_1, C_2, and L_2, C_3, C_4 are driven by matched oscillators so that they both resonate at some frequency near 1 Mc. The small variable capacitors C_2 and C_3 are equipped with Vernier dials so that the setting corresponding to resonance at any given frequency can be determined precisely. Initially the capacitors are adjusted so that the resonant frequencies are the same within 1 or 2 Hz. The effect of the change in the dielectric of C_3 that results from the addition of some methanol vapor is measured by determining the change in the Vernier reading that is needed to make the two frequencies equal again.

To determine the difference in the two frequencies a small amount of power is withdrawn from each circuit through a pickup coil. The resulting signals are then amplified and multiplied together in a mixing circuit. Since we have

$$\sin(\omega_1 t + \delta_1) \cdot \sin(\omega_2 t + \delta_2)$$
$$= \tfrac{1}{2}\cos\left[(\omega_1 + \omega_2)t + \delta_1 + \delta_2\right] + \tfrac{1}{2}\cos\left[(\omega_1 - \omega_2)t + \delta_1 - \delta_2\right],$$

it follows that the output of the mixer will be the sum of two cosine signals, of which the frequency of one is the sum of the two input frequencies and the frequency of the other is the difference of the two input frequencies. Thus, if the input frequencies differ by 10 Hz, the output will contain a component that is modulated at 10 Hz. This is the phenomenon of "beats" which is well-known in acoustics and is illustrated in Fig. 3.58. The output of the mixer is filtered to remove the high-frequency component of the signal and the lower frequency is then measured with a frequency meter. The addition of a

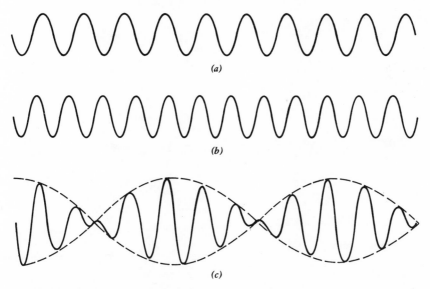

(a)

(b)

(c)

Fig. 3.58 (a) and (b), Sine waves with repetition frequencies in the ratio 5:4. (c) Sum of (a) and (b), showing beats with repetition frequency $\tfrac{1}{4}$ of the repetition frequency in (a) and $\tfrac{1}{5}$ of that in (b). In (c) the signal has the form $2\sin\tfrac{1}{2}(\omega_1 + \omega_2)t$.

small loudspeaker enables the pitch of the difference frequency signal to be monitored by ear, once the frequency difference is within audio range. Since it is not difficult to compare frequencies near a megacycle to within 1 Hz, we have here an example of a measurement that can be made with a precision of 1 part in 10^6, using relatively simple and inexpensive apparatus.

References

Condon, E. U. and H. Odishaw, Eds., *Handbook of Physics*, 2nd ed., New York: McGraw-Hill, 1967.

Fundamentals of Selecting and Using Oscilloscopes. Tektronix Inc., Beaverton, Oregon.

Owen, D., *Alternating Current Measurements*, 3rd ed., London: Methuen and Company, 1950.

Soisson, H. E., *Electronic Measuring Instruments*. New York: McGraw-Hill, 1961.

Chapter **IV**

ELECTRONIC COMPONENTS
Leon F. Phillips

---

1 INTRODUCTION: SIGNALS AND SIGNAL MODIFIERS

The Nature and Transmission of Electrical Signals

Sources of electrical signals can be either current or voltage generators or both. In the general case, in which both current and voltage may change simultaneously, a signal consists of a measurable change in the *power output*

149

of the generator. As mentioned in Chapter III in connection with Norton's and Thevenin's theorems, an ideal current generator has infinite internal resistance, whereas an ideal voltage generator has negligible internal resistance. Many signal sources encountered in practice approximate to one or the other of these extremes so that their output is a pure current or voltage change; nevertheless the relevant quantity for deciding whether the signal can be detected in the presence of noise or for deciding the degree of amplification required before the signal can operate an output transducer is always the amount of signal *power* available. It follows that it is important to be able to transfer as much as possible of the available power between the signal generator and the load, the load in this case being the input impedance of the amplifier, output transducer, or other device connected to the generator.

For a battery of internal resistance R_S in series with a resistive load R_L (Fig. 4.1a) it is a simple exercise in calculus to show that with a fixed value of

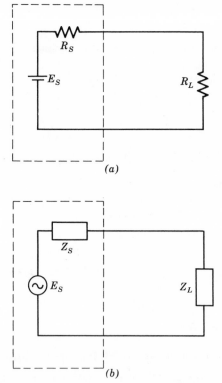

(a)

(b)

Fig. 4.1   Maximum power theorem: (a) for a dc source, optimum $R_L = R_S$; (b) for an ac source, optimum $Z_L = Z_S$.

R_S the power dissipated in the load, $E^2 R_L/(R_L + R_S)^2$, is maximum when R_L and R_S are equal. This is the *maximum power theorem*. For the more general case of an ac generator in series with a load impedance Z_L (Fig. 4.1b) the situation is more complicated because Z_S and Z_L have to be combined vectorially according to the formula

$$Z_{L+S} = [(R_L + R_S)^2 + (X_L + X_S)^2]^{1/2}, \tag{4.1}$$

where

$$Z_L^2 = R_L^2 + X_L^2, \tag{4.2a}$$

and

$$Z_S^2 = R_S^2 + X_S^2, \tag{4.2b}$$

and R and X are the resistive and reactive components, respectively, of the impedance Z. Here only the resistive components actually dissipate power. In practice, however, these complications are ignored, and the optimum load impedance Z_L is assumed to be equal to the source impedance Z_S; when this equality holds, the impedances are said to be matched.

A more interesting case of impedance matching occurs when power is transferred through a *transmission line* to a load some distance from the source. Two common types of transmission line, *coaxial* and *parallel*, are illustrated in Fig. 4.2a and b. The antenna connections of television receivers normally take one or the other of these forms. A length of transmission line behaves as an inductor because of the magnetic interaction of the current in the two conductors and also as a capacitor because of the electrostatic interaction of the charges on the conductors. Thus the line has *distributed* inductance and capacitance along its entire length, and a short section of the line can be represented by the ladder network of Fig. 4.2c, where L and C are the inductance and capacitance of a small increment of length. If we now focus attention on the last ladder section plus the load R_L (which is assumed to be purely resistive), as in Fig. 4.2d, we can calculate by the methods of Chapter III that the total impedance Z of this section is given by

$$Z = j\omega L - \frac{R_L^2 j\omega C}{1 + R_L^2 \omega^2 C^2} + \frac{R_L}{1 + R_L^2 \omega^2 C^2}. \tag{4.3}$$

In this equation C is the capacitance of an increment of length which we can choose to be as small as we like. Hence the quantity $R_L^2 \omega^2 C^2$ can always be made negligible in comparison with unity, and the total impedance becomes

$$Z = j\omega L - R_L^2 j\omega C + R_L, \tag{4.4}$$

which is the impedance of the equivalent series circuit of Fig. 4.2d. Now for maximum transmission of power from source to load the total impedance Z should be just equal to R_L (as in a series resonant circuit) and the effects of the distributed capacitance and inductance should vanish. For the short section of line that we have been considering this gives the requirement

$$R_L = \left(\frac{L}{C}\right)^{\frac{1}{2}}. \tag{4.5}$$

When (4.5) holds, the short section of line plus the load is equivalent, from the viewpoint of the signal, to the load by itself, and so we can add any number of similar ladder sections in front of the load without affecting the total impedance. The important quantity $(L/C)^{\frac{1}{2}}$, measured in ohms, is the square root of the ratio of inductance per unit length to capacitance per unit length of the line and is known as the *characteristic impedance* of the line. We therefore have the result that for optimum transmission of power the

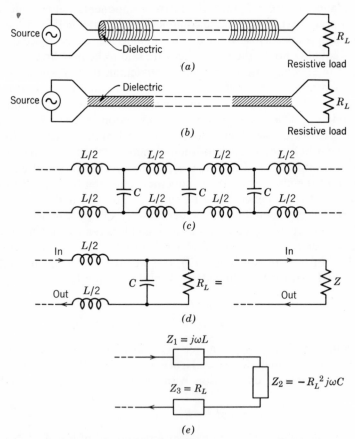

Fig. 4.2   Transmission lines: (*a*) coaxial line; (*b*) parallel line; (*c*) equivalent ladder circuit of a short length of transmission line; (*d*) last ladder section and resistive load; (*e*) series circuit with the same total impedance Z as the parallel circuit of (*d*).

Table 4.1 Types of Electrical Signal

Signal Type	Continuous Alternating Current	Discrete Pulses
Form of information carried	Analog	Digital
Usual source	Oscillator	Switch
Kind of amplifier	Narrow bandwidth	Wide-band
Other modifiers	Rectifier (detector), integrater, differentiater, chopper	Height discriminater, integrater, differentiater, shaper, counter
Mechanical output	Servo motor, meter, pen recorder	Mechanical counter, stepping motor, display tube, tape or card punch or printer
Typical origin in physical experiments	Chopped dc signal, chopped light source, radiofrequency radiation	Geiger tube, scintillater, discrete photon source, threshold relay

transmission line should be terminated by a load equal to its characteristic impedance.* Typical values of characteristic impedance for low-power transmission lines lie in the range from 20 to 1000 Ω. In an ideal situation the output impedance of the signal source, the characteristic impedance of the transmission line, and the input impedance of the load would all be equal. So far we have neglected the resistance of the conductors in a line; this does not affect the characteristic impedance, but it does lead to dissipation of power in the line as well as in the load, that is, to attenuation of the signal by the line. Thus transmission lines are also characterized by an *attenuation factor*, which is usually expressed in *decibels* (dB) per hundred feet. If the power entering the line from the source is P_1 and the power entering the load from the line is P_2, the total attenuation in decibels is equal to $10 \log (P_1/P_2)$.

When we consider the detailed form of the current or voltage changes that constitute a signal, we discover that there are two extreme types, namely continuous ac signals and discrete pulse signals, and most signals correspond purely to one or the other of these. The two types are compared in Table 4.1.

* An ac signal traveling along a transmission line is inevitably accompanied by an electromagnetic wave, due to the magnetic and electrostatic fields of the conductors, which can equally well be regarded as the medium by which energy is transferred. It can be shown that in an improperly terminated transmission line the wave is partially reflected from the load back to the source, whereas in a properly terminated line the wave is completely absorbed by the load.

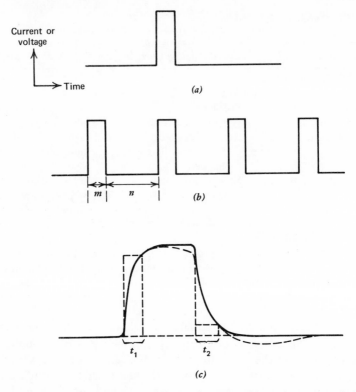

Fig. 4.3 (a) Ideal rectangular pulse; (b) ideal pulse train with mark: space ratio $= m/n$; (c) realistic pulse with rise time t_1 and fall time t_2.

As outlined in Chapter III, a continuous ac signal is characterized by its angular frequency ω, amplitude E_0 or I_0, and phase angle δ [cf. (3.5) and (3.6)]. An ideal pulse signal, as illustrated in Fig. 4.3a, is characterized only by its height and its width or duration. A repetitive pulse train, shown in Fig. 4.3b, may also be characterized by its *mark-to-space ratio*, which in this example is m/n. If a sharp-edged rectangular pulse is to be synthesized by the superposition of a large number of sine or cosine signals, it is necessary for the sum to contain terms up to very high frequencies; otherwise the corners of the rectangle will be rounded rather than sharp. This is the reason for using wide-band amplifiers with pulse signals. The usual effect observed with electrical pulses in practice is shown in Fig. 4.3c. In addition to simple rounding of the corners, there is also a delay at the beginning and end of the pulse due to the time required to charge and discharge stray capacitance or to build up or reduce the current in unwanted inductance. This leads us to define a characteristic *rise time* t_1, equal to the time required for 90%

of the voltage or current change to occur on the way up, and a *fall time* t_2, equal to the time required for 90 % of the change to occur on the way down. It is also sometimes convenient to define a *delay time* and a *storage time* equal to the times required for the first 10 % of the voltage or current change on the way up and on the way down, respectively. If the bandwidth of the amplifier does not extend all the way to direct current at the low-frequency end, it is also likely that the top of the pulse will have a slope and the trailing edge of the pulse will be depressed below the base line, as indicated by the dotted line in Fig. 4.3c.

The distinction between analog and digital forms of information, indicated in Table 4.1, warrants some further discussion. In an analog device the signal current or voltage behaves in a manner strictly analogous to the behavior of the quantity being measured. Thus a thermocouple and a millivoltmeter together constitute an analog thermometer in which the voltage signal varies in exactly the same way as the temperature. A graph of signal voltage versus time could be almost exactly superimposed on a graph of temperature versus time, as obtained by some other means. In contrast, the temperature control unit in most thermostat baths is a digital device with just two states such that the heater is on when the temperature is below a predetermined value and off when the temperature is above this value. A series of such temperature control units, set for different temperatures and having indicator lamps in place of heaters, could function as a digital thermometer; for example, with seven units and representing an unlighted lamp by 1 and a lighted lamp by 0, the following temperature scale might be obtained:

$$
\begin{aligned}
0000000 &= \text{below } 18^\circ\text{C} \\
0000001 &= \text{between 18 and } 19^\circ\text{C} \\
0000011 &= \text{between 19 and } 20^\circ\text{C} \\
0000111 &= \text{between 20 and } 21^\circ\text{C} \\
0001111 &= \text{between 21 and } 22^\circ\text{C} \\
0011111 &= \text{between 22 and } 23^\circ\text{C} \\
0111111 &= \text{between 23 and } 24^\circ\text{C} \\
1111111 &= \text{above } 24^\circ\text{C}
\end{aligned}
$$

The electrical state of the system would convey quite precise information about the temperature of the bath, but the variation of the electrical signals would not resemble the temperature variations. In an *analog computer* the electrical circuitry is adjusted so that a current or voltage is constrained to obey the same differential equations that apply to a physical system of interest. Thus by observing the time development of the current or voltage, with various initial boundary conditions, it is possible to simulate and ultimately to understand the behavior of the physical system without having to solve the equations mathematically. In a *digital computer*, on the other hand, information and operating instructions are converted into binary digits, stored, and manipulated in accordance with the laws of arithmetic and digital logic. Analog and digital techniques in electronics have their own fields of competence in which they frequently complement one another and seldom compete. With some instrumentation problems the best outcome can be achieved with a hybrid of the two techniques.

Signal Modifiers

It was indicated in Chapter I that a basic measuring instrument consists of an input transducer, one or more signal modifiers, and an output transducer. It is the modifiers that contain most of the electronics. The essential features of a modifier for voltage or current signals are shown in Fig. 4.4. As in any four-terminal network, there are characteristic input and output impedances which can be transformed by appropriate source transformations into corresponding input and output admittances (cf. Fig. 3.35). However, the most important feature of the modifier is the functional relationship

$$E_{\text{out}} = E(E_{\text{in}}, I_{\text{in}}) \tag{4.6}$$

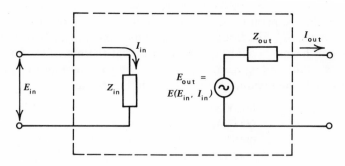

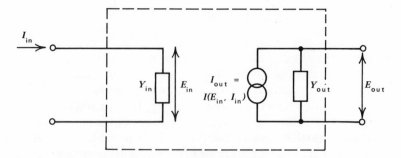

Fig. 4.4 Alternative representations of a modifier for electrical signals.

Table 4.2 Some Modifiers of Voltage Signals
(For current signals simply replace E by I throughout)

Amplifier	$E_{out} = A \cdot E_{in}$ + constant	(A = gain)
Rectifier (for continuous ac)	$E_{out} = \frac{1}{2}E_{pp}$	(E_{pp} = peak-to-peak value of E_{in})
	$= 1.4 \times E_{rms}$	(E_{rms} = root-mean-square of E_{in})
Differentiater	$E_{out} = dE_{in}/dt$	
Integrater	$E_{out} = \int_{0}^{t} E_{in} \cdot dt$	(t = time)
Chopper	$E_{out} = E_{in}$, t in range $t_1 \rightarrow t_2$, $t_3 \rightarrow t_4$, $t_5 \rightarrow t_6$, etc.	
	$E_{out} = 0$, t in range $t_2 \rightarrow t_3$, $t_4 \rightarrow t_5$, $t_6 \rightarrow t_7$, etc.	
Level discriminater	$E_{out} = E$, $E_{in} > E_0$ (E is a constant)	
	$E_{out} = 0$, $E_{in} < E_0$	
Pulse-height discriminater	$E_{out} = E_{in} - E_0$, $E_{in} > E_0$	
	$E_{out} = 0$, $E_{in} < E_0$	
Pulse shaper	$E_{out} = E(t)$, $\Delta E_{in} > E_{threshold}$	
Pulse counter	$E_{out} = nE_0$, $E_{in} > 0$ at times $t_1 \rightarrow t_n$, $E_{in} = 0$ otherwise	
Gate	$E_{out} = E_{in}$, $E_{gate} > E_0$	
	$E_{out} = 0$, $E_{gate} < E_0$	
Mixer	$E_{out} = K \cdot E_{in}(1) \cdot E_{in}(2)$	

or

$$I_{out} = I(E_{in}, I_{in}), \tag{4.7}$$

which holds between the input and output signals. In many cases the functional dependence can be treated as essentially linear, but in general there is no guarantee that the functions involved are even well behaved; for example, there may be discontinuities or there may be ranges in which the functions are many-valued.

Some of the more important modifiers are listed in Table 4.2. In Section 2 of this chapter we mainly consider modifiers that are commonly used with continuous ac (i.e., analog) signals, while in Section 3 we consider some modifiers for pulse signals. The last section of this chapter contains a discussion of power supplies.

2 AMPLIFIERS

The Properties of Active Devices

Resistors, capacitors, and inductors are passive components in electronic circuits—they serve as standard bearers and spear carriers while the main action in center stage is being performed by such active components as

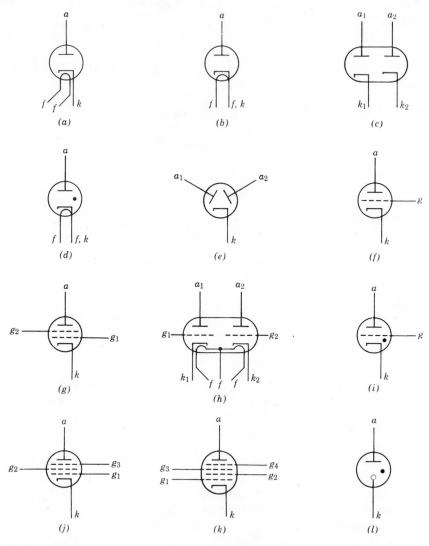

Fig. 4.5 Symbols for vacuum tubes: a = anode, f = filament (heater), k = cathode, g = grid. (*a*) Diode with indirectly heated cathode; (*b*) diode with directly heated cathode; (*c*) double diode, filaments not shown; (*d*) mercury rectifier with directly heated cathode (dot signifies gas filled); (*e*) full-wave rectifier diode; (*f*) triode; (*g*) tetrode; (*h*) double triode showing the usual arrangement for filament connections; (*i*) gas-filled triode (thyratron); (*j*) pentode; (*k*) hexode; (*l*) gas-filled discharge-tube (voltage reference tube).

vacuum tubes, transistors, or tunnel diodes. Correspondingly the history of electronics is essentially a history of the development of active devices, from the invention of the triode tube at the beginning of this century, through the ascendancy of the semiconductor "crystal" diode around 1920 and the rise of the vacuum tube from 1930 to 1950, to the vast resurgence of semiconductor devices that has occurred since 1955. The present state of the art is such that it is necessary to consider both tubes and solid-state devices, tubes still being capable of superior performance in the areas of very low current, high voltage, very high frequency, or very low noise. However, it is clearly only a matter of time before the advantages possessed by the solid-state devices, namely, much smaller size and much greater reliability, become available for all applications of electronics, and "hollow-state" devices become relegated to museums of technology.

We consider vacuum tubes first. Tubes are classified as diodes, triodes, tetrodes, pentodes, hexodes, heptodes, and so on, according to the number of electrodes inserted into the vacuum envelope. The envelope is usually glass but may be metal. Often two or more tubes are contained in the same envelope to conserve space. Circuit symbols for a number of different types of tube are given in Fig. 4.5.

The simplest tube is the vacuum diode, which contains an anode, or "plate," a cathode, and a cathode heater; a typical mode of construction is illustrated in Fig. 4.6a. The cathode is usually heated indirectly by a filament with which it is in thermal but not electrical contact, but tubes with electrical contact between cathode and heater or with a directly heated cathode are also fairly common.

When the diode is in use, the cathode becomes surrounded by a cloud of evaporated electrons which constitute a "space charge" and which produce an electric potential minimum a short distance from the cathode. When a positive potential is applied to the anode, some of the electrons in the cloud are attracted and a current flows, but most of the electrons that leave the cathode are repelled by the space charge without passing the potential minimum. In this condition the current is said to be space-charge limited. As the potential on the anode is increased the current increases and the effect of the space charge decreases until finally all of the electrons leaving the cathode can get to the anode. Thus we obtain the characteristic curve of Fig. 4.6b. The current does not go exactly to zero at zero anode voltage because the thermal energy is sufficient in the case of a small number of electrons for them to reach the anode unaided. The essential feature of a vacuum diode is that it conducts electricity in one direction only, namely from anode to cathode in terms of the conventional positive current.

If a vacuum diode is used in the high-voltage regime, with all of the electrons that leave the cathode being accelerated to reach the anode, the heating of

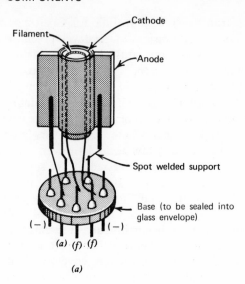

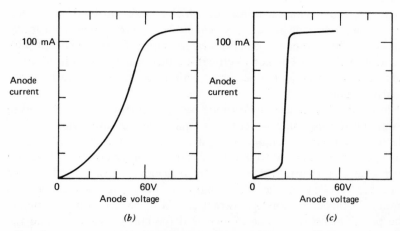

Fig. 4.6 (a) Construction of low-power vacuum diode with indirectly heated cathode; (b) typical vacuum diode characteristic; (c) diode characteristic with mercury vapor added.

the anode is usually sufficient to destroy the tube. This effect can be overcome by adding a small amount (0.1 torr) of gas, usually mercury, to the tube. Then, when the energy acquired by electrons on the way to the anode is sufficient to ionize the mercury (about 15 V per electron is needed), the positive ions so formed diffuse into the space charge region and remove the potential minimum. Consequently all of the electrons that leave the cathode can be attracted to the anode at the price of only a slight further increase in anode voltage. The characteristic curve that results is shown in Fig. 4.6c. Mercury rectifiers were formerly widely used in laboratory power supplies as an efficient means of converting mains ac power to dc, despite their disadvantage of requiring a warm-up time of two or three minutes during which the mercury slowly vaporizes. They have been largely superseded by equivalent semiconductor devices that require no warm-up time, take up much less space, and consume less power. If the anode voltage is applied before a tube is properly warmed up, there is a large voltage drop across the tube and the oxide coating on the cathode is "poisoned" or even destroyed as a result of bombardment with positive ions, formed from residual gas in the tube, which have been accelerated by the large anode potential. Positive ion bombardment of the cathode is one of the commonest mechanisms that lead to failure of vacuum tubes. The properties of some typical vacuum diodes are summarized in Table 4.3.

The usual mode of construction of a vacuum triode is shown in Fig. 4.7a. In a triode the control over the anode current formerly exercised by the space charge is taken over by the grid, a third electrode, which consists of an evenly spaced spiral of fine wire interposed between cathode and anode. The dependence of anode current on anode voltage at fixed grid potential is similar to that for a vacuum diode, as shown in Fig. 4.6b, but a different curve is obtained for each value of grid voltage. A typical set of anode characteristics is shown in Fig. 4.7b. The grid potential is normally slightly negative with respect to the cathode; otherwise some of the electrons from

Table 4.3 Properties of Some Vacuum Diodes

Designation	1AD2	5U4GB	6BC7	866A
Type*	Half-wave	Full-wave	Triple diode	Mercury, half-wave
Cathode heating	Direct	Direct	Indirect	Direct
Heater voltage	1.25 V	5 V	6.3 V	2.5 V
Heater current	0.2 A	3 A	0.45 A	5 A
Peak inverse-voltage rating†	26,000 V	1550 V	330 V	5000 V (at 60°C max)
Peak anode-current rating	50 mA	1 A (each plate)	54 mA (each section)	1 A

* A half-wave rectifier is simply a diode and a full-wave rectifier is a diode with two separate anodes. The reasons for these names will become apparent when we discuss power supplies. A triple diode is three separate and independent diodes in the same envelope.

† The maximum permissible reverse voltage between anode and cathode.

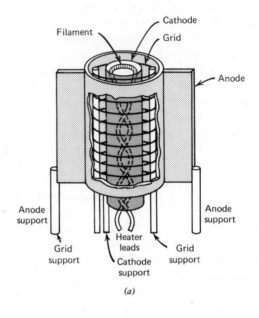

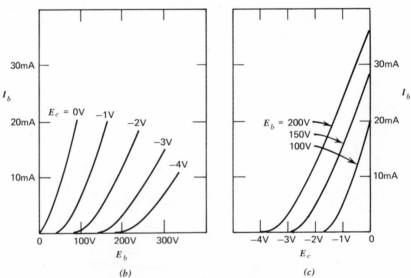

Fig. 4.7 Vacuum triode: (*a*) internal construction; (*b*) plate characteristics; (*c*) mutual characteristics.

the cathode attracted to the grid, "grid current" flows, and the grid loses its control over the anode current. The dependence of anode current on grid potential is shown by the mutual characteristics of Fig. 4.7c. It is the control exercised by the grid over the anode current that gives the triode its ability to act as an amplifier or switch.

In general the anode current of a tube is a function of both the anode voltage and the control-grid potential; that is, we can write

$$I_b = I(E_b, E_c),\qquad(4.8)$$

where I_b is the anode current, E_b is the anode voltage, and E_c is the control-grid voltage.* Hence the differential of I_b is

$$dI_b = \left(\frac{\partial I_b}{\partial E_b}\right) dE_b + \left(\frac{\partial I_b}{\partial E_c}\right) dE_c\qquad(4.9)$$

$$= \frac{dE_b}{r_p} + g_m \cdot dE_c,\qquad(4.10)$$

where r_p is known as the *plate resistance* of the tube and g_m is the *mutual conductance* or *transconductance*. For a triode it is usual also to define a quantity μ, the *amplification factor*, given by

$$\mu = g_m \cdot r_p = -\left(\frac{\partial E_b}{\partial E_c}\right)_{I_b}\qquad(4.11)$$

Triodes are classified as high mu, low mu, or medium mu, according to whether μ is more than 50, less than 10, or between these two values. The value of r_p is commonly in the range 5 to 50 K, and g_m is typically 1 to 5 mA/V (milliamperes per volt; unfortunately g_m is almost invariably stated in tube manuals in terms of the barbarous units *micromhos*, where 5000 μmho = 5 mA/V). The properties of some representative triodes are compared in Table 4.4.

In a triode tube the direct capacitance between grid and anode is typically about 1.5 pF. This is not significant at audiofrequencies, but at radio-frequencies and above it has two deleterious effects, namely those of reducing the input impedance at the control grid and of providing a direct signal path between the input at the grid and the output at the anode (this is for a tube in the commonest amplifier configuration; see Fig. 4.8). These effects are discussed in more detail later in this section; their relevance at present stems from the fact that attempts to overcome them led to the development of tetrodes and pentodes.

* This is the American Standard notation; a list of commonly used equivalents for these and other symbols is given in Appendix 4.2.

Table 4.4 Properties of Some Vacuum Triodes

Designation	12AU7	12AX7 (ECC83)	12AT7 (ECC81)	6AM4*	6080
Type	medium mu	high mu	high mu	high mu	low mu
Heater voltage	6.3/12.6	6.3/12.6	6.3/12.6	6.3	6.3
Heater current	0.3/0.15 A	0.3/0.15 A	0.3/0.15 A	0.225 A	2.5 A
Maximum E_b	300 V	300 V	300 V	200 V	250 V
Plate (anode) dissipation P_p	2.75 W	1.0 W	2.5 W	2.0 W	13 W
g_m	2.8 mA/V	1.4 mA/V	4 mA/V	9.8 mA/V	7 mA/V
μ	18.5	100	60	85	2.0
r_p	7 K	70 K	15 K	8.7 K	0.3 K
Measured at I_b	11 mA	0.8 mA	3.7 mA	10 mA	100 mA

* This is a single triode intended for high-frequency applications. The others are double triodes, with data given for one triode section alone.

In a tetrode the capacitance between grid and anode is reduced by the interposition of a second grid (the screen grid) between control grid and anode. This is successful as far as it goes, but the usefulness of the simple tetrode is limited by a new phenomenon, namely the emission of secondary electrons from the anode. In a typical application the cathode of the tube would be at earth potential, the control grid would be a few volts negative, the screen grid would be at about $+100$ V, and the anode, at about $+150$ V. Electrons striking the anode would have an energy of more than 100 V, which is sufficient to produce secondary emission of electrons with energies of a few tens of volts. The secondary electrons would form a cloud between anode and screen and many of them would actually be attracted to the screen, with a consequent reduction in anode current. This effect would be greater, the lower the anode voltage, and the result would be a characteristic curve of the form shown in Fig. 4.9. The region of negative slope in the anode

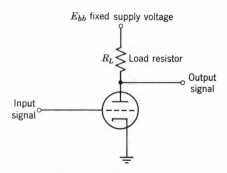

Fig. 4.8 Grounded-cathode amplifier configuration.

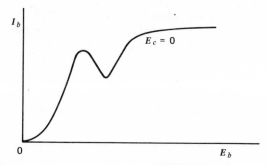

Fig. 4.9 Form of tetrode plate characteristic that results when secondary emission is important.

characteristic is undesirable because it leads at best to nonlinearity in the response of the tube and at worst may produce instability and oscillation in any amplifier of which the tube is made a part. If the anode current were arranged to be concentrated into a tight beam, the resulting space charge would tend to repel the secondary electrons back to the anode and would thus restore the usefulness of the tube. This is the approach that is used in "beam power" tubes. The electrons are concentrated into a beam by what is basically a crude grid in the form of a slotted plate, internally attached to the cathode; such a tube can be regarded as a pentode in which one grid is not able to be controlled independently. The properties of some typical beam-power tubes are summarized in Table 4.5.

In a pentode the secondary emission of electrons from the anode is overcome by the introduction of the suppressor, a third grid between anode and screen. The suppressor grid wires are normally rather widely spaced, so as not to interfere with the anode current, and in most applications are held at cathode potential. Secondary electrons continue to be emitted by the anode, but they are repelled back by the suppressor's much more negative

Table 4.5 Beam-Power Tubes

Designation	6Y6-GA	6V6	6146 A
Heater	6.3 V, 1.25 A	6.3 V, 0.45 A	6.3 V, 1.25 A
Capacitance, anode-G_1	0.66 pF	0.7 pF	0.24 pF
E_b maximum	200 V	350 V	600 V
Maximum G_2 dissipation	1.75 W	2.2 W	3 W
Maximum plate dissipation, P_p	12.5 W	14 W	20 W
g_m	7.1 mA/V	4.1 mA/V	7.0 mA/V
r_p	15 K	50 K	Not listed
Measured at I_b	60 mA	45 mA	100 mA

potential. The number of electrons that reach the anode becomes almost independent of the anode potential so that the anode characteristics have the form shown in Fig. 4.10a. The current is considerably affected by the screen (G_2) potential, so a different set of characteristics is obtained for each potential. This is shown explicitly by the mutual characteristics of Fig. 4.10b.

Once the initial "knee" is past, the very low slopes of the graphs of anode current versus anode voltage in Fig. 4.10a correspond to values of plate

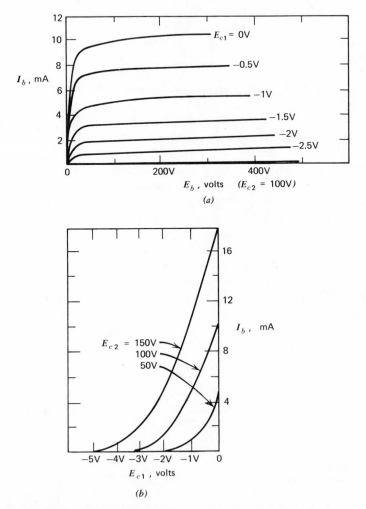

Fig. 4.10 Pentode 6AU6 characteristics; (a) plate characteristics at fixed screen grid voltage (E_{c2}); (b) mutual characteristics at $E_b = 250$ V. Note that suppressor voltage E_{c3} is zero throughout.

Table 4.6 Some Representative Pentodes

Designation	6SJ7	6AU6	18FW6A
Type*	Sharp cutoff	Sharp cutoff	Remote cutoff
Capacitance A-G_1	0.005 pF	0.0035 pF	0.0035 pF
E_b maximum	300 V	330 V	150 V
Maximum G_2 dissipation	0.7 W	0.7 W	0.6 W
Maximum plate dissipation, P_p	2.5 W	3.3 W	2.5 W
g_m	1.65 mA/V	5.2 mA/V	4.4 A/V
r_p	1.2 M	1 M	250 K
Measured at I_b	3.0 mA	10.6 mA	11 mA

* A pentode is described as sharp cutoff, semiremote cutoff, or remote cutoff, according to whether the negative control-grid voltage required to reduce the anode current to zero (the "grid base") is less than 10, 10 to 20, or more than 20% of the screen-grid voltage. This property is governed by the uniformity of the control-grid spacing.

resistance in the megohm range; it will be seen later that this considerably enhances the amplifying ability of a pentode in comparison with a triode. The amplification factor μ is not usually quoted for a pentode (the value of μ would be high because of the high value of r_p), the important parameters being just g_m and, for high-frequency applications, the capacitance between the anode and G_1. The properties of some representative pentodes are listed in Table 4.6.

Tubes with six or more electrodes invariably possess more than one control grid, their usual function being to mix two signals by allowing them to modulate the same anode current (cf. the heterodyne beat apparatus described at the end of Chapter 3). Apart from the presence of an extra control grid and an extra screen between the two control grids, such tubes are little different from the tetrodes and pentodes we have been considering.

A number of special tubes and related devices have been designed for use as generators and amplifiers of radiofrequency power in the ultra-high-frequency and microwave range (about 100 MHz to 100,000 MHz). These include disk-seal triodes, klystrons, magnetrons, masers, traveling-wave tubes, and quadrupole amplifiers. In general the complexity of operation of these devices and the degree of understanding required to exploit their special properties are an order of magnitude greater than for the tubes we have been considering. Even the appearance of what corresponds to an electrical circuit tends to be bizarre when the wavelength of the electromagnetic radiation associated with a signal approaches the physical dimensions of the circuit. Therefore, although techniques for handling microwave signals are of considerable importance to chemists working with electron

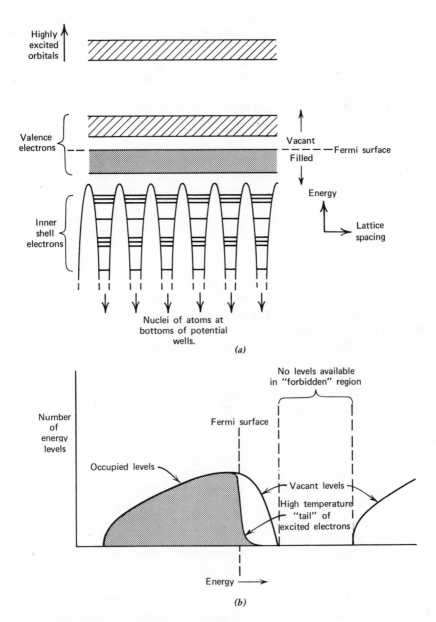

Fig. 4.11 Energy band model: (a) energy versus internuclear distance (for an insulator); (b) shows typical degeneracy of levels and Fermi surface (for a metal).

spin resonance or microwave spectrometers, they are not discussed in this chapter. Sources of microwave radiation are treated separately in Chapter V, and some topics relating to the detection of microwaves are covered in Chapter VI.

We next consider solid-state amplifiers—the class of electronic devices that exploits the electrical properties of semiconductors. The electrical conduction of a semiconductor is intermediate between that of a metal and that of an insulator, and, unlike conduction in a metal, increases with increasing temperature. This behavior is accounted for in terms of the *energy-band model*, which is illustrated qualitatively in Fig. 4.11. When atoms are packed together in a solid, the inner electrons are relatively unaffected and remain closely bound to their home nuclei at an energy level well below the outer or valence electrons. The inner electrons occupy the levels shown within the potential wells associated with nuclei in Fig. 4.11. The valence electrons, on the other hand, are in proximity to similar electrons on adjacent atoms and their orbitals are strongly affected. With only two atoms the outer orbitals combine in pairs, each pair forming one bonding and one antibonding molecular orbital in the usual way. The orbitals of a third atom can then mix with the orbitals of similar energy in the combined system, thereby adding to the number of levels, and so on as more and more atoms are added. By the time enough atoms have been added to constitute a crystal each outer orbital or group of degenerate orbitals in the individual atoms has given rise to a virtually continuous band of bonding energy levels, spaced by an energy gap from a similar band of antibonding levels. Further bands can be visualized as formed by overlap of the higher energy orbitals which are unoccupied in the ground-state atoms. The electrical properties of the resulting crystal depend on how completely these energy bands are filled with electrons.

Electrons obey Fermi-Dirac statistics, which means that the individual energy levels that make up a band become completely filled by the addition of just two electrons, which must be paired with opposite spins. Thus the available valence electrons in the crystal have to be placed in successively higher levels, two at a time, until all have been allocated places. For simplicity we suppose initially that the crystal is at $0°K$. Then the electrons will form a "sea" that will occupy all levels up to some maximum energy at the surface (the "Fermi surface"), at which point there are no more electrons to allocate. We can now distinguish three simple cases:

1. All levels in both bonding and antibonding bands are just completely filled with electrons. This would be true in a crystalline rare gas like argon or a molecular crystal in which the units are stable molecules like N_2 or CO_2. Such a crystal is necessarily an *insulator*.

2. One of the energy bands is not completely filled because of the lack of sufficient valence electrons. The unfilled band may be made up of bonding orbitals (sodium, copper) or of antibonding orbitals (bismuth, tellurium). The resulting crystal has metallic character and is a *conductor*, since the addition of a minute amount of energy is sufficient to excite an electron from the top of the sea into a level in which it is free to move throughout the crystal.

3. The band composed of bonding orbitals is completely filled, whereas the band composed of antibonding orbitals is entirely empty. In this case we have a strong molecular crystal of the type exemplified by diamond or silicon. At 0°K this crystal is also a perfect insulator. At any higher temperature, however, the statistics require that some electrons be excited into the vacant band. The result is that electrons are free to move in both bands, for the current is carried by the electrons themselves ("negative carriers") in the higher band and appears to be carried by the "positive holes," because of the absence of some electrons, in the lower band. The material is then an *intrinsic semiconductor*. The conductivity is governed by the number of electrons excited at a given temperature, which to a good approximation is given by the Boltzmann distribution law in the form

$$N_e = N_A \cdot \frac{Q_e \cdot Q_+}{Q_A} \times \exp\left(\frac{-\Delta E}{RT}\right), \qquad (4.12)$$

where N_e, the number of electrons excited, is equal to the number of positive holes left behind, N_A is the number of neutral atoms, the Q's are partition functions of the excited electron, the positive hole, and the neutral atom, and ΔE is the energy gap expressed in the same units as the gas constant R (recall that 1 eV = 23.06 kcal/mole). The two most commonly used semiconductor materials, germanium and silicon, have energy gaps of 0.72 and 1.03 eV, respectively. In an insulator the spacing from the filled level to the first unoccupied level is an order of magnitude greater, and at moderate temperatures the conduction is negligible; nevertheless the difference is one of degree rather than of kind.

It is not necessary in an intrinsic semiconductor for the same amount of current to be carried by each type of carrier; in fact it is unlikely. The carriers responsible for most of the conduction are termed "majority carriers"; the others are termed "minority carriers." If the majority carriers are electrons, we have an *n-type semiconductor*, and if they are positive holes we have a *p-type semiconductor*. The nature of the majority carriers can be determined unequivocally by measurements of the *Hall effect*, whose main features are shown in Fig. 4.12. The semiconductor, in the form of a flat

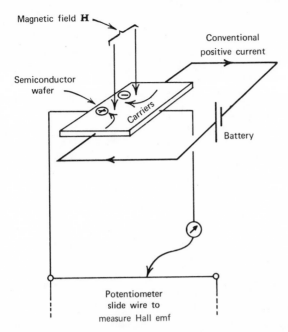

Fig. 4.12 Hall-effect experiment to determine the nature of the majority carriers in a semiconductor.

sheet or ribbon, is placed in a magnetic field and a voltage is applied between the ends of the ribbon. Carriers moving through the magnetic field under the influence of the applied voltage are deflected in a direction given by the right-hand rule so that charge tends to pile up along one edge of the ribbon. Since a current of positive carriers moving in one direction is equivalent, from the point of view of the right-hand rule, to a current of electrons moving in the opposite direction, the direction in which the carriers are deflected is the same for both. Thus the sign of the Hall emf, which develops between the edges of the ribbon, indicates the nature of the majority carriers, and the magnitude of the emf is an indication of the extent to which one carrier predominates, that is, of the size of the majority.

The materials used in solid-state electronic devices are *extrinsic semi-conductors*—very pure intrinsic semiconductors to which tiny amounts of impurities have been added to produce the desired amount of *n* or *p* character. Impurities are classified as donors or acceptors according to whether they contain more or fewer valence electrons than the host lattice; for example, an aluminum atom in a silicon lattice is an acceptor because it contributes one less valence electron than the silicon atom it replaces. Consequently a

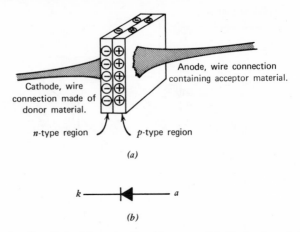

Cathode, wire connection made of donor material.

Anode, wire connection containing acceptor material.

n-type region   *p*-type region

(a)

k ———▸|— a

(b)

Fig. 4.13   Junction diode: (*a*) construction (diagrammatic); (*b*) circuit symbol.

positive hole is formed in the energy band, and silicon doped with aluminum is a *p*-type semiconductor. Similarly, germanium doped with arsenic is an *n*-type semiconductor. Other common acceptors are boron, gallium, and indium and other donors are phosphorus and antimony. The amount of impurity added is so small—typically 1 part in 10^9—that the production of satisfactory doped semiconductors was dependent on the invention of such techniques as zone refining for producing very pure crystals of host material.

Solid-state electronic devices consist of single crystals in which regions of *n*-type material are adjacent to *p*-type regions. The simplest example is the *junction diode,* which is illustrated in Fig. 4.13. There are many ways of forming a *p-n* junction between different regions of a crystal; for the present we shall ignore the constructional details. In the absence of an applied voltage the positive and negative carriers in the region of the junction experience a concentration gradient that tends to make them diffuse into the adjacent region of opposite type. This diffusion occurs until a balance is set up between the concentration gradient and the electric-field gradient that results from the diffusive movement of the electrical charges. Now a negative carrier finding itself in a *p*-type region will almost immediately drop into a hole in the lower energy band, whereas a positive hole in an *n*-type region will similarly be filled by one of the excess electrons from the higher band—in effect, the positive and negative carriers *recombine* with one another. The net result is a loss of some carriers, that is, the formation of a narrow *depletion layer* in the vicinity of the junction. If a voltage is applied across the diode in such a way that both types of majority carrier tend to be driven toward the junction, this counteracts the field gradient set up by diffusion across the depletion layer and further movement of charges across the junction becomes possible. Once the field gradient is completely overcome a steady current flows, for positive and negative carriers are created continuously where the current enters the crystal and lost continuously by recombination at the junction. In this condition the diode is said to be *forward-biased*.

If a voltage is applied across the diode in the reverse direction, the majority carriers migrate away from the junction, thereby increasing the thickness of the depletion layer. In this condition the diode is said to be *reverse-biased* and the only current that flows is the very small "leakage current" due to the minority carriers. Because of the larger energy gap, the number of minority carriers, and therefore the leakage current, is much less in silicon than in germanium; on the other hand, the forward voltage drop required to overcome the initial field gradient is about 0.5 V in silicon as opposed to only 0.2 V in germanium. A typical diode current-voltage characteristic is shown in Fig. 4.14.

If the reverse voltage across a *p-n* junction is made large enough, a phenomenon called breakdown occurs. The allowable-peak inverse voltage of a diode in normal use is governed by this phenomenon. The usual mechanism of breakdown is that minority carriers are accelerated by the large voltage difference across the depletion layer until they acquire sufficient energy to excite electrons across the energy gap and thus to create majority carriers forcibly in the layer. The voltage at which this occurs is termed the *Zener voltage*. Once the Zener voltage is reached a large current can be

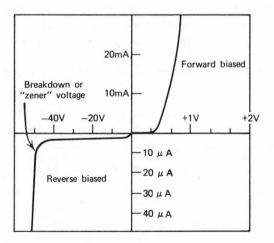

Fig. 4.14 Junction diode characteristics. Note different scales in forward and reverse quadrants.

made to flow with very little voltage increase; that is, the device has the useful property that the voltage drop is almost independent of the amount of current flowing. The use of Zener diodes as voltage standards in regulated power supplies is discussed in the last section of this chapter. The breakdown region is shown at the extreme left of the diode characteristic in Fig. 4.14. Too large a reverse current leads ultimately to destruction of the junction, after which the device may behave either as a short circuit in both directions or as an open circuit. The properties of some representative diodes and Zener diodes are compared in Table 4.7.

The device on which most of the semiconductor industry is presently founded is the transistor, of which two main types exist, namely, the *junction transistor* and the *field-effect transistor* (abbreviated FET). The word transistor by itself usually denotes a junction transistor, the first to be developed and used on a large scale, and still produced and used in greater numbers than the FET. The *point-contact transistor,* an early version of the junction transistor, is now obsolete and not considered here.

The construction of an alloy-junction transistor is shown in Fig. 4.15. The description "alloy-junction" refers to the mode of formation of the junctions, which governs the physical configuration of the device and also has a considerable effect on its electrical properties. The other basic configuration is planar, or "mesa," in which both junctions are formed on one surface of a disk-like crystal. In the alloying process small dots of indium, to take a specific example, are placed on opposite sides of a very thin wafer of germanium, which in this case would be n-type, and the whole is heated in vacuum. The molten indium attacks the germanium, in which it dissolves, and on cooling and recrystallization forms a region of p-type material on each side of the wafer with only a very thin n-type region near the center. The result is a *pnp* transistor. It happens, because of relative ease of fabrication, that most germanium transistors are of the *pnp* type, whereas most silicon transistors are *npn*. If the wafer is kept hot long enough for a significant amount of diffusion of the indium to occur, the result is a "diffused junction"

Table 4.7   Properties of Some Silicon Diodes and Zener Diodes

Designation	1N456	1N3070	1N3016B	1N2838	1N1128	1N2920
Use	General	Switching	Zener	Zener	Rectifier	Rectifier
V breakdown	30 V	200 V	6.8 V ($\pm 5\%$)	100 V ($\pm 2\%$)	600 V	5500 V
I maximum	135 mA	150 mA	-100 mA	-120 mA	3 A	250 mA
I surge	700 mA	2 A	-740 mA	-400 mA	10 A	2 A
Dissipation	200 mW	250 mW	1 W	50 W	Use heat sink	2.5 W
V forward	1 V	1 V	—	1.5 V	1.1 V	11 V
At I forward	40 mA	100 mA	—	10 A	1 A	250 mA
I reverse	0.025 μA	0.1 μA	—	—	10 μA	0.5 μA

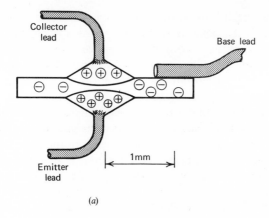

(a)

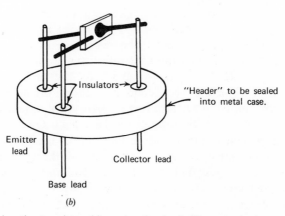

(b)

Fig. 4.15 Alloy-junction transistor: (a) construction (*pnp*); (b) mounted prior to encapsulation.

transistor in which transitions between the *p* and *n* regions are much less sharp and in which the pure *n*-type region is exceedingly narrow. These are both desirable properties, especially in transistors that are to operate at high frequencies. Many refinements of the diffusion process have been developed for use with transistors having the planar configuration, almost all with the aim of obtaining better performance at high frequencies, and the alloying process in its original form has been almost discarded. There is one other basic approach for obtaining suitable junctions, namely the *epitaxial technique*, which consists of growing from the vapor phase a thin layer of material of known properties on a single crystal substrate with different properties. By the use of suitable masks and a combination of vapor deposition, etching, and oxidation (to produce insulating layers of

SiO$_2$) it becomes feasible to build up complicated patterns of controlled resistance and p or n character on small sections of crystal. This, in turn, has made it possible to fabricate complete transistor circuits that occupy the space formerly occupied by single devices. We consider some of the features of these *integrated circuits* later in this chapter.

To return to the transistor of Fig. 4.15 we note that the thin central region is called the base and the two alloyed regions form the collector and emitter, respectively. The base is the control element corresponding to the grid of a tube, and the collector and emitter are analogous to the plate and cathode. When the transistor is in operation, the base-emitter junction constitutes a forward-biased diode and the base-collector junction constitutes a reverse-biased diode; the directions of the arrows in the circuit symbols of Fig. 4.16a correspond to the allowed direction of flow for the conventional positive current through the base-emitter diode. Since the collector-base junction is reverse-biased, most of the potential difference applied across the transistor actually occurs across a depletion layer at the base-collector junction (Fig. 4.16b). We can describe the operation of a *pnp* junction transistor in simple terms: under the influence of the applied voltage positive holes travel through the depletion layer produced by diffusion of carriers at the emitter-base junction and enter the base region. Since the base region as a whole must be electrically neutral, the number of positive holes from the emitter must always be balanced by an equal number of electrons that have entered through the base lead. Once inside the base region a positive hole has two possible fates: either it can be lost by recombination with a negative carrier or it can diffuse through the base to the depletion layer at the base-collector junction. Any positive hole that reaches the collector depletion layer encounters a strong voltage gradient and is immediately swept into the collector region. In the steady state a fraction

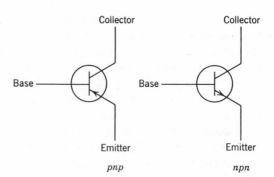

Fig. 4.16a   Circuit symbols for junction transistors.

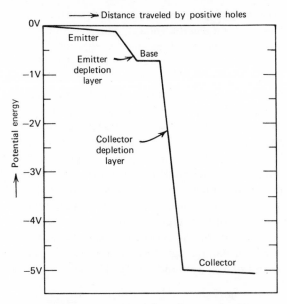

Fig. 4.16*b* Potential gradients in a *pnp* transistor.

$(1 - \alpha)$ of the positive holes is lost by recombination, and a corresponding current of electrons must flow in through the base lead to keep the base potential constant, despite recombination losses. The remaining fraction α of the positive holes constitute the collector current. The current gain β of the transistor is then given by the ratio of collector current to base current, that is,

$$\beta = \frac{\alpha}{1 - \alpha}. \tag{4.13}$$

To take a numerical example, if the current from emitter to base (in terms of the conventional positive current) is 1 mA and 1 % of the positive holes are lost by recombination in the base, the current flowing from base to collector is 0.99 mA, the current leaving via the base lead is 0.01 mA, and the current gain is 99. We see that, unlike a vacuum tube in which the anode current is controlled by the input voltage signal at the control grid, a transistor is a current-operated device, the collector current being controlled by the input current signal at the base. Correspondingly, the input resistance at the grid of a vacuum tube is very high—never less than $10^6 \ \Omega$, provided the grid remains negative with respect to the cathode, whereas the input resistance at the base of a transistor is at most a few thousand ohms.

In addition to its strong dependence on the base current, the collector current is also a function of collector voltage. This dependence is a consequence of two separate effects. The first effect is that any increase in the collector voltage relative to the emitter appears almost entirely as an increase in collector-base voltage and so results in an increase in the thickness of the depletion layer between these two regions. The thickness of the region through which carriers must diffuse is decreased, which leads to a small increase in collector current. This effect contributes to a "collector resistance" r_{ce} analogous to the plate resistance r_p of a tube. To understand the second effect we refer to Fig. 4.17a, which shows a simple form of equivalent circuit for a transistor. In this figure r_c is the resistance of the reverse-biased collector-base diode, which is usually a few megohms, r_b is the internal resistance of the base, typically a few hundred ohms, and r_e is the resistance of the forward-biased emitter-base diode, which is typically about 20 Ω. Now suppose that the emitter is connected to earth and consider the effect of applying a small voltage δv at the base. This voltage signal will be amplified by the gain of the transistor into a current $\delta i(\beta + 1)$ in the emitter. Hence

$$\delta v = \delta i(r_b + [\beta + 1]r_e);   (4.14)$$

that is, the effective resistance between the base and earth is $r_b + [\beta + 1]r_e$, and the circuit of Fig. 4.17a can be transformed into the simpler one of Fig. 4.17b. Now, if the collector voltage changes by an amount δV_c, a fraction μ of the change appears between the base and earth, where

$$\mu = \frac{r_b + (\beta + 1)r_e}{r_b + (\beta + 1)r_e + r_c},   (4.15)$$

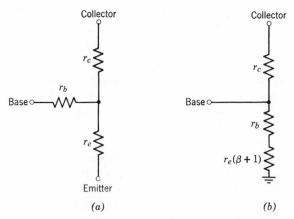

Fig. 4.17 Equivalent circuits for a transistor to illustrate *Early feedback* of voltage from collector to base.

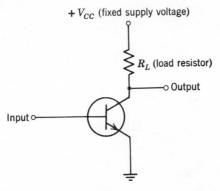

Fig. 4.18 Simplest transistor amplifier configuration (common-emitter configuration).

With $r_b = 200\ \Omega$, $\beta = 99$, $r_e = 20\ \Omega$, and $r_c = 4$ M, we should have $\mu = 4.5 \times 10^{-4}$, which would be a fairly typical value. If the collector of an *npn* transistor is connected to a fixed positive voltage supply through a load resistor, as in Fig. 4.18, an increase in collector voltage corresponds to a *decrease* in collector current. A fraction μ of the voltage increase is felt at the base, however, where it produces an increase in the base current and so a corresponding increase in the collector current; that is, it tends to counteract the original decrease in current. This is a type of internal negative feedback, which is sometimes referred to as "Early feedback."

The behavior of the collector current as a function of base current and collector voltage is summarized in the collector characteristics which are given for a typical low-power transistor in Fig. 4.19. The collector characteristics are similar in form to the pentode plate characteristics of Fig. 4.10*a*, except that the curves are labeled with particular values of base current rather than grid voltage. Also, the knee in the collector characteristic occurs below 1 V, whereas in the pentode characteristic it came at about 20 V; therefore a transistor will operate satisfactorily from a much lower voltage supply than is required for a tube. The analogy between the transistor and pentode characteristics is stronger because we have chosen an *npn* transistor for purposes of illustration. With a *pnp* transistor the collector voltage, the collector current, and the base current would all be of opposite sign to those in Fig. 4.19.

Corresponding to the pentode mutual characteristics of Fig. 4.10*b* there are the two transistor input characteristics of Fig. 4.20. In Fig. 4.20*a* it is seen that the dependence of collector current on base current at constant collector voltage is extremely linear; however, in Fig. 4.20*b* it is seen that the corresponding dependence of collector current on base voltage cannot be treated as linear except in the case of a small current variation.

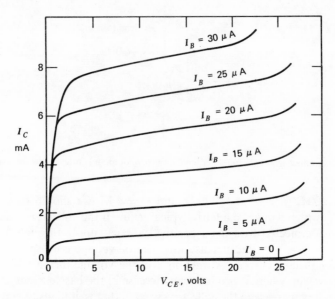

Fig. 4.19 Collector characteristics of silicon *npn* transistor (2N929), 25°C.

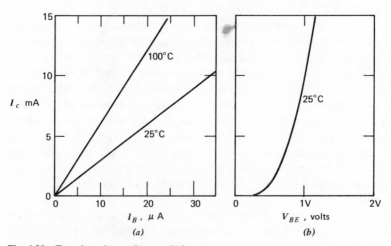

Fig. 4.20 Transistor input characteristics.

The electrical performance of a transistor can be summarized mathematically by formulas similar to (4.9) or (4.10), but the situation is more complicated for a transistor because there is a base and a collector current as well as a base and collector voltage to be considered. In general *two* equations are needed simultaneously to relate these quantities to one another. Any pair of the four quantities may be chosen as the dependent variables; the most convenient choice is usually the base voltage V_b and collector current I_c. For a transistor in the configuration of Fig. 4.18 this leads to the equations

$$dV_b = h_{ie} \cdot dI_b + h_{re} \cdot dV_c, \tag{4.16}$$

$$dI_c = h_{fe} \cdot dI_b + h_{oe} \cdot dV_c. \tag{4.17}$$

Here the *h*-parameters* are related to the quantities we have introduced so far as follows:

$$h_{ie} = r_b + (1 + \beta)r_e, \qquad h_{re} = \mu, \qquad h_{fe} = \beta; \qquad h_{oe} = 1/r_{ce}.$$

Strictly, the quantity β defined earlier was the dc gain rather than the ratio of a small change in collector current to the corresponding change in base current at constant collector voltage, that is, the small-signal current gain of (4.17), but the difference is not very great in practice. If necessary the large-signal or dc parameters can be distinguished from small-signal parameters by using upper-case subscripts, for example, h_{FE} or h_{IE}. The parameters are read in full as "*h*-input-emitter," "*h*-reverse-emitter," "*h*-forward-emitter," and "*h*-output-emitter." The emitter part of the subscript indicates that the parameters are defined for a transistor in the *common-emitter configuration* of Fig. 4.18, that is, with the emitter grounded or earthed and thus common to both the input and output circuits. Parameters defined for other configurations are discussed later in this chapter. For many purposes the only parameter it is essential to keep in mind is the current gain $\beta = h_{fe}$, partly because the other parameters have less to do with the over-all performance of an amplifier and partly because the control that manufacturers exercise over transistor parameters is much less than in the case of tube parameters; for example, two transistors of nominally the same type may have values of h_{fe}, measured under identical conditions, which differ by a factor of 2 or 3. Manufacturing techniques steadily improve, however, and the production of transistors in large quantities makes it feasible to select devices whose important parameters are specified within quite narrow ranges, so that the number of situations in which there is an

---

* The "hybrid" parameters, so-called because the dependent variables are a current and a voltage, not two currents, which would give admittance or *y*-parameters, nor two voltages, which would give impedance or *z*-parameters.

Table 4.8   Representative Junction Transistors

Designation	2N930	2N2243	2N428	2N514
Type	Si-*npn*	Si-*npn*	Ge-*pnp*	Ge-*pnp*
Construction	Planar	Epitaxial planar	Alloy-junction	Alloy-junction
Use	Small-signal	Fast, medium power	Low-power switch	High-power
BV_{CB}*	45 V	120 V	30 V	60 V
BV_{CE}	45 V	80 V	20 V	50 V
BV_{EB}	5 V	7 V	20 V	30 V
I_c maximum	30 mA	1 A	400 mA	25 A
Maximum dissipation	600 mW	2.8 W	150 mW	150 W
Current gain	150–600	40–120	20–30	20–60
Measured at $I_c =$	1 mA	150 mA	10 mA	25 A
Measured at $V_{CE} =$	5 V	10 V	0.35 V	2 V

* The symbol BV_{CB} stands for the breakdown voltage of the collector-base junction. BV_{EB} is the breakdown voltage of a reverse-biased emitter-base junction.

advantage to be gained by using the complete equations (4.17) and (4.18) can only increase. The properties of some representative junction transistors are compared in Table 4.18.

Among the properties compared in Table 4.8 one of the most important in practice is the maximum power dissipation, which is governed by the maximum allowable temperature in the device and the *thermal resistance*, in degrees centigrade per watt, between the collector junction and the surroundings at ambient temperature. It is dependent on such mechanical factors as the presence or absence of a heat sink and the proximity of other heat-generating components. All transistor parameters depend on temperature, and the extent of this dependence for the parameters of interest is one of the most important pieces of information to be gained from the transistor manufacturer's data sheets. Some mechanical mountings and heat sinks for transistors are described in Chapter II.

The principle of a *field-effect transistor* is shown in Fig. 4.21. Unlike Fig. 4.15, it is not to be regarded as an illustration of an actual device; field-effect transistors normally have a planar configuration, with quite complicated geometry of the different layers. In the *n*-channel FET of Fig. 4.21 the negative carriers in the body of the device must pass through a thin channel on their way from the *source*, shown as being at earth potential, to the positive *drain*. On either side of the *n*-type channel is the *p*-type *gate*. The gate is at a negative potential and the diode formed by the gate and channel is reverse-biased.

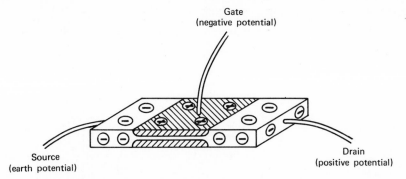

Fig. 4.21 Principle of operation of an *n*-channel field-effect transistor.

Consequently a depletion layer is present between gate and channel, and the thickness of this depletion layer is controlled by the size of the negative gate voltage. The thicker the depletion layer, the narrower the channel for carriers to flow from source to drain, and thus the lower the drain current. The source is seen to be analogous to the cathode of a tube, and the gate and drain are analogous to the control grid and plate, respectively. In the circuit symbols of Fig. 4.22 the arrows show the direction of easy flow of positive current through the gate-channel diode; since this diode is reverse-biased when the device is in operation, the input resistance is large (typically greater than 5 M) and the FET is electronically more like a tube than a junction transistor. The drain and transfer characteristics of an *n*-channel FET, shown in Fig. 4.23, are similar to the corresponding pentode characteristics of Fig. 4.10, except for the lower knee voltage and the presence of the break-down region at the high voltage end of each drain characteristic. The high input resistance of the FET gives it a definite superiority over the junction

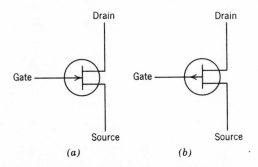

Fig. 4.22 Circuit symbols for field-effect transistors: (*a*) *n*-channel; (*b*) *p*-channel. (Sometimes the source and drain connections are distinguished by drawing the gate connection closer to the source.)

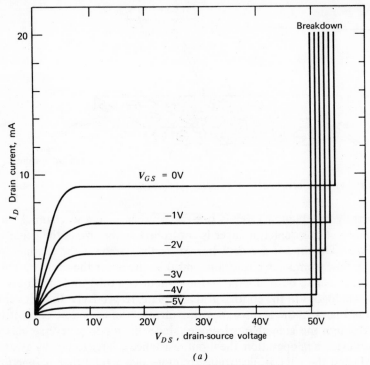

(a)

Fig. 4.23a   Drain characteristics of *n*-channel FET (2N4222).

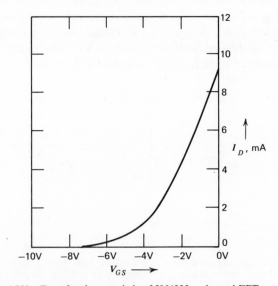

Fig. 4.23b   Transfer characteristic of 2N4222 *n*-channel FET.

transistor in some applications; in addition the FET usually has markedly better internal noise characteristics and is more resistant to damage by ionizing radiation—both advantages that are usually attributed to vacuum tubes.

Earlier we noted in passing that it is possible to form an insulating layer on a silicon substrate by controlled oxidation of the surface to SiO_2. If a very thin layer of SiO_2 is interposed between the gate and channel of an FET, the resulting device has an input resistance of the order of 10^{12} or 10^{13} Ω, combined with electrical characteristics basically similar to those of an ordinary field-effect transistor. This is the principle of what is variously termed a MOSFET, MOST, or IGFET; MOST is short for *metal-oxide semiconductor transistor*, IG is short for *insulated-gate*, and FET has its usual significance. The ultra-high input resistance gives the MOSFET many interesting characteristics and potential applications. The device has two drawbacks in practice, namely that the internal noise level is fairly high and that the layer of SiO_2 is easily punctured and the transistor ruined by too large a gate voltage. Such a voltage can easily be generated as static electricity during ordinary handling of the leads, and to avoid puncturing the SiO_2 layer it is advisable to keep the gate and source leads in electrical contact until after the device has been installed in a circuit. Alternative circuit symbols for a MOSFET are given in Fig. 4.24.

As with a pentode the most important quantity for deciding the performance of an FET as an amplifier is the rate of change of current through the device with changing voltage on the control element. In a pentode this change is given by the mutual conductance g_m; in an FET the corresponding parameter is termed the *forward-transfer admittance* (for the common-source configuration) y_{fs} and has a value that is typically in the range 1 to 5 mA/V. Corresponding to the high plate resistance r_p of the pentode, the FET has a low value of common-source *output admittance*, y_{os}, which is typically 20–100 μA/V (20–100 μmho). Thus in the usual low-voltage transistor circuits the dependence of drain current on drain-source voltage can generally be neglected. As with a junction transistor the possible spread of the numerical values of important parameters is so large for an FET that there is usually no point in using elaborate formulas to predict the behavior of an amplifier. If, however, either specially selected or experimentally characterized devices are available, it becomes worthwhile to consider, in addition to y_{fs} and y_{os}, (a) the finite resistance of the reverse-biased gate-channel diode, as described by the common-source *input admittance* y_{is}, and (b) the fraction of the output signal at the drain that is transferred back to the gate by a potential-divider effect, that is, the reverse-transfer admittance y_{rs}, analogous in its effect to h_{re} or μ of a junction transistor. Typical values for y_{is} and y_{rs} are 0.2 μA/V and 0.1 μA/V, respectively. In terms of these

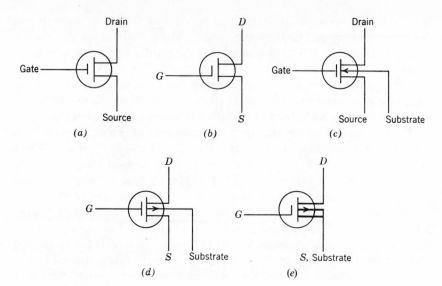

Fig. 4.24 Alternative circuit symbols for a field-effect transistor with an insulated gate (MOSFET): (*a*) simplest form; (*b*) with source distinguished from drain; (*c*) with separate connection to the substrate on which the device is grown and an arrow to show that it is an *n*-channel device; (*d*) as in (*c*) but *p*-channel; (*e*) Motorola representation, substrate internally connected to source, *p*-channel.

y-parameters, the behavior of a field-effect transistor in the configuration of Fig. 4.25 is described by the equations

$$dI_G = y_{is} \cdot dV_{GS} + y_{rs} \cdot dV_{DS}, \tag{4.18}$$

$$dI_D = y_{fs} \cdot dV_{GS} + y_{os} \cdot dV_{DS}, \tag{4.19}$$

where I_G and I_D are the gate-source and drain-source currents and V_{GS} and V_{DS} are the gate-source and drain-source voltages. The properties of some representative FET's and MOSFET's are compared in Table 4.9.

Table 4.9 Representative Field-Effect Transistors

Designation	2N4222	TIXS67	2N2500	2N3823	2N3796
Type	FET	MOSFET	FET	FET	MOSFET
Channel type	*n*	*p*	*p*	*n*	*n*
Use	General	High R input	Low noise	High frequency	Small signal
Dissipation	300 mW	360 mW	500 mW	300 mW	200 mW
BV_{DS}	30 V	−25 V	−20 V	30 V	25 V
y_{fs}	2.5–6.0 mA/V	3.0–6.5 mA/V	1.0–2.2 mA/V	3.2 mA/V*	0.9–1.8 mA/V
y_{os}	40 μA/V	250 μA/V	20 μA/V	200 μA/V*	12 μA/V
y_{is}	10^{-9} mho	10^{-13} mho	<0.2 μA/V	200 μA/V*	10^{-13} mho

* Measured at 200 MHz.

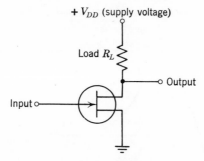

Fig. 4.25   Common-source amplifier configuration for an *n*-channel FET.

The remaining active amplifying device that we have to consider is the *tunnel diode*, which is a small two-terminal *p-n* device in which the *p* and *n* regions are heavily doped. Because of the heavy doping, the depletion layer which is formed by diffusion across the junction is extremely thin—only of the order of 100. Å. To account for the characteristics of the device we consider the energy-band model in Fig. 4.26. The energy levels of the *p*- and *n*-type regions are displaced relative to one another, as a consequence of the electric field produced by diffusion of carriers across the junction, and with no applied voltage the highest filled levels in the *p*-type region are of similar energy to the lowest vacant levels of the *n*-type region. Thus, if a small external

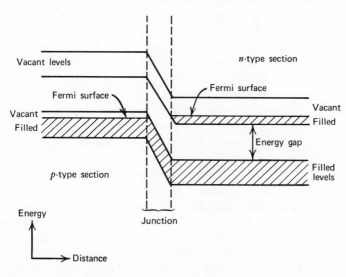

Fig. 4.26   Energy band model for a tunnel diode.

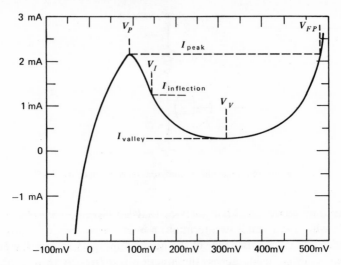

Fig. 4.27   Typical characteristic and static parameters for a germanium tunnel diode.

voltage is applied in either direction, the device will conduct by quantum-mechanical tunneling of the electrons across the thin junction. A positive voltage applied to the n-type region causes a further lowering of the energy bands on that side of the junction so that the device continues to conduct heavily in the direction corresponding to reverse bias in an ordinary diode. If, however, a negative voltage is applied to the n-type region, the energy levels on that side of the junction are raised and the tunneling current falls off. Normal forward-biased diode conduction then sets in when the applied voltage is sufficient to overcome the potential set up by diffusion, that is, when corresponding bands on opposite sides of the junction are at about the same energy level. The resulting tunnel diode characteristic is illustrated in Fig. 4.27. The usual circuit symbol for a tunnel diode is shown in Fig. 4.28a; a less common alternative is shown in Fig. 4.28b.

The most interesting feature of the tunnel diode is that the behavior shown in the characteristic of Fig. 4.27 is maintained over an extremely large range of frequencies—typically from dc to 10^{12} cps (1 THz). Thus the tunnel diode is an attractive device for use as an amplifier or oscillator at ultrahigh and microwave frequencies. Its ability to amplify or oscillate is a consequence of the presence of a *negative resistance* region in the characteristic, between the peak and valley currents of Fig. 4.28. By negative resistance we understand that dI/dV is negative, that is; if the device is biased at the inflection point by a suitable dc voltage, a small increase in the applied voltage results in a decrease in the current and vice-versa. If a signal

Fig. 4.28 (a) Usual tunnel diode symbol; (b) less common alternative.

generator of internal resistance R_s is in series with a properly biased tunnel diode of dynamic resistance $dV/dI = -R_d$ together with a load R_L, as in Fig. 4.29, the signal power transferred to the load is

$$W_L = \frac{E_S{}^2 R_L}{(R_s - R_d + R_L)^2},$$ (4.20)

where E_S is the output of the generator, and for this simple illustration the frequency is assumed to be low enough that reactances in the circuit can be neglected (in most applications of tunnel diodes this is definitely not true). It follows that the presence of the tunnel diode results in a *power gain* given by

$$A_p = \frac{(R_s + R_L)^2}{(R_s - R_d + R_L)^2}.$$ (4.21)

The available gain is limited by the condition that the tunnel diode must remain in its negative resistance region and by the practical observation that if the gain of an amplifier is made too high it becomes impossible to

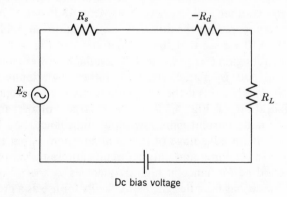

Fig. 4.29 Basic tunnel diode amplifier.

prevent the output from interacting with the input in such a way that the circuit is transformed into an oscillator.

In what follows we confine our attention almost exclusively to circuits containing tubes or transistors rather than tunnel diodes, since most chemical instruments involve signals of relatively low frequency and because tunnel diodes are less versatile than the other amplifying devices we have considered.

Basic Amplifier Configurations

So far when we have discussed the amplifying property of a tube or transistor we have always considered it in one of the configurations of Fig. 4.30a, that is, with the input signal applied to the control element—grid, base, or gate—and an output signal appearing across a load R_L in series with the anode, collector, or drain. In this configuration the cathode, emitter, or source is grounded. It is common to both input and output circuits and in naming the configuration we apply the epithet "grounded" or "common" to the appropriate one of the three elements. There is nothing, however, to prevent us from trying some other combination of input and output electrodes, and in this way we are led to the grounded grid, common base, and grounded-gate amplifiers of Fig. 4.30b and to the cathode-follower, emitter-follower, and source-follower amplifiers of Fig. 4.30c. The last three could equally well be termed common anode, common collector, and common drain, but the "follower" nomenclature, which arises from the fact that these amplifiers have a voltage gain close to unity so that the output voltage precisely follows the variations of the input voltage, is deeply ingrained by usage. Each type of configuration has its peculiar characteristics that can render it the most useful of the three in a particular situation.

Referring to Fig. 4.31, we note that an amplifier can be characterized by its input and output impedance or admittance and by its voltage gain A_v or current gain A_i. The gain is positive if the input and output signals are in phase with one another and negative if they are 180° out of phase. These properties are compared for the different configurations in Table 4.10.

From Table 4.10 we see that the configuration of Fig. 4.30a gives both voltage and current gain (hence the highest available power gain for a single amplifier stage) and is characterized by rather high input and output impedances. In practice this is the most commonly used configuration.

The configuration of Fig. 4.30b gives a large voltage amplification, combined with unity current gain, low input impedance, and high output impedance. The main advantage of this configuration is that the isolation it affords between the input and output circuits allows the amplifier to give particularly good performance at high frequencies. A special type of tube, the disk-seal triode, has been designed specifically for use as a grounded-grid amplifier at frequencies of 100 Mc and above.

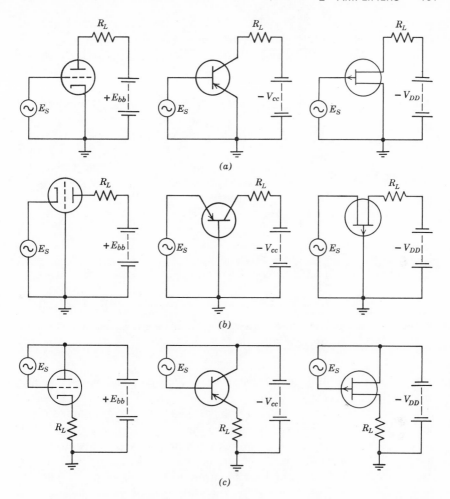

Fig. 4.30   Basic amplifier configurations: (*a*) common (or *grounded*) cathode, common emitter, and common source configurations: (*b*) grounded grid, common base, and common drain configurations; (*c*) cathode-follower, emitter-follower (common collector), and source-follower (common drain) configurations.

The configuration of Fig. 4.30*c* is used mainly as an *impedance transformer;* that is, it converts a signal at a high impedance level at which it would be susceptible to the integrating effects of stray capacitance to an identical voltage signal at a low impedance level at which there is sufficient current output available to make distortions due to charging stray capacitance entirely negligible. It is usual for a multistage amplifier to include a follower

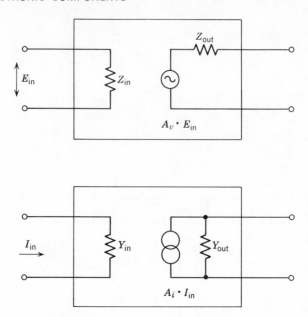

Fig. 4.31 (*a*) Voltage amplifier (cf. Thevenin's theorem); (*b*) current amplifier (cf. Norton's theorem): $Y_{in} = 1/Z_{in}$; $Y_{out} = 1/Z_{out}$.

output stage to ensure against distortion of the signal en route to the next modifier or transducer. In addition, most output transducers have low input impedance so that it is convenient to have the follower stage ready to match the output impedance of an amplifier to the input impedance of any likely transducer. Finally, if the output of an amplifier is taken to a transmission line, which is terminated by its characteristic impedance, it is usually desirable to match the amplifier's output to this impedance. Since the

Table 4.10   Gain and Impedance Characteristics of Simple Amplifier Stages

Configuration	Voltage Gain	Current Gain	Input Impedance	Output Impedance
Grounded cathode	Large negative	Large negative	Very high	High
Common emitter	Large negative	Large negative	Fairly high	Fairly high
Common source	Large negative	Large negative	Very high	High
Grounded grid	Large positive	+1.0	Low	High
Common base	Large positive	+1.0	Very low	High
Grounded gate	Large positive	+1.0	Low	High
Cathode follower	+1.0	Very high	Very high	Low
Emitter follower	+1.0	High	High	Very low
Source follower	+1.0	Very high	Very high	Low

characteristic impedances of commonly used transmission lines are low, the use of a final amplifier stage of low output impedance is indicated, which in turn implies that the final stage is probably a cathode, emitter, or source follower.

Assume that we wish to design an amplifier stage and have decided, on the basis of input and output impedance and gain requirements, which of the three types of configuration to use. Assume further that we have some grounds for having chosen a particular kind of active device, such as the availability of suitable power supplies, the need for a large final voltage signal (tube circuit indicated), the desire for safe, low-voltage operation and compactness (transistor circuit preferred), or for these qualities combined with low noise or with high input impedance in the configuration of Fig. 4.30a (FET circuit indicated). The next problems are to choose a particular type of tube or transistor in accordance with power and voltage requirements and to ensure that the one selected is incorporated into a circuit in such a way that the current and voltage in absence of an input signal are in the correct range for satisfactory operation. These are the problems of *selection* and *biasing*. To show how solutions are arrived at in practice we devote the rest of this subsection to the design of some typical amplifier stages. In the next subsection we consider how individual stages may be combined into a multistage amplifier.

For the first example suppose that we require a simple tube amplifier in the grounded cathode configuration to respond to small signals in the audiofrequency range (roughly 20 to 20,000 Hz) and to have a voltage gain of 30 or 40 with no great power output. These modest requirements can be met most economically by choosing a high-mu triode, which may be a single unit such as a 6AB4 ($\mu = 60$) or 6AN4 ($\mu = 70$), or one section of a double unit such as a 12AT7, which contains two triodes similar to the 6AB4, a 12AX7, which contains two units in which $\mu = 100$, or a 6AW8A, which contains a triode with $\mu = 70$ plus a sharp-cutoff pentode. For simplicity we suppose that the tube chosen is the 6AB4. The plate characteristics of this tube are given in Fig. 4.32 and the form of circuit to be used is shown in Fig. 4.33.

First we need to fix a few of the quantities that appear in Fig. 4.33. The maximum rated plate voltage for this tube is 300 V, and therefore it is safe to choose this same value for the supply voltage E_b. The capacitors C are required to conduct the input and output signals at frequencies of the order of 20 cycles; with the relatively high impedance levels that are characteristic of tube circuits it should certainly be adequate to choose $C = 1.0\ \mu\text{F}$, which corresponds to a reactance of about 8 K at 20 Hz. Small plastic-dielectric capacitors with voltage ratings above 300 V are easily obtained for this kind of application. The grid resistor R_g should be large in comparison with the

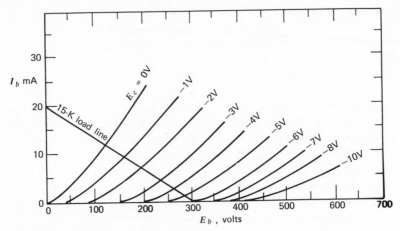

Fig. 4.32   Plate characteristics of 6AB4 triode.

reactance of C but not so large that the tube's grid current, which may be 0.1 μA, will produce an appreciable voltage drop on flowing through R_g to earth. We choose $R_g = 1$ M.

The next step is to decide on a suitable operating point for the tube, that is, a suitable combination of plate voltage and plate current. In general R_L will be much larger than R_k, and we can assume that the total voltage $E_{bb} = 300$ V will divide itself between the plate voltage E_b and the drop across the load resistor, $I_b \cdot R_L$, and write

$$E_{bb} = E_b + I_b \cdot R_L = 300. \tag{4.22}$$

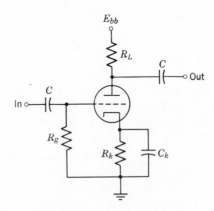

Fig. 4.33   Basic triode amplifier circuit.

This is the equation of a line, the *load line*, which can be superimposed on the curves of Fig. 4.32 to cut the horizontal axis at $E_b = 300$ V and the vertical axis at $I_b = 300/R_L$. For the sake of illustration the load line for $R_L = 15$ K has been drawn in the figure. The optimum load line should cut the characteristics approximately at right angles, since this would give the greatest variation of E_b, that is, the largest output signal, for a given variation of E_c. The only limitation here is set by the maximum plate dissipation, which in this instance is 2.5 W, and cannot be exceeded with $R_L = 15$ K. Now, if we choose a point on the 15-K load line with $E_c = -1$ V, we note that a change of E_c by 1 V in either direction moves the point along the line in such a way that E_b changes by about 40 V; therefore with $R_L = 15$ K the circuit has a gain of about 40 and is satisfactory for our purpose. The value of R_k is now fixed by the fact that the voltage drop produced by the plate current I_b when it flows through R_k must equal the value of $-E_c$ at the chosen operating point. If we choose the operating point at $E_c = -1.5$ V on the 15-K load line, this gives $I_b = 8$ mA and the value of R_k works out to be 187 Ω. Low-precision resistors (and capacitors below about 1 μF) are available with values* that are multiples of numbers in the series 1.0, 1.2, 1.5, 1.8, 2.2, 2.7, 3.3, 3.9, 4.7, 5.6, 6.8, 8.2, 10; in this case we can use $R_k = 180$ Ω. This resistor dissipates little power and its wattage rating hardly matters; however, the load resistor R_L is required to dissipate 8 mA × 120 V = 960 mW, so at least a 1 W rating is indicated. Finally, the purpose of the "bypass capacitor" C_k is to short-circuit the cathode to earth from the point of view of alternating current so that the cathode potential remains constant in the presence of an incoming ac signal. The criterion for fixing the value of C_k is that its reactance should be about 10% or less of R_k at the lowest frequency for which the amplifier is designed. Therefore in the present circuit we should have $C_k = 500$ μF. A miniature electrolytic capacitor with a voltage rating of 5 to 10 V would be satisfactory. The final triode amplifier is shown in Fig. 4.34.

Instead of estimating the gain of the amplifier from the load line, we could obtain a more precise value by using the equation

$$dI_b = \frac{dE_b}{r_p} + g_m \cdot dE_c. \tag{4.10}$$

Here we have $dE_{\text{in}} = dE_c$, and $dE_{\text{out}} = dE_b = -R_L \cdot dI_b$ (the minus sign is important). Hence

$$-dE_{\text{out}}\left(\frac{1}{R_L} + \frac{1}{r_p}\right) = g_m \cdot dE_{\text{in}} \tag{4.23}$$

---

* These are usually termed the "preferred" values of resistance and capacitance. With 5% tolerance resistors the intermediate values 1.1, 1.3, 1.6, 2.0, 2.4, 3.0, etc., are available.

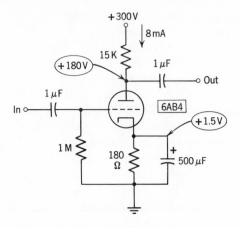

Fig. 4.34   Practical triode amplifier.

or

$$A_v = \frac{dE_{\text{out}}}{dE_{\text{in}}} = \frac{-g_m \cdot r_p \cdot R_L}{R_L + r_p} \tag{4.24}$$

$$= \frac{-\mu R_L}{R_L + r_p} \tag{4.25}$$

The negative gain corresponds to the fact that the input and output signals are 180° out of phase, that is, a positive-going input signal produces a negative-going output signal. For the present circuit we have $\mu = 60$, $R_L = 15$ K, $r_p = 12$ K, and a voltage gain of -33.

In connection with the problem of fixing the operating point of a tube a useful general rule is that the cathode of a tube which is conducting a current is normally only a few volts more positive than the control grid. This is especially true of tubes that are suitable as amplifiers of small signals. Thus in the circuit of Fig. 4.35 the current through the tube, which need not even be a triode, is approximately 35 V divided by 3.9 K, or 9 mA, no matter what kind of tube within reasonable limits is actually used. The load R_L should not be so large that E_b is unusually small (e.g., less than 100 V), and if a high value of E_{bb} is used (assuming that the tube has a high rating) the voltage to which the control grid is tied needs to be raised in proportion. Provided these restrictions are kept in mind, it becomes a simple matter either to fix the operating point of an amplifier stage without more than passing reference to tube characteristics or, alternatively, to design a stage in which the operating point is stabilized against variations in characteristics during the life of a tube, or from one tube to another.

If our tube amplifier were required to have a much greater value of the product of gain and bandwidth than we previously supposed, it would be necessary to use a pentode or two triodes in the form of a cascode amplifier, as described in the next subsection. For a pentode stage we use as our example a 6EW6, which is a miniature sharp-cutoff pentode with a plate resistance of 200 K and a transconductance of 14 mA/V. (For most pentodes g_m is half this value or less.) The plate characteristics are given (with the screen-grid characteristics) in Fig. 4.36, and the basic circuit of a pentode amplifier is given in Fig. 4.37. In this example we again fix $E_{bb} = 300$ V (the rated maximum for E_b is 330 V), the coupling capacitors C are chosen to be 1 μF, and R_g is set at 1 M. The characteristics of Fig. 4.36 are for a tube with a screen (G_2) potential of 125 V; we should therefore choose the value of R_s so that the screen current in absence of an input signal produces a potential drop of 175 V across R_s. The screen current depends on the control-grid potential, and this must be decided first. A reasonable value is $E_{C1} = -1$ V, which gives $I_{C2} = 2.5$ mA and I_b approximately 8 mA. With $I_{C2} = 2.5$ mA we require $R_s = 175$ V/2.5 mA $= 70$ K and we use the nearest preferred value which is 68 K. The purpose of the capacitor C_s is to prevent the screen potential from varying appreciably in the presence of an incoming signal; using the same criterion as for a cathode bypass capacitor, we find that at 20 Hz a reactance of 6.8 K corresponds to a capacitance of 1.2 μF, and to be on the safe side we use $C_k = 2$ μF. This capacitor should be rated to withstand more than 300 V in case the 300 V supply should come on before the tube heater has had time to warm up. Since the control grid is at earth potential, it is necessary for the total cathode current of 10.5 mA to produce

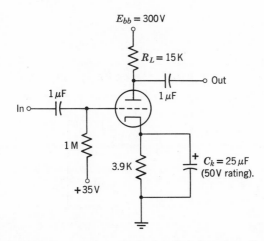

Fig. 4.35 Circuit in which the operating point is virtually independent of tube characteristics.

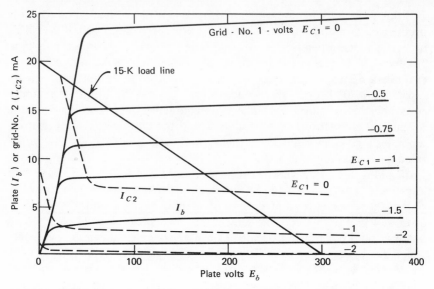

Fig. 4.36 6EW6 plate and screen characteristics; G_3 connected to cathode, G_2 at $+125$ V.

a potential drop of 1 V on flowing through R_k. Hence R_k must be 100 Ω, and for the cathode bypass capacitor C_k we can insert a small electrolytic capacitor of about 1000 μF. Finally we must choose a value for the anode load R_L. In general the greater the value of R_L the higher the gain at moderate frequencies and the more limited the high-frequency response. As a reasonable compromise we again choose $R_L = 15$ K and estimate from the load

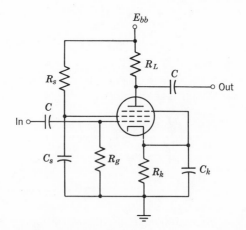

Fig. 4.37 Basic pentode amplifier.

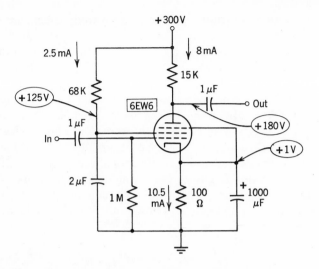

Fig. 4.38 Practical high-gain pentode amplifier.

line drawn in Fig. 4.36 that the gain is about 200. The resulting practical pentode amplifier stage is shown in Fig. 4.38.

Once again, to obtain a precise value of the gain we can work from (4.10) by using the result

$$A_v = \frac{-g_m \cdot r_p \cdot R_L}{r_p + R_L},$$ (4.24)

which for a pentode will normally reduce to

$$A_v = -g_m \cdot R_L$$ (4.26)

because of the high value of r_p. In the present example r_p has the relatively low value of 200 K, while $g_m = 14$ mA/V and $R_L = 15$ K. Using the complete equation (4.24), we obtain $A_v = -195$. The current dissipation in the 68-K resistor is 430 mW and therefore a $\frac{1}{2}$ W resistor will suffice; in the 15-K resistor the dissipation is 960 mW and at least a 1-W rating is indicated. It is usual to be more conservative with the rating of R_L because the gain depends directly on its value, which is likely to vary significantly with temperature.

In both amplifiers the input impedance is provided by the 1-M grid resistor in parallel with the interelectrode capacitances that are the main limitation on the gain at high frequencies. The output impedance in each case is provided by the parallel combination of anode load and plate resistance and therefore amounts to 6.7 K for the 6AB4 and 14 K for the

6EW6, again with a contribution from interelectrode capacitances at high frequencies.

Before leaving tube amplifiers let us consider briefly the grounded-grid amplifier of Fig. 4.39 and the cathode-follower of Fig. 4.40. In both circuits the operating point for the 6AB4 tube has been fixed by the method of referring the grid to a fairly large positive potential and then choosing the cathode resistor R_k to obtain the desired plate current. In the grounded-grid stage the grid is short-circuited to earth, from the point of view of an ac signal, by the 2-μF capacitor. This type of circuit is intended mainly for high-frequency signals and quite small coupling capacitors can be used. Alternatively, the cathode circuit may contain the secondary winding of one interstage transformer and the anode circuit the primary winding of another. The calculation of gain and input and output impedances is based on (4.10):

$$dI_b = \frac{dE_b}{r_p} + g_m \cdot dE_c, \qquad (4.10)$$

where

$$dE_{\text{out}} = -R_L \cdot dI_b, \qquad dE_b = dE_{\text{out}} - dE_{\text{in}}, \qquad dE_c = -dE_k$$

and

$$dE_k = dE_{\text{in}} = R_k \cdot dI_b.$$

With the aid of these relationships we can transform (4.10) into

$$A_v = \frac{dE_{\text{out}}}{dE_{\text{in}}} = \frac{(\mu + 1)R_L}{R_L + r_p}, \qquad (4.27)$$

which is positive, showing that the input and output signals are in phase.

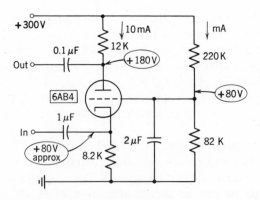

Fig. 4.39   Grounded-grid amplifier.

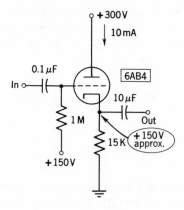

Fig. 4.40 Cathode-follower.

Using $\mu = 60$, $R_L = 12$ K, and $r_p = 12$ K, we obtain $A_v = 30$. The output impedance consists of the plate resistance and load resistance in parallel, that is, 6 K, together with the anode-grid capacitance of 1.5 pF and any stray wiring capacitances that may be present. The input impedance of the tube alone is defined as $(\partial E_{in}/\partial I_b)$ with $dE_{out} = 0$; putting $dE_b = 0$ into (4.10), we find that the input impedance is $-1/g_m$ or $-200\ \Omega$ when $g_m = 5$ mA/V. The negative sign merely means that a positive current from the point of view of the input signal corresponds to a decrease in the current through the tube and does not have the same significance as the negative resistance of, say, a tunnel diode. To calculate the net input impedance we ignore the minus sign and consider the 200 Ω to be in parallel with the 8.2-K cathode resistor, which gives a final value of about 190 Ω.

For the cathode-follower of Fig. 4.40 the coupling capacitor on the input side can be quite small because the circuit has an inherently high input impedance (roughly 1 M in this example). On the output side, however, the coupling capacitor should in general be large because here the signal is at a low impedance level. The voltage gain and output impedance are again calculated from (4.10). We have

$$dE_c = dE_{in} - dE_{out}, \qquad dE_b = -dE_{out}$$

and

$$dE_{out} = R_k \cdot dI_b,$$

where we have written the load resistor as R_k to show it is attached to the cathode. With the aid of these relationships we can transform (4.10) into

$$A_v = \frac{dE_{out}}{dE_{in}} = \frac{\mu R_k}{(\mu + 1)R_k + r_p} \sim \frac{\mu}{\mu + 1}. \qquad (4.28)$$

For the present example the exact equation yields $A_v = 0.972$ and the form $\mu/(\mu + 1)$ gives $A_v = 0.983$. Both values are close to unity, and in practice the difference between E_{in} and E_{out} would usually be negligible. With $dE_{in} = 0$ we obtain from (4.10) the result

$$dI_b = \frac{-dE_{out}}{r_p} - g_m \, dE_{out} \tag{4.29}$$

or

$$\frac{\partial E_{out}}{\partial I_b} = \frac{-r_p}{\mu + 1} \sim \frac{-1}{g_m}, \tag{4.30}$$

where again the minus sign has no practical significance. Thus the net output impedance consists of 200 Ω in parallel with the 15-K cathode resistor, which gives a final value of about 195 Ω.

Transistor amplifier circuits can be designed by procedures that are entirely analogous to those we have used with tubes. The main point of difference lies in the large variations in transistor parameters that can occur as a result of changes in temperature or on going from one individual device to another of the same type. To overcome these effects it is invariably necessary to use a biasing arrangement similar to that in Fig. 4.35. Junction transistors operate at much lower voltage and impedance levels than vacuum tubes, so that transistor circuits typically contain low-valued resistors and high-valued capacitors. As noted before, in this respect field-effect transistors resemble tubes more than they resemble junction transistors.

To consider the factors involved we refer to the two small-signal amplifiers of Fig. 4.41. In the 2N930 stage of Fig. 4.41a the collector current is chosen to be rather small (100 μA) because silicon transistors have better noise properties at low collector currents. The dc current gain at this collector current is about 200, and only about 0.5 μA is required to flow in through the base lead. The base potential is fixed at 6.1 V by the potential divider made up of the 2.2-M and 560-K resistors and the emitter potential will normally be about 0.6 V more negative than this. Therefore the emitter current, which is fixed by the emitter potential and the emitter resistor, must be close to the desired value of 100 μA. With the emitter at 5.5 V the remaining potential drop to be shared between the transistor and the collector load is about 24 V; with a 120-K load the potential drop is evenly divided, and an incoming signal can cause the collector potential to swing almost 12 V positive or negative before serious distortion occurs. As before, the emitter-bypass capacitor is chosen to have its reactance less than 10% of the value of the emitter resistor at a frequency near 20 cycles (20 Hz), this being the arbitrary lower frequency limit that we previously chose for the tube amplifiers. The 10 μF values shown for the coupling capacitors would be

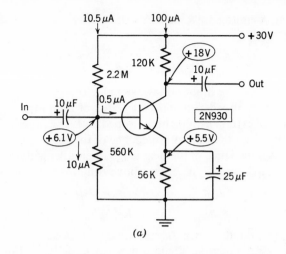

(a)

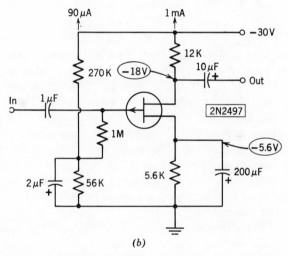

(b)

Fig. 4.41 Small signal amplifiers: (a) junction transistor common-emitter stage; (b) FET, common-source.

fairly typical for this kind of circuit. The collector characteristics of the 2N930 are not given on a sufficiently large scale to allow the 120-K load line to be drawn (cf. Fig. 4.19), and in order to calculate the gain of the amplifier we have to use the equations

$$dV_b = h_{ie} \cdot dI_b + h_{re} \cdot dV_c \qquad (4.16)$$

$$dI_c = h_{fe} \cdot dI_b + h_{oe} \cdot dV_c \qquad (4.17)$$

For a common-emitter stage we can write

$$dV_b = dE_{in}$$

and

$$dE_{out} = -R_L \cdot dI_c = dV_c.$$

(This assumes that the input voltage signal is obtained from a generator of negligible output impedance and is detected at the output by an amplifier or transducer of extremely high input impedance. In a practical case it would be necessary to add the output impedance of the generator in series with h_{ie} and the input impedance of the next stage in parallel with R_L.) We can now eliminate dI_b, dV_b, and dI_c from the above equations and obtain

$$A_v = \frac{dE_{out}}{dE_{in}} = \frac{-h_{fe} \cdot R_L}{(h_{ie} + R_L[h_{ie}h_{oe} - h_{fe}h_{re}])}. \qquad (4.31)$$

In this expression the term Δh in square brackets is usually neglected, although its effects may be significant when R_L is large. For the 2N930 at $I_c = 100\ \mu A$ and $T = 25°C$ we find typically* $h_{fe} = 250$, $h_{ie} = 75$ K, $h_{oe} = 12\ \mu A/V$, and $h_{re} = 3.5 \times 10^{-3}$. With these values the term in square brackets is 0.04 and the voltage gain is -400. The power gain is given by the product of current and voltage gain, the current gain from the simplest viewpoint being just h_{fe}. In practice, however, the output current divides itself between the load R_L and the following amplifier or transducer and the input signal current divides itself between the output admittance of the generator and h_{ie} so that h_{fe} really amounts to an upper limit for the gain. Taking the current gain to be 250, we find that the available power gain A_p is 10^5, or 50 dB (50 decibels). The input impedance of the amplifier at moderate frequencies is simply h_{ie}, or 75 K, and the output impedance is given by the parallel combination of R_L and $1/h_{oe}$, which in the present case works out to be 63 K. The power dissipated in the whole circuit is only 3.3 mW, and the power ratings of the components do not need to be considered. This is not a typical transistor circuit because the choice of a very small collector current has resulted in the use of high-valued resistors. If the collector current is multiplied by 100 and the values of all resistors are decreased by the same factor, the collector current becomes 10 mA and the collector dissipation is still below the limit of 300 mW, which is permitted for this particular transistor at an air temperature of 25°C. We now have typically $h_{fe} = 370$, $h_{ie} = 5.2$ K, $h_{oe} = 0.24$ mA/V, and $h_{re} = 3.0 \times 10^{-3}$. The term in square brackets in (4.31) is 0.14 and the voltage gain A_v is -90. The input impedance at moderate frequencies is now 5.2 K and the output impedance is 1.2 K in parallel with $1/h_{oe}$, or 1 K.

---

* The Texas Instruments data sheets for the 2N930 give a mixture of common-emitter and common-base parameters. Formulas connecting these quantities are given in Appendix 4.1.

The 2N2497 amplifier of Fig. 4.41*b* is designed in accordance with the same principles as the one we just considered, but in this case the excellent noise properties of the device tend to deteriorate at very low operating currents and the initial design is for a drain current of −1 mA. To preserve the high input impedance characteristic of the FET the gate is connected through a 1-M resistor to the potential divider which is used to fix the source potential (via that of the gate). The midpoint of the potential divider is bypassed, or "decoupled," with a 2-μF capacitor as a means of reducing pickup of unwanted signals and in order to keep the voltage provided by the potential divider constant in the presence of a large input signal. According to the typical drain characteristics of Fig. 4.42, a current of −1 mA corresponds to a gate potential of about +0.5 V; since the midpoint of the potential divider is at −5.1 V, the source is therefore at −5.6 V and the source current is 1 mA as specified. The 12-K load resistor therefore takes half the remaining potential drop of 24 V between the source and the power supply. The 12 K load line in Fig. 4.42 is drawn for a supply voltage

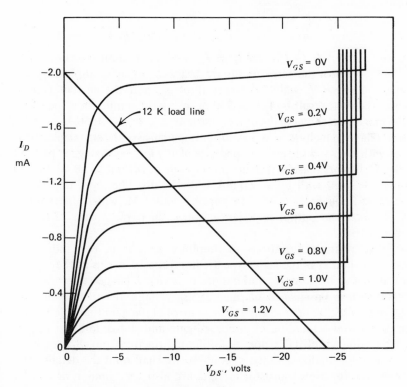

Fig. 4.42 Drain characteristics of 2N2497 FET.

of 24 V, since the 5.6-V drop across the source resistor is not available to contribute to the output signal. From the load line the voltage gain A_v is estimated to be -17. For a more precise estimate we can use the equations

$$dI_G = y_{is} \cdot dV_{GS} + y_{rs} \cdot dV_{DS}, \tag{4.18}$$

$$dI_D = y_{fs} \cdot dV_{GS} + y_{os} \cdot dV_{DS} \tag{4.19}$$

with $y_{is} = 0.2 \ \mu A/V$ (maximum), $y_{rs} = 0.1 \ \mu A/V$ (maximum), y_{fs} is between 1.0 and 2.0 mA/V, and $y_{os} = 20 \ \mu A/V$ (maximum). To calculate the voltage gain we need use only the second equation with $dE_{in} = dV_{GS}$ and $dE_{out} = -R_L \cdot dI_D = dV_{DS}$ to obtain

$$A_v = \frac{dE_{out}}{dE_{in}} = \frac{-y_{fs} \cdot R_L}{1 + y_{os} \cdot R_L}. \tag{4.32}$$

This result is the FET analog of (4.24). For the present example it yields $A_v = -24$ as a maximum value and $A_v = -10$ as a minimum "worst-case" value. From (4.18) and (4.19) together we can calculate the current gain in the form

$$A_i = \frac{dI_{out}}{dI_{in}} = \frac{y_{fs}}{y_{is} + R_L[y_{is} \cdot y_{os} - y_{fs} \cdot y_{rs}]}, \tag{4.33}$$

where we have put $I_D = I_{out}$ and $I_G = I_{in}$. For our present example, using maximum y-values, the term in square brackets when multiplied by R_L becomes $-2.36 \ \mu A/V$, which is larger than y_{is}, and the current gain is negative. The final result is $A_i = -930$ or, using the minimum value of y_{fs} with the maximum values of the other y-parameters, $A_i = -1050$. In practice we should have to include here the output impedance of the signal generator in series with $1/y_{is}$ and the input impedance of any following stage in parallel with R_L. The "worst-case" available power gain works out to be 40 dB and the value obtained with $y_{fs} = 2.0$ mA/V is 43.5 dB. The input impedance at moderate frequencies is $1/y_{is}$ in parallel with 1 M, which amounts to 800 K, whereas the output impedance is $1/y_{os}$ in parallel with 12 K and amounts to 10 K.

The large possible variations in amplifier gain from one individual transistor to another of the same type are not quite as serious as they might appear at first sight, since by making use of *feedback* (as described later in this chapter) it is possible to sacrifice excess voltage or current gain and thereby obtain highly precise and stable control of the gain that is left.

The design and evaluation of grounded-gate and source-follower stages, using FET's and MOSFET's, does not differ in principle from what we have done already for analogous tube circuits, so we shall omit the details. The corresponding junction transistor circuits are also very similar, as can be seen by comparing Figs. 4.43 and 4.44 with Figs. 4.39 and 4.40.

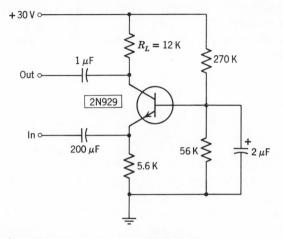

Fig. 4.43 Common-base amplifier stage.

In Fig. 4.43 we have used a 2N929 in preference to the more expensive 2N930 because a high value of h_{fe} is not important in the common-base configuration. The biasing conditions are essentially the same as for the FET amplifier of Fig. 4.41b. To calculate the voltage gain we could draw a 15-K load line on the common-base collector characteristics, if these were available, or work from the equations

$$dV_e = h_{ib}\, dI_e + h_{rb}\, dV_c, \tag{4.34}$$

$$dI_c = h_{fb}\, dI_e + h_{ob}\, dV_c, \tag{4.35}$$

which are the common-base analogs of (4.16) and (4.17). The relations

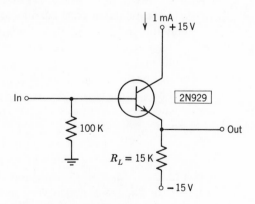

Fig. 4.44 Emitter-follower.

between h-parameters for the different configurations are given in Appendix 4.1; for the present we may note that $h_{ib} = r_e$ and $h_{fb} = -\alpha$, while h_{ob} is essentially the reciprocal of the resistance of the reverse-biased collector-base junction. Using $dV_e = dE_{in}$ and $dV_c = -R_L \cdot dI_c = dE_{out}$, we can obtain a voltage gain expression analogous to (4.31), namely,

$$A_v = \frac{dE_{out}}{dE_{in}} = \frac{-h_{fb} \cdot R_L}{h_{ib} + R_L[h_{ib}h_{ob} - h_{fb}h_{rb}]}. \qquad (4.36)$$

Inserting appropriate values for the h-parameters, we find that the term in square brackets amounts to $+1.8 \times 10^{-4}$ and makes a difference of 10% in the value of the denominator, h_{ib} being $20\ \Omega$. With $h_{fb} = -0.995$ the value of A_v works out to be $+540$. In practice it would hardly be necessary to use (4.36), since almost all of the signal current that flows into the emitter must flow out through the collector, neglecting only the very small base current, and the voltage gain must equal the ratio of output impedance to input impedance. The output impedance is provided by $1/h_{ob}$ in parallel with R_L, which in this case is 14 M in parallel with 12 K and so amounts to just 12 K, whereas the input impedance is provided by $h_{ib} = 20\ \Omega$ (from the viewpoint of an external circuit this is in parallel with the 5.6-K biasing resistor which does not affect the gain). The ratio of 12 K to $20\ \Omega$ gives a value of 600 for A_v, which differs from the previous value through what amounts to neglect of the term in square brackets in (4.36). A common-base stage can give more voltage gain and better high-frequency response than a common-emitter stage based on the same transistor, but the power gain is much less, and the combination of low input impedance and high output impedance is the opposite of what is usually desirable.

We have also specified a 2N929 transistor for the emitter-follower of Fig. 4.44, in which a center-tapped power supply is used so that the input may be close to earth potential. The anticipated base current of 5 μA fixes the base potential at -0.5 V and the emitter potential is about -1.2 V. To calculate the voltage gain of this arrangement we could set up equations analogous to (4.34), (4.35), and (4.36) and insert the h-parameters appropriate to the common-collector configuration. This would largely obscure what is going on, however, and it is more instructive to carry out an approximate but still quite accurate calculation. We have $dV_{be} = dE_{in} - dE_{out}$ and $dI_b = dV_{be}/(r_b + [\beta + 1]r_e) = dV_{be}/h_{ie}$. Now

$$dI_e = (\beta + 1) \cdot dI_b = (h_{fe} + 1) \cdot dI_b$$

and

$$dE_{out} = R_L \cdot dI_e,$$

so we can eliminate dV_{be}, dI_b, and dI_e to obtain the result

$$A_v = \frac{dE_{out}}{dE_{in}} = \frac{R_L(h_{fe} + 1)}{h_{ie} + R_L[h_{fe} + 1]}. \tag{4.37}$$

For the present circuit we have $R_L = 15$ K, $h_{fe} = 200$, and $h_{ie} = 6$ K; hence $A_v = 0.998$ and the difference between dE_{in} and dE_{out} would be entirely negligible in practice.

To calculate the input impedance we note that the input current dI_b is equal to $(dE_{in} - dE_{out})/h_{ie}$; using (4.37), we therefore obtain

$$Z_{in} = \frac{dE_{in}}{dI_b} = h_{ie} + R_L(h_{fe} + 1) \sim R_L \cdot h_{fe}. \tag{4.38}$$

This is an interesting result because it shows that the impedance at the output of the transistor is effectively multiplied by h_{fe} from the viewpoint of a signal generator at the input. For the present case we find $Z_{in} = 3$ M, and as far as the source of the input signal is concerned the lowest impedance in sight is the 100-K bias resistor! In practice we should have to include the input impedance of any following circuit in parallel with R_L, which would lower the input impedance of the transistor to a small extent.

The output impedance of the emitter-follower consists of the impedance at the emitter of the transistor in parallel with R_L. We ignore R_L for the present and consider the case in which the total resistance between the base and earth is R_s (Fig. 4.45). Strictly, this should be considered as an impedance, but the result we are about to obtain is easily generalized. With no input signal, a voltage change dE at the output will result in a current dI in the emitter and a current $dI/(h_{fe} + 1)$ in the base circuit which contains R_s. The voltage change at the output is equal to the sum of the potential drop produced by dI flowing through r_e and the potential drop produced by

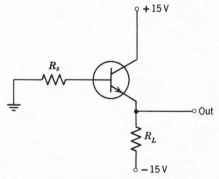

Fig. 4.45 Calculation of the output impedance of an emitter-follower.

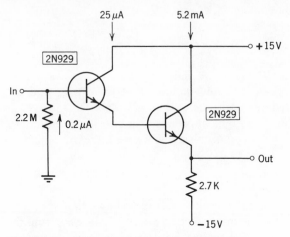

Fig. 4.46   Darlington configuration for two transistors.

$dI/(h_{fe} + 1)$ flowing through r_b and R_s in series; that is,

$$dE = r_e \cdot dI + r_b \cdot \frac{dI}{h_{fe} + 1} + R_s \cdot \frac{dI}{h_{fe} + 1}$$

$$= (h_{ie} + R_s)\frac{dI}{h_{fe} + 1}$$

and we have, replacing R_s with an impedance Z_s,

$$Z_{\text{out}} = \frac{dE}{dI} = \frac{h_{ie} + Z_s}{h_{fe} + 1} \sim \frac{h_{ie} + Z_s}{h_{fe}}. \tag{4.39}$$

Thus from the point of view of the output of the circuit the impedance at the input is effectively divided by the current gain of the transistor. With the present circuit the maximum value Z_s could have is 106 K and the maximum value of the output impedance is about 500 Ω.

This kind of impedance transformer action can be greatly increased by using two (or more) transistors in the *Darlington configuration* of Fig. 4.46. In this configuration the two transistors behave as a single device whose current gain is the product of the two h_{fe} values and whose base-emitter voltage is the sum of the separate voltages. In a germanium transistor there is an appreciable temperature-dependent leakage current across the collector-base junction which amounts to an internal base current and which makes the operating point of the transistor rather strongly temperature-dependent. For this reason it is not advisable to use a germanium transistor in place of the first silicon transistor in Fig. 4.46, but for the second transistor this restriction would not apply. The Darlington configuration is often used in power supplies and other situations in which a large current gain is required.

Multistage Amplifiers

An interesting multistage amplifier involving two triodes is the *cascode amplifier*, of which a practical example is given in Fig. 4.47. The circuit amounts essentially to a grounded-cathode stage followed directly by a grounded-grid stage and is very conveniently built around a high-mu double triode, such as the 12AT7 or 12AX7. Its main advantages are a large gain-bandwidth product, which may be appreciably greater than that of most pentodes, and low internal noise; it commonly appears as the input stage of a wide-band tube amplifier for handling small pulse signals.

Using (4.10), we have for the lower triode

$$dI_b = \frac{dE_{b1}}{r_p} + g_m \cdot dE_{\text{in}}$$

and for the upper triode

$$dI_b = \frac{dE_{\text{out}}}{r_p} - g_m \cdot dE_{b1},$$

where

$$dE_{\text{out}} = -R_L \cdot dI_b.$$

We have neglected dE_{b1} in comparison with dE_{out} in substituting dE_{out} for

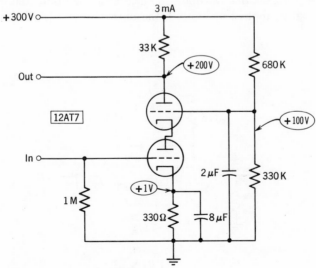

Fig. 4.47 Cascode amplifier.

dE_b of the upper triode. These equations can be rearranged to give the expression

$$dI_b = \frac{dE_{out}}{R} + g_m \cdot dE_{in} \qquad (4.40)$$

where

$$R = \frac{g_m \cdot r_p^2 \cdot R_L}{R_L + r_p}, \qquad (4.41)$$

so that the cascode amplifier behaves as if it were a single tube of plate resistance equal to r_p multiplied by $\mu \cdot R_L/(R_L + r_p)$ and of amplification factor equal to μ multiplied by the same factor. For the circuit of Fig. 4.47 we have $R_L = 33$ K, $r_p = 14$ K, $g_m = 4.2$ mA/V, and $\mu = 60$. The effective plate resistance is 590 K and the voltage gain works out to be -140.

An extremely useful two-stage amplifier is the *long-tailed pair*, of which three examples are given in Fig. 4.48. In each of these circuits a center-tapped power supply is used so that the input may be near earth potential; this is often convenient but by no means essential. The input resistors could be taken to the midpoint of a potential divider, provided sufficient decoupling capacitance were used to prevent the input signals from interacting. If input 2 is held at a fixed potential, the long-tailed pair may be regarded as a follower stage driving a grounded-grid, common-base, or grounded-gate stage, the low output impedance of the first being matched to the low input impedance of the second. The long-tailed pair has important applications:

1. As a *phase-splitter:* If input 2 is held at a fixed potential and a sinusoidal signal is applied at input 1, the output of one triode or transistor

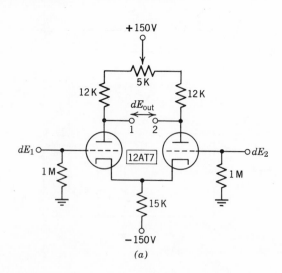

(a)

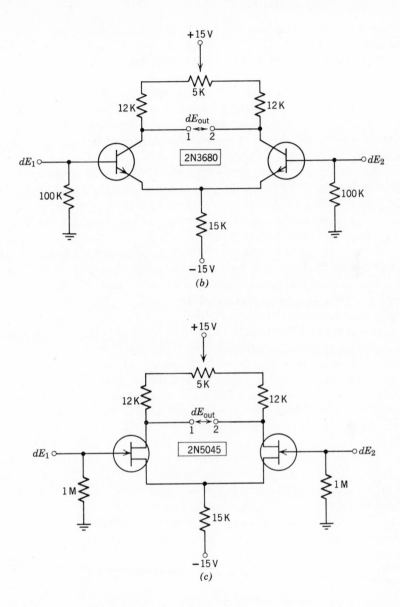

Fig. 4.48 Long-tailed pairs: (a) based on double triode tube; (b) using a dual junction transistor; (c) using a dual FET. In each case $dE_{in} = dE_1 - dE_2$.

section is 180° out of phase with the output of the other section, and the amplitudes of the two out-of-phase signals may be exactly equalized by adjusting the potentiometer (whose value in these examples is 5 K) that controls the relative sizes of the loads in the two sections.

2. As a *differential amplifier:* If two identical signals are applied at the inputs, the difference between the output voltages, shown in the figure as dE_{out}, is zero to a good approximation. Only when there is a difference between dE_1 and dE_2 does an appreciable signal appear between the output terminals.

3. As a *dc amplifier:* If an amplifier is built without reactive components, it is able to amplify very slow changes of dc voltage levels. The long-tailed pair circuit has the advantage of not requiring cathode, emitter, or source-decoupling capacitors so that it must merit consideration for this kind of application. The main difficulty with dc amplifiers is that slow changes in the ambient temperature, supply voltage, tube filament voltage, or the characteristics of the devices themselves can give rise to drifts in the output that may be mistaken for the consequences of an input signal. The long-tailed pair largely avoids these problems, since the changes in ambient temperature and filament voltage should affect both active devices simultaneously, and the differential output is insensitive to changes in the supply voltage. Furthermore, the 12AT7 consists of two triodes in the same envelope, which were necessarily assembled at the same time and are subject to the same influences throughout the lifetime of the unit. Therefore, if a tube is selected initially to have matched plate characteristics in its two triode sections, the matching can be expected to remain good. In a semiconductor device there are more parameters to match, notably the base-emitter or gate-source voltage, the temperature coefficient of this voltage, and the gain for small signals, h_{fe} or y_{fs}. With germanium junction transistors it would also be necessary to balance the collector leakage current. The 2N3680 and 2N5045 transistors of Fig. 4.48 are, in fact, *dual* devices, each consisting of a pair of transistors grown on the same silicon "chip" and selected for careful matching of the abovementioned parameters. The 2N5045 is also selected to have a low internal noise level at low frequencies. The long-tailed pair does not represent the ultimate in low-drift dc amplifiers, but it has the advantage of simplicity, combined with a drift-rate that is small enough to be tolerable in most applications.

It is not difficult to work through the algebra involved in obtaining expressions for the voltage gains of the circuits in Fig. 4.48; to save time, however, we use a simpler approach. Suppose, initially, that the potential at input 2 is fixed. The input impedance at the cathode, emitter, or source of the second device of the pair is low, and if a signal current appears at this point by follower action from input 1 it will flow largely through this low impedance in preference to the 15-K resistor. Hence the potential drop along the 15-K resistor must remain almost constant, which means that the total current through the two devices is also almost constant. Thus, if the signal at input 1 is positive, it increases the current by an amount dI in the first device and simultaneously decreases the current by dI in the second device. If the load resistors are matched and equal to R, there is a signal $-R \cdot dI$ at output 1 and a corresponding signal $+R \cdot dI$ at output 2. An identical input signal applied at input 2 would cancel both output signals exactly; an equal negative input at 2 would double the output signals. With equal and opposite input signals, the cathode, emitter, or source potential is exactly constant, and the gain at each output, relative to the nearest input, is the same as that calculated for a simple grounded-cathode, common-emitter, or common-source stage. We therefore have the result that for a symmetrical system the over-all gain $dE_{\text{out}}/(dE_1 - dE_2)$ is equal to the gain that would be given by one of the sections in a common-cathode, common-emitter, or common-source configuration with the same value of load resistor.

A number of grounded-cathode, common-emitter, or common-source amplifiers may be connected in the manner of Fig. 4.49 to make an *RC-coupled amplifier* of large over-all voltage gain. The output stage of the amplifier is normally a follower so that the output impedance will be low. The number of stages that give voltage gain is usually limited to three or four because of the instability that arises when the over-all gain becomes very large; to reduce interactions that could occur by way of the voltage supply it is usual to decouple the input stage with an RC network with a long time constant, as shown in the figure. The input impedance of each stage preferably should be high, since this input impedance is in parallel with the load

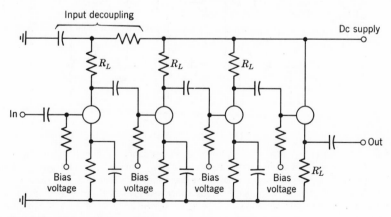

Fig. 4.49 *RC*-coupled amplifier.

resistor of the preceding stage; if it is too low, the gain of the preceding stage is reduced. From this point of view tubes and field-effect transistors are more suitable than junction transistors for incorporation into this type of amplifier, and in a transistor amplifier it may be desirable to alternate common-emitter and emitter-follower stages. The alternative is to use *transformer coupling* as in Fig. 4.50. This form of coupling has some advantages: for example, it becomes possible to cascade common-base stages in which high gain does not depend directly on the possession of high h_{fe} (at high frequencies the transformer coils can be tuned to a narrow bandwidth by the addition of a small amount of parallel capacitance) and it greatly simplifies the problem of working with a small current signal from a low impedance source such as a thermocouple. To obtain a high impedance ratio in a transformer it is necessary to have a high ratio of the number of turns in the primary coil to the number in the secondary, which in turn implies the use of a voltage step-down transformer and a reduction in the size of the signal voltage. Since the impedance ratio of a transformer is equal to the square of the turns ratio, the voltage reduction is less than might have been expected; with a well-designed transformer the *power* available from the secondary is almost the same as the power supplied to the primary.

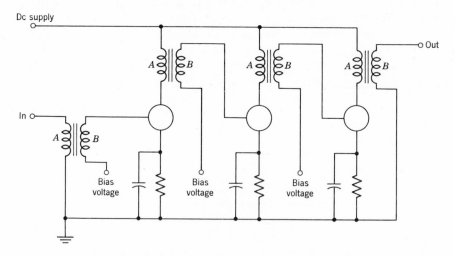

Fig. 4.50   Transformer-coupled amplifier; A = high impedance winding, B = low impedance winding. (This is either for junction transistors or for grounded-grid and grounded-gate configurations.) The power supply to the input stage may be decoupled, if necessary, as in Fig. 4.49. In a radiofrequency amplifier the transformers usually lack the iron cores shown here, and primary and secondary windings may be tuned by the addition of a small capacitor in parallel with each winding.

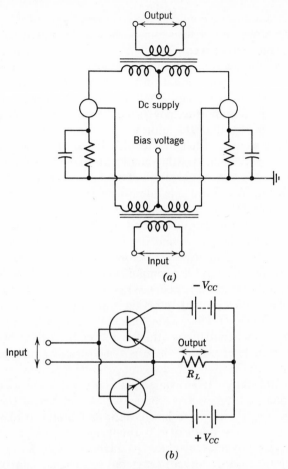

Fig. 4.51 Push-pull amplifiers: (*a*) with transformer coupling; (*b*) with direct-coupled complementary *pnp* and *npn* transistors. (Biasing here is for approximately Class B operation.)

In amplifiers designed to handle large amounts of power impedance matching assumes great importance and transformer coupling is used almost exclusively. Other methods of improving the efficiency of *power amplifiers* include the use of paired tubes or transistors in *push-pull* operation, as illustrated in Fig. 4.51, and the replacement of class A operation by class B or class C operation. In *class A* operation the active device is biased in the middle of its operating range so that with a sine-wave input signal of maximum amplitude the current just reaches zero at one peak in each cycle and is a maximum, with zero voltage across the device, at the opposite peak. It can be shown that in class A operation the maximum proportion of the supply power that can be converted into output signal is 50%. In *class B* operation two tubes or transistors in push-pull are biased so that in the absence of a signal neither is conducting, but a very small positive signal will cause one to conduct and a very small negative signal will bring the other into conduction and leave the first turned off. With this arrangement each device is turned off for an average of half the time that a signal is present, and the theoretical maximum efficiency of conversion of supply power into output signal is 78.5%. If all the information of interest is contained in the amplitude of the signal so that the detailed shape of the waveform is not important, the tubes can be biased to conduct for less than half the time and the output signal becomes a succession of brief pulses. This is *class C* operation, in which the theoretical maximum efficiency approaches 100% and efficiencies of 60 to 80% are realizable in practice.

In a power amplifier, under conditions of optimum load, half the output signal power and all the power that is not converted into output signal is dissipated in the amplifier itself. Therefore it is always necessary to give attention to cooling the amplifier components (e.g., with an air blower) and to provide good thermal contact between power transistors and heat-sinks. A difficulty that develops with junction transistors is that the dc gain increases quite rapidly with increasing temperature; if the increasing current gain leads to an increased dissipation of power in the transistor, and a consequent rise in temperature, there is the possibility of a catastrophic "thermal runaway." This difficulty does not occur with field-effect transistors, but at present the only FET's available are low-power devices. It can be shown that thermal runaway is impossible provided less than half the supply voltage appears between the collector and emitter of the transistor. This condition is easily fulfilled in a small-signal amplifier; in a power amplifier it is generally unacceptable. The quantity that determines whether a regenerative (i.e., self-catalyzed) temperature increase can occur is the product $\theta \cdot (\partial P_c/\partial T)$, where θ is the thermal resistance in degrees centigrade per watt between the collector junction and the ambient temperature and $\partial P_c/\partial T$ is the rate of increase of collector dissipation with the junction temperature. This product should not exceed 0.5 for operation at the limits of safety, and it should be evaluated for the worst possible combination of component tolerances, supply voltage fluctuations, and device parameters. The quantity θ is normally listed in the manufacturer's data sheets for the transistor. For a particular circuit $\partial P_c/\partial T$ can be evaluated from (a) the listed value of the transistor's leakage current I_{cbo} at room temperature and the temperature coefficient of this leakage current, as given by the Boltzmann factor (4.12), with the appropriate value of the energy gap ΔE, together with (b) the temperature coefficient of h_{FE}, which amounts to approximately $+1\%$ per degree for both silicon and germanium transistors. With a silicon

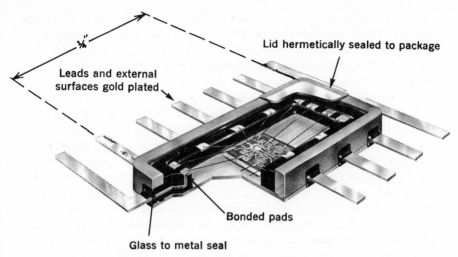

Lid hermetically sealed to package

Leads and external
surfaces gold plated

Bonded pads

Glass to metal seal

Fig. 4.52 Cutaway diagram of a typical "flat-pack" integrated circuit (Texas instruments series 54/74 digital logic).

transistor the effect of the leakage current is usually negligible. Another effect that can be allowed for is the decrease of the base-emitter voltage with increasing temperature; this amounts to 2 mV per degree for both silicon and germanium. The factors that can lead to thermal runaway in a power amplifier are identical with those that lead to thermal drifts in a dc amplifier based on junction transistors.

A form of multistage amplifier remarkable for its combination of economy, versatility, and compactness is the *linear integrated circuit,* of which many varieties are now available commercially. (There are even more varieties of digital integrated circuits; these are discussed in the next section.) As mentioned earlier, integrated circuits are made by selective deposition, oxidation, and etching of semiconductor material on the surface of a small chip of crystalline *n-* or *p*-type substrate. In the circuits that result transistors can be precisely matched because they are grown simultaneously and the cost per active device in the circuit is only a fraction of what it would be if the circuit were built with discrete components. Versatility of operation is obtained by providing external connecting leads to several points in the amplifier, while the input impedance can be varied by choosing between a common-emitter stage, an emitter-follower, a Darlington stage, an FET, or a MOSFET for the input stage. Because of lower cost and reliability that is one to three orders of magnitude greater than for discrete-component circuits, the continuing trend is toward the large-scale use of integrated circuits in industry and instrumentation. A cutaway diagram of a typical integrated circuit is shown in Fig. 4.52.

Some examples of linear integrated circuits are given in Fig. 4.53. In this type of circuit forward-biased diodes are commonly used for temperature compensation, the change with temperature of the voltage across the base-emitter diode of a transistor being balanced by the change of the forward voltage of a diode that forms part of the biasing network. All three of the circuits are direct-coupled, which is not unusual, since even a very small capacitor takes up a relatively large area of the substrate chip and the relative costs of components are directly related to the areas they occupy. As a result of the direct coupling it is a common practice to use balanced circuit configurations, such as the long-tailed pair, to reduce thermal drift. The basic long-tailed pair arrangement is generally improved by the replacement of the "tail" emitter resistor by a constant current generator; that is, a transistor whose emitter current is controlled by a temperature-compensated base voltage and a fixed emitter resistor. Another feature of these circuits is the relatively small range of resistance values employed. In general the cost

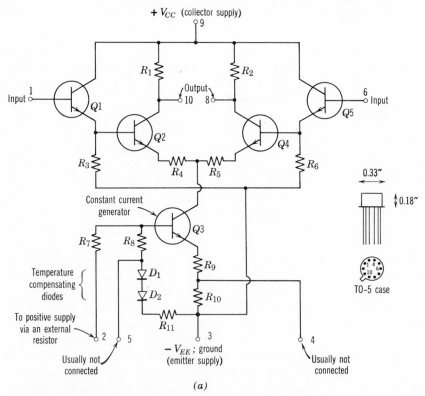

Fig. 4.53 Three examples of linear integrated circuits: (*a*) RCA type CA3000 differential-input dc amplifier; (*b*) Motorola type MC1554 power amplifier (1 W, dc—300 kc); (*c*) Texas Instruments type SN5510 video amplifier (dc—40 Mc).

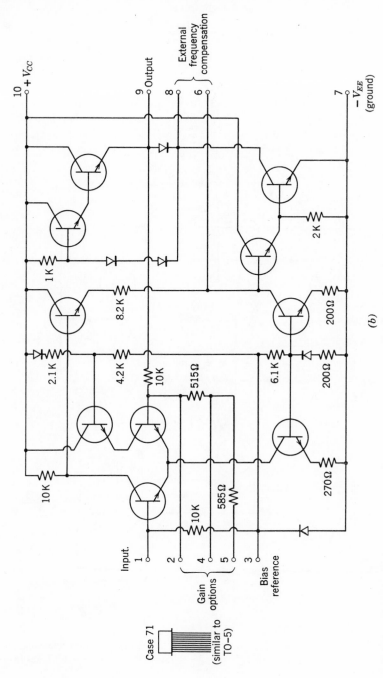

Fig. 4.53 (*Continued*)

221

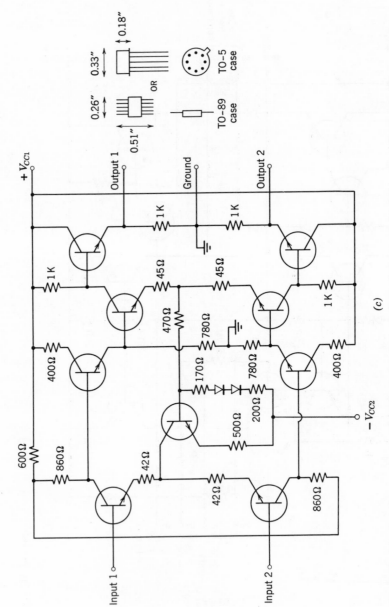

Fig. 4.53 (*Continued*)

222

per resistor is about optimum for a value of 300 Ω, but rises sharply for values more than 10 times or less than one tenth of this. Integrated circuits contain a much higher proportion of active devices than comparable circuits built of discrete components, partly because the lack of high-valued resistors makes it difficult to obtain high gain from a single stage of amplification. "Hybrid" circuits, which contain an integrated circuit plus a few discrete components in one package, combine some of the best features of both forms.

As shown by the examples in Fig. 4.53, linear integrated circuits are available to perform a variety of different amplifying functions, so that one approach to the problem of obtaining a suitable amplifier for a particular purpose must be to combine one or more integrated circuits with a small number of discrete components and a compatible power supply. A more general approach, which preceded the development of integrated circuits and is now in the process of profiting from this development, involves the use of high-gain *operational amplifiers* in circuits with *feed-back* such that the output is constrained to be some desired function of the input. This approach has proved to be extremely powerful and versatile and at present undoubtedly offers the most effective way of exploiting a minimum knowledge of electronics in order to obtain maximum success in the design of electronic equipment.

Feedback and Operational Amplifiers

Feedback is the operation that takes some of the output of a signal modifier and returns it to the input. If the signal is returned in such a way that it tends to reinforce the original input signal, the process is termed *positive feedback*, and if the feedback is such that it tends to reduce the size of the original input signal, it is termed *negative feedback*. Negative feedback is invariably a stabilizing influence in any system in which it occurs, whereas positive feedback is generally a source of instability. In chemical systems a self-catalyzed reaction, a branched-chain reaction, and a thermal explosion are all examples of phenomena in which an initial disturbance is built up by positive feedback to the point at which the system can go no further. Two chemical examples of negative feedback are a reaction in which one of the products is an inhibitor and the common thermostat bath. Feedback can change from positive to negative in the same system; for example, in the presence of a large food supply an animal population grows exponentially because of positive feedback between the number of young produced and the number of animals available to have offspring. However, once the population reaches a certain size the competition for food and the tendency of large groups of animals to attract predators provide paths for negative feedback between the number of animals born and the number that survive to produce young, and so the population becomes stabilized. In electronics the occurrence of

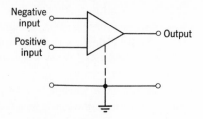

Fig. 4.54   Operational amplifier symbol.

positive feedback is normally limited to oscillators and other forms of signal generator, though it can also appear unintentionally in any piece of carelessly constructed equipment. Negative feedback, on the other hand, has a large number of applications, which include automatic control systems and servomechanisms, regulated power supplies, and gain-stabilized amplifiers. The applications of negative feedback appear to particular advantage in circuits based on *operational amplifiers.*

In a sense any amplifier that can be treated as a building block in a large instrument is eligible to be called an operational amplifier; the term, however, is generally understood to refer to a voltage amplifier of rather high gain that extends from dc to high frequencies with a prescribed form of "roll-off," that is, decrease of gain with increasing frequency, at the high frequency end. Many operational amplifiers have a differential input (cf. the long-tailed pair) but this is not essential. Included in the definition are amplifiers that range from large multistage tube affairs to small, monolithic integrated circuits, with input impedances ranging from 10^4 to 10^{12} Ω and dc voltage gains ranging from 10^3 to 10^8.

The basic circuit symbol for an operational amplifier is given in Fig. 4.54. In this diagram the triangle that represents the amplifier points in the direction of signal flow and the dashed line between the triangle and ground implies an earth reference point for the signals. In the absence of an input signal the output is at ground level. The negative input is such that at moderate frequencies the input and output signals are 180° out of phase; when the positive input is used, the input and output signals are exactly in phase. In a single-ended (i.e., nondifferential) amplifier and in many applications of the double-ended type the positive input is tied to ground. Positive feedback occurs when some of the output is returned to the positive input; negative feedback similarly results when signals are returned to the negative input. To calculate the effect of negative feedback in a general case we refer to Fig. 4.55. Here an input x (at the negative input of the amplifier) is added at the "summing point" to a fraction β of the output $-y$ of the circuit. Thus the net input to the amplifier is the "error signal" $(x - \beta y)$, and we have

$$\frac{-y}{x - \beta y} = -A$$

or

$$y = \frac{+Ax}{1 + \beta A}. \tag{4.42}$$

Note that the quantities x and y in this equation are defined in such a way that both are positive. Equation 4.42 is the basic feedback equation; all quantities in the equation are positive; hence the gain is $A/(1 + \beta A)$, which is less by the factor $(1 + \beta A)$ than in the absence of negative feedback. If we had been considering positive feedback, the denominator would have been $(1 - \beta A)$, and as the fraction β tended to $1/A$ the gain would have gone to infinity; that is, the circuit would have become a self-sustaining oscillator. In the most general case the quantities x and y in (4.42) can be current or voltage signals and the quantity β is not necessarily a fraction but may represent a functional relationship between the output and the signal fed back to the input. If the gain A of the amplifier, usually termed the *open-loop gain*, is very large so that $A\beta \gg 1$, then (4.42) reduces to

$$y = \frac{x}{\beta} \tag{4.43}$$

and the relationship between the output and input signals is determined entirely by the properties of the feedback loop. In obtaining this last result we have in effect put the error signal $(x - \beta y) = x/(1 + \beta A)$ equal to zero. The loop gain $(1 + \beta A)$, or βA approximately, is the factor by which the gain is increased when the negative feedback loop is opened; that is, it is the surplus gain of the system and can be regarded as the agency that enforces compliance of the output signal with (4.43). The magnitude of the error signal is a measure of the lack of compliance with this formula.

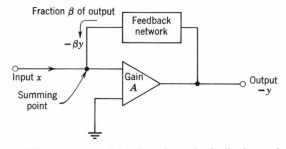

Fig. 4.55 Calculation of the effect of negative feedback on gain.

When the error signal can be neglected, the summing point becomes a virtual ground; that is, no matter what the input signal, the potential of the summing point remains constant. Thus, if the input and output signals are currents, the summing point presents a low impedance to the signal source, the input impedance of the amplifier being effectively reduced by the factor $(1 + \beta A)$. If, however, the both signals are voltages, the voltage signal "seen" by the input to the amplifier is reduced by the factor $(1 + \beta A)$, and so the effective input impedance of the amplifier, which is a measure of the amount of current that the amplifier draws from the voltage source, is increased by the factor $(1 + \beta A)$. A little reflection about these results leads to the conclusion that the effect on the input impedance depends only on the nature of the *output* signal fed back; that is, if a voltage is fed back, the effect is to increase the input impedance, since any voltage change at the input is thereby partly canceled and prevented from delivering current. However, if a current is fed back, the effect is similarly to reduce the input impedance, since the voltage change due to a given input current is reduced. To see the effect of negative feedback on the output impedance we suppose that the input signal is zero and let the output impedance in the absence of feedback be Z_{out}. For an amplifier in which the input signal is normally a voltage (Fig. 4.56) a signal y volts applied to the output results in a signal βy volts at the input and a signal $-A \cdot \beta \cdot y$ at the signal generator which, in accordance with Thevenin's theorem, we visualize as being in series with Z_{out}. Therefore the current drawn from the amplifier is due to a voltage $y(1 + \beta A)$ across the impedance Z_{out}, and so Z_{out} is effectively reduced by the factor $(1 + \beta A)$. If the input signal is normally a current, we use the Norton's theorem picture of Fig. 4.57, in which the output of the amplifier consists of

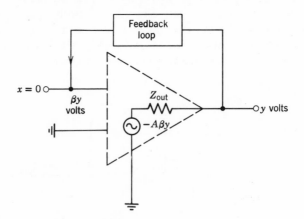

Fig. 4.56   Output impedance calculation for amplifier with voltage input signal.

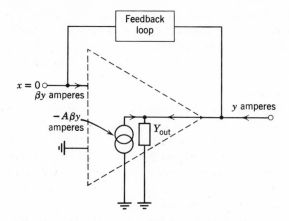

Fig. 4.57   Output admittance calculation for amplifier with current input signal.

a current generator in parallel with an admittance $Y_{out} = 1/Z_{out}$. A signal y Amperes applied at the output now results in a signal βy at the input, and a signal $-A \cdot \beta \cdot y$ at the current generator. The minus sign implies that this current is in the opposite direction to y, as shown by the arrows in the figure. Thus the total current through Y_{out} is $y(1 + \beta A)$, and the voltage produced at the output by the current y is equal to $y(1 + \beta A)/Y_{out}$, or $y(1 + \beta A) \cdot Z_{out}$. Therefore, if the input signal is a current, the output impedance is increased by the factor $(1 + \beta A)$ over the open-loop value. Note that from the point of view of a circuit attached to the output of the amplifier the equivalent output circuits of Figs. 4.56 and 4.57 are indistinguishable, and our choice of equivalent circuit has been dictated solely by the nature of the input signal. A further point to note is that in general the feedback loop will contain reactive elements, but the results obtained in this discussion will still apply, provided β is regarded as a complex quantity (i.e., one that contains the square root of -1), and the reactances and impedances are treated by the methods that were developed in Chapter 3.

Earlier it was mentioned that the gain of an operational amplifier is required to fall off in a prescribed manner with increasing frequency. The reason for this requirement is that phase changes, which can occur in the amplifier or the feedback loop, may cause the feedback to change from negative to positive at high frequencies, and, unless the gain has fallen off sufficiently to make $|\beta \cdot A|$ smaller than unity, when this occurs the result will be an unstable circuit or even an oscillator. An idealized gain-versus-frequency plot is shown on a logarithmic scale in Fig. 4.58. The gain falls off at the rate of 6 dB per octave (20 dB per decade), which means, since the gain in decibels is 20 log A, that the current or voltage gain is proportional to

$1/\omega$ (or $1/f$). Also indicated on the plot are the closed-loop gain (with feedback), which remains constant up to the frequency at which the open-loop and closed-loop gains become equal, and the loop gain, which decreases steadily with increasing frequency. With the ideal characteristic the open-loop gain would become infinite with a dc signal; in practice the low frequency gain levels off at some large but finite value. At the high frequency end the gain passes through unity at the frequency f_T. The phase shift behavior of an ideal operational amplifier is such that in the dc region in which the gain is constant the phase shift is zero; then in the region in which the 6 dB per octave roll-off begins the phase shift changes quite rapidly to a 90° lag, which remains essentially constant up to the frequency f_T. In practice the effects of stray capacitance cause the lag to become greater than 90° some time before f_T is reached.

Since an operational amplifier has a response that extends right to direct current, it is necessary to take steps to reduce the drifts that normally characterize dc amplifiers. With a long-tailed pair configuration of matched tubes or transistors the input drift is still of the order of millivolts per hour, which for many purposes is not satisfactory. Therefore it is necessary to try another approach, which consists of using an ac amplifier, with a switch or "chopper" to convert the input signal to alternating current, and another switch synchronized with the input chopper to convert the ac signal back to direct current at the output of the amplifier. A simple circuit for performing this function is given in Fig. 4.59. This particular circuit is arranged so that only the positive-going part of the ac signal that leaves the amplifier is able

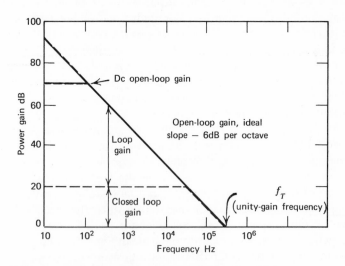

Fig. 4.58 Frequency response of an operational amplifier.

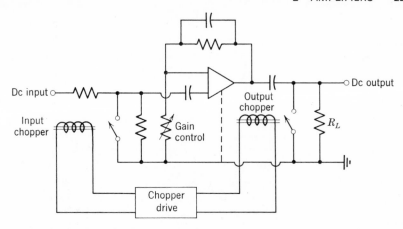

Fig. 4.59 Essential elements of a chopper-stabilized dc amplifier.

to drive a current through the load R_L, the negative-going part being short-circuited to earth when the chopper contacts close. Consequently the average current through R_L is in the positive direction, and if this current were applied to an integrating network a steady signal, proportional to the original dc input, would result. The ac gain of the amplifier is shown as being stabilized by feedback to the negative input. We shall return to this part of the circuit shortly. If a mechanical chopper or field-effect chopper is used at the input, this type of circuit can have a drift rate that is only of the order of microvolts per hour in normal operation. The main cause of drift in a chopper-stabilized amplifier is the presence of a temperature dependent *offset* voltage or current, which in a mechanical chopper is due mainly to thermal electromotive forces generated between the contacts, and in a transistor chopper to temperature-dependent voltage differences across *pn* junctions; for example, in the junction transistor chopper of Fig. 4.60*a*, with no input signal the voltage between the collector and emitter of the transistor when the base is at $+1$ V, that is, when the "switch" is closed, is the difference between the voltages across the forward-biased collector-base and emitter-base diodes. This voltage, which in general is not zero, constitutes a finite offset voltage and so produces a drift-prone signal at the input to the ac amplifier. This source of offset voltage does not exist in an FET chopper, such as that of Fig. 4.60*b*, in which the conduction path when the switch is closed (i.e., with the gate at 0 V) is purely resistive. Even in this case, however, there remains a very small offset current, due to leakage from the gate to the channel, which produces a corresponding small voltage signal at the input to the ac amplifier. In the MOSFET chopper of Fig. 4.60*c* the leakage between gate and channel is entirely negligible, so that this source of offset is also

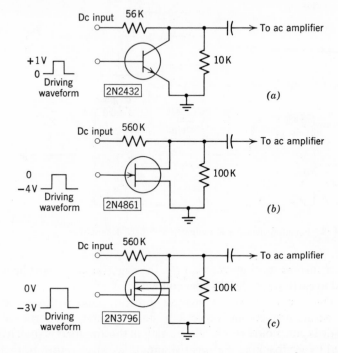

Fig. 4.60 Transistor choppers: (a) using a silicon junction transistor; (b) FET; (c) MOSFET.

essentially zero. If the dc amplifier is not to have a limited frequency response
it is necessary for the chopping frequency to be fairly high; present mechanical
choppers are limited to frequencies below a few kilocycles (kHz). Field-effect
choppers, though slightly inferior in other respects, can go considerably
higher than that, the upper limit being set by the ability of the circuit to
tolerate feed-through of the driving waveform, via the gate input capacitance,
to the ac amplifier. If the driving waveform is a square wave, as is usual, the
feed-through is in the form of sharp spikes which result from differentiation
of the square wave on its way through the gate-drain capacitance. For the
2N4863 FET this capacitance is about 26 pF; for the 2N3796 MOSFET it
is about 6 pF. Normally only one of these spikes will appear in the output,
where it will be integrated and so contribute to the output signal. The gate
input capacitance is a function of temperature, and the offset signal arising
from spike feed-through will drift with time. The effect can be reduced by
using a driving waveform with a more gradual switching action (a sine wave
is sometimes satisfactory), by making sure that the spikes are not significantly
integrated by stray capacitance at the input to the amplifier, and by altering
the mark-space ratio of the driving waveform for the output chopper so that

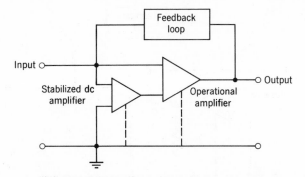

Fig. 4.61 Use of a chopper-stabilized amplifier to control drift in an operational amplifier.

spikes from the input chopper arrive either too early or too late to contribute to the dc output signal.

The best method of employing chopper stabilization with an operational amplifier is to use what is basically a separate stabilized amplifier, as shown in Fig. 4.61. If the voltage at the negative input in this circuit attempts to stray away from earth potential, the positive input is driven strongly in the opposite direction by the chopper-stabilized amplifier. The resulting signal at the output is fed back so that it cancels out all of the initial deviation with the exception of the extremely small error signal. A way of indicating specifically that an operational amplifier is stabilized in this way is shown in Fig. 4.62. If the direct connection between the signal and the operational amplifier is replaced by a capacitor, as in Fig. 4.63, the resulting circuit draws much less current from the signal source and continues to respond to signals that are above the frequency range of the chopper-stabilized amplifier. With both circuits of Fig. 4.61 and 4.63 the amplifier is chopper-stabilized at low frequencies without being limited by the speed of the input chopper at high frequencies. The time-constant RC is chosen to minimize any discontinuity at the transition from the chopper-stabilized region to the high-frequency region of the response curve (Fig. 4.58).

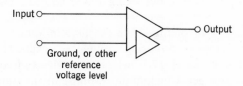

Fig. 4.62 Circuit symbol intended to show that an operational amplifier is stabilized as in Fig. 4.61. Note that the amplifier now lacks a free positive input terminal.

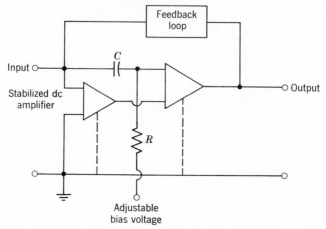

Fig. 4.63   Stabilized operational amplifier with dc blocking of negative input.

In the circuit in Fig. 4.63 the negative input of the amplifier is taken through a high resistance to a source of bias voltage rather than directly to earth. By this means any small remaining offset voltage or current between the input terminals can be compensated by adjusting the bias so that the output voltage is exactly zero in the absence of an input signal. Various types of temperature-compensated bias circuit have been developed to reduce drifts caused by changes of the offset with temperature. Many commercial operational amplifiers incorporate these circuits, whereas others have external terminals to which compensated circuits of a type recommended by the manufacturer can be attached. For details of such specialized biasing arrangements it is advisable to refer to the manufacturer's data sheets for the particular amplifier or to the references that are given at the end of this chapter. Other refinements of the basic circuit include the provision of protection circuits at the input of the amplifier and of "bounds" circuits to limit the voltage excursions at the output. If the output is permitted to become cut off, or saturated, the recovery time of the amplifier can be up to 10^4 times as long as the normal response time for a small signal, longest overload recovery times being observed with chopper-stabilized amplifiers.

With the arrangement of Fig. 4.64a the parallel diodes do not conduct until the necessary forward-biasing voltage is reached; this limits the differential input to about ± 0.7 V, which at moderate frequencies is more than sufficient to produce a maximum response at the output. The diodes should be low-leakage, low-capacitance signal diodes such as the 1N914, 1N4444, 1N4449, and similar types. To protect the amplifier against large

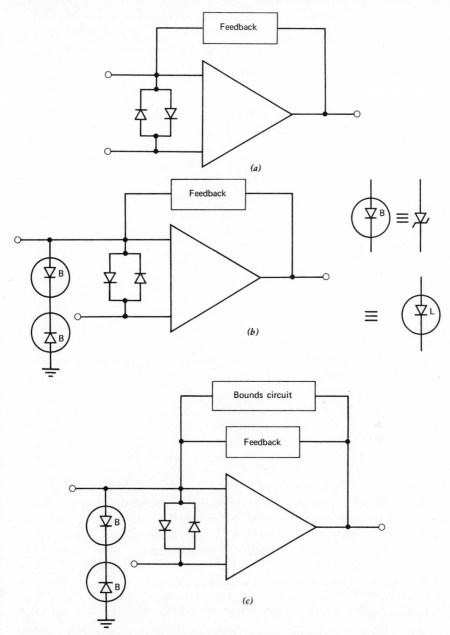

Fig. 4.64 Input protection: (a) limitation of size of differential input with silicon diodes; (b) addition of common-mode limitation to circuit (a); (c) insertion of bounds circuit in feedback loop to limit output excursions; (d) simple reverse-biased diode bounds; (e) zener diode bounds; (f) leakage-suppression circuit.

233

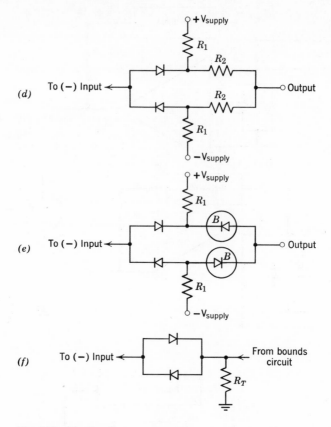

Fig. 4.64 (*Continued*)

common-mode signals, that is, signals applied simultaneously to both inputs, it is possible to use paired zener diodes as in Fig. 4.64*b*. (Note the three commonly used circuit symbols for a zener diode). The zener diodes would typically be chosen to have a breakdown voltage of about 12 V, with a wattage rating to suit the impedance of the signal source, and should have very low leakage. A list of suitable 12-V types would include the IN4106 (250 mW), the 1N759 (400 mW), 1N3022 (1 W), and such "back-to-back" devices as the double-anode 1N4834 (1.2 W). To prevent large excursions of the output signal it is possible to insert an additional feedback loop containing a bounds circuit, as in Fig. 4.64*c*. The bounds circuit behaves as a very large resistance, provided the size of the output signal is less than some predetermined value, but once this value is exceeded the feedback loop comes into operation and reduces the closed-loop gain. In the diode bounds circuit of Fig. 4.64d the diodes remain reverse-biased until the output signal exceeds $R_1 \cdot V_{\text{supply}}/R_2$, where R_2 limits the over-all gain when the bounds circuit is in operation. In the zener diode bounds of Fig. 4.64e the ordinary diodes are reverse biased until the output signal is sufficient to exceed the breakdown voltage of one or both zener diodes. In place of these relatively complicated networks one could simply use a pair of zener diodes between the output and the negative input, similar to the pair between input and ground in Fig. 4.64b. This simple arrangement is satisfactory, provided the leakage through the diodes and the additional high-frequency roll-off due to capacitance associated with the zener diode functions are tolerable. The leakage can be reduced by inserting one or more "tee" sections similar to that in Fig. 4.64f, where R_T is of the order of 1 K and serves to shunt the leakage current to earth, away from the input.

This completes our discussion of the essential properties of the operational amplifiers themselves. Next we consider some applications. A large number of useful circuits have been designed, and for a fuller account, especially of topics relating to analog computers, the reader should consult the references listed at the end of this chapter.

The first application is to an ac amplifier whose gain is stable and can be varied in a convenient manner by altering a resistor in the feedback loop. A typical circuit is shown in Fig. 4.65. The operational amplifier used here is a Philbrick P55A, which is a relatively low-cost amplifier with a high-impedance differential input and a minimum voltage gain of 20,000. For

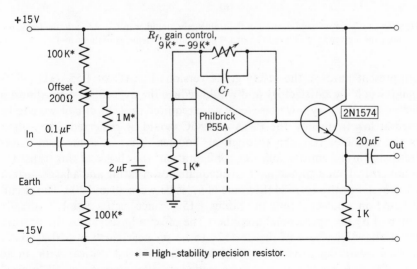

Fig. 4.65 Stable-gain ac amplifier.

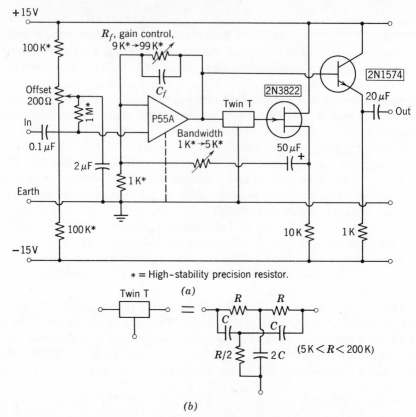

Fig. 4.66 (*a*) Narrow-band version of the stable-gain amplifier in Fig. 4.65; (*b*) the frequency of peak gain is given by $f = 1/2\pi RC$, when R and C are the elements of the twin-T.

the present purpose the utility-grade versions P55AU or P55AHU (wide-band) would be satisfactory and would reduce the over-all cost by almost a factor of 2. If a very low noise level were required or if the circuit were to be used at low frequency, the P85A or P85C would be preferred. The output of the amplifier is taken through a "booster," that is, a medium-power transistor in the emitter-follower configuration; the choice of this transistor is not critical but it should have an adequate power rating and a large current gain (h_{fe}). For the 2N1574 the value of h_{fe} is between 80 and 200. The circuit is based on a power supply providing ± 15 V, since such a supply is already required by the operational amplifier. The offset adjustment at the positive input allows the base of the 2N1574 to be set near earth potential under normal operating conditions. This adjustment is not critical with an ac amplifier and should not need to be made very often; hence a small "preset" potentiometer could be used. The voltage gain is essentially given by the ratio $(R_f + 1 \text{ K})/1 \text{ K}$ which in this example can usefully be varied in steps between 10 and 100. The high-frequency response is limited by the capacitor C_f which is chosen to suit the particular application. Generally C_f is made as small as possible, the lower limit being set by the tendency of the circuit to become unstable at high frequencies; a typical value would be 1000 pF. The low-frequency response is limited by the capacitors at the input and output.

The basic amplifier of Fig. 4.65 can be converted to a narrow-band audio-frequency amplifier by the application of feedback through a selective RC network. It should be recalled that the twin-T network which was discussed in Chapter III is such that when a complex signal is passed through the network the component of one particular frequency is completely attenuated by the network, signals of other frequencies being only partly attenuated. Hence, if a twin-T, constructed to attenuate some chosen frequency, is inserted in a loop that gives a large amount of negative feedback, the over-all gain will be low for all frequencies except the one that is filtered out. It is necessary to ensure that the twin-T operates into a high impedance, since this was assumed in the derivation given in Chapter III. It then becomes necessary to add an extra follower stage to the circuit of Fig. 4.65. The resulting narrow-bandwidth amplifier is shown in Fig. 4.66. The particular choice of n-channel FET in the twin-T feedback loop is not critical. An advantage of the FET, apart from its high input impedance, is that the source electrode is necessarily positive with respect to the gate, and if the offset control is used to set the base of the 2N1574 at earth potential, or slightly positive, correct polarity of the 50 μF electrolytic capacitor in the loop is ensured.

The amplifiers we have just considered can be regarded as elaborations of the basic voltage follower circuit shown in Fig. 4.67. In this circuit there is 100% negative feedback so that, just as in a cathode-follower, emitter-follower, or source-follower, the output and input voltages differ only by the very small error signal required to make E_{out} different from its quiescent, no-signal value. The circuits of Figs. 4.65 and 4.66 are followers with gain,

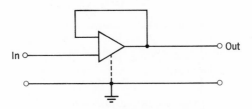

Fig. 4.67 Basic voltage follower.

that is, followers in which the fraction β is less than 100%. The common-mode input impedance, which is measured between the positive and negative inputs, is large in a follower circuit because only the small fraction $1/(1 + \beta A)$ of a voltage change at the input actually appears between the input terminals of the operational amplifier. For the P55A the common-mode input impedance without feedback is about 100 K, the minimum value of A is 20,000, and β is 0.01 when the over-all gain is set at 100 and 0.10 when it is set at 10; thus at maximum closed-loop gain the common-mode impedance is at least 20 M and at minimum gain it is at least 200 M. The impedance from the positive input to ground is stated to be around 15 M; hence the net input impedance is essentially governed by the 1-M input resistor. A disadvantage of the follower configuration is that for most wideband operational amplifiers the frequency response is specified relative to the negative input only and that relative to the positive input may be less by a factor of 10 or more. To obtain the maximum frequency response for a signal applied to the positive input an amplifier specially designed to have this feature (e.g., Analog Devices Model 102) must be used.

Another basic kind of circuit is the current-to-voltage converter in Fig. 4.68. This circuit is particularly useful with high-impedance current sources such as electron multipliers and particle counters, and with photovoltaic cells, which must operate into a very low impedance if the output is to be a linear function of light intensity. The action of the operational amplifier is to hold the potential of the summing point constant by arranging for a negative feedback current to substract from the positive input current. Since all but the fraction $1/(1 + \beta A)$ of the input current is thus made to flow through R_f and βA is extremely large, it follows that the output voltage is just $-I_{in} \cdot R_f$. As before, C_f is used to limit the response of the circuit at high frequencies. For the very best performance in measuring small currents a low-noise, low-offset current, high-gain operational amplifier is required; suitable types would probably include the Philbrick model P25A, Burr-Brown model 1552/15, and Melcor model 1673.

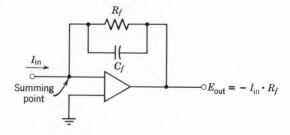

Fig. 4.68 Current-to-voltage converter.

If R_f is made very large, as in the measurement of currents of 10^{-9} A or less, shielding from external fields, insulation resistance between the input and ground, and stray capacitance become important matters for consideration. Shielding, in particular, has a major influence on the effectiveness of a circuit for detecting small signals, and it may be necessary in extreme cases to resort to multiple shields or driven shields (cf. the oscilloscope probe with driven shield in Fig. 3.51c). Normally the shield should surround the whole circuit with a minimum number of small apertures for input and output leads and should be connected to a low-resistance ground lead at just one point. Leads through which appreciable signal current flows to ground should be isolated from one another or if possible twisted together with the return lead for the same current. Power supply lines and the ground lead should each be in the form of a heavy wire "bus," and all signal voltages should have the ground bus as their reference point. Ground loops, that is, systems of earth connections that form closed loops, should be avoided because they usually give rise to pickup, although in multiple power-supply systems unavoidable ground loops may result from the necessity of tying each power-supply ground to a common bus bar. All transformers in mains-operated equipment should be magnetically shielded and if possible isolated some distance from sensitive inputs. It is often worthwhile to obtain high-permeability shielding such as mu-metal to overcome low-frequency pickup (below 100 Hz) due to varying magnetic fields. Sensitive input leads, especially when connected to ground through a high impedance, need to be as short as possible so that any unwanted influences that do penetrate the shielding have as little as possible to act on. Poor insulation gives rise to drift-prone and noisy leakage currents. In some cases the insulator itself may experience dielectric absorption currents and other polarization effects that interfere with the ability of the circuit to respond faithfully to moderately rapid changes in voltage. The best insulation is a vacuum or dry air; reasonable alternatives include Teflon, polystyrene, polyethylene, mica, and treated glass, in an approximate order of preference. Stray capacitance is undesirable mainly because of the effect it has on response time; for example, with a resistance of 10^{11} Ω a capacitance of 5 pF has a time constant of half a second. With very small currents the measuring process may in any case involve a wait of seconds or even minutes for sufficient charge to accumulate to produce a steady-state voltage at each point in the circuit. This delay can be minimized by minimizing stray capacitance.

Amplifiers designed to measure currents of less than about 10^{-7} A or to respond to voltage changes in circuits containing a resistance of 10^8 Ω or more are usually termed *electrometers*. To be effective such an amplifier should itself have an input resistance of at least 10^{10} Ω, combined with very low input capacitance. This is the case with many solid-state operational amplifiers; for example, the Philbrick P25A (10^{11} Ω and 6 pF differential, i.e., between inputs, 10^{12} Ω and 6 pF common-mode, i.e., between each input and ground), Burr-Brown 1552/15 (10^{11} Ω differential and common-mode input resistances, response to 100 kHz), and Melcor 1673 (10^{10} Ω differential, 10^7 Ω common-mode, response to 200 kHz) which were mentioned in connection with the current-to-voltage converter. The differential input impedance can be enhanced by using a follower or follower-with-gain configuration. The smallest current that can be measured with a simple electrometer is of the order of 10^{-15} A; the extremely high input resistance necessary for this class of measurement is obtained by the use of a special *electrometer tube* to provide the first stage of amplification.

In an ordinary vacuum tube there is an input current offset due to the *grid current* which is typically around 10^{-8} A in a tube with negative grid bias. If a current of 10^{-15} A is to be measured, it is first necessary to reduce the grid current to a similar magnitude; otherwise fluctuations and drifts in the grid current will mask the effect that is meant to be observed. The main sources of grid current are (a) positive ions evaporated from the heated cathode are attracted to the grid, (b) electrons emitted by the cathode can have sufficient thermal velocity to reach the grid, (c) residual gas in the tube can be ionized and the ions formed attracted to the grid; (d) light incident on metal parts of the tube, and especially the control grid, can cause the emission of photoelectrons; and (e) electrons striking the anode can cause the emission of soft x-rays, which in turn generate photoelectrons from the grid and other metal surfaces. In an electrometer tube these effects are reduced by operating the cathode at a very low temperature (typical filament current 13 mA at 1.25 V) so that the thermal energy of the electrons is too low for them to reach the grid and few positive ions are emitted, by having an extremely good vacuum inside the tube so that there is little residual gas to be ionized, by keeping the tube in the dark to prevent photoemission, and by using a very low anode voltage (typically 4–12 V) so that ionization of residual gas and emission of soft x-rays from the anode are both prevented. Surface leakage on the outside of the tube and through or over insulators also contributes to the offset currents; hence fingerprints and moisture on the surfaces must be avoided and the physical size of insulators must be kept to a minimum. It is invariably necessary to enclose the electrometer tube in a metal shield or box; the possibility of moisture condensing on surfaces inside the shield can then be reduced by inserting a small container of drying agent or by adding a resistor that is dissipating a steady 2 or 3 W (dc) in the tube compartment. It is good practice to leave an electrometer circuit switched on continuously so that drifts due to temperature changes in components are kept to a minimum. A typical electrometer input stage is shown in Fig. 4.69; with this circuit the 1-K potentiometer is adjusted so

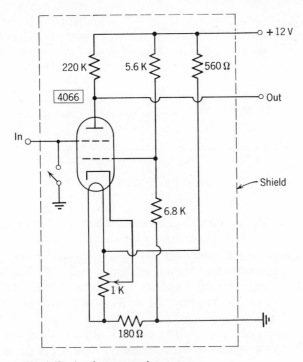

Fig. 4.69 An electrometer input stage.

that in the absence of an input signal the output is not dependent on whether the input grid is grounded or floating. The over-all voltage gain is less than unity, but this is less important than the circumstance that with proper shielding the circuit can be used to measure signals of the order of millivolts across a 10^{10}- or 10^{11}-Ω resistor. For critical low-drift applications it is possible to obtain matched pairs of electrometer tubes for use in balanced configurations such as the long-tailed pair. For precise measurements of current of the order of 10^{-15} A, however, and to detect changes of the order of 10^{-17} A (about 60 electrons per second!) it is necessary to go to a circuit that combines an electrometer with a chopper-type, low-drift input. This is the principle of vibrating reed electrometers, such as the Cary 401, in which the vibrating unit forms one plate of a small capacitor (the so-called "dynamic capacitor") and the voltage produced by a fixed charge q on the plates of the capacitor is modulated at the frequency of vibration in accordance with the relationship

$$q = CV,$$

where C is inversely proportional to the varying distance between the plates.

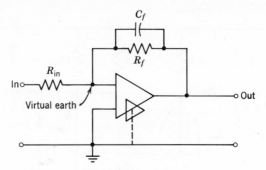

Fig. 4.70 Inverting dc amplifier.

A circuit closely related to the current-to-voltage converter is the inverting amplifier of Fig. 4.70. The potential of the summing point is held constant by the operational amplifier, so that the input current E_{in}/R_{in} must flow through R_f as in the converter circuit, and so $E_{out} = -E_{in} \cdot R_f/R_{in}$. In Fig. 4.70 a chopper-stabilized amplifier has been specified that will permit the circuit to perform well at zero frequency. If R_f/R_{in} is not too large and C_f is made large to limit the bandwidth for noise, a very precise and stable dc amplifier results; for example, if the amplifier were a Philbrick SP656, with $R_{in} = 50$ K and $R_f = 500$ K, both precision resistors, and C_f were a low-leakage computer-grade polystyrene capacitor of 0.04 μF, the gain would be 10.000, with an accuracy limited only by the precision of the resistors and by the uncertainty, due to offset, of less than 5 μV in the potential of the summing point. For the SP656 we have $A_v = 5 \times 10^7$, and here β would be 0.1 and the loop gain would be 5×10^6. The bandwidth of the amplifier would be approximately 5 Hz.

The high precision with dc signals obtained by the use of a chopper-stabilized amplifier in Fig. 4.70 provides an incentive for designing a follower circuit, such as those in Figs. 4.65 and 4.67, based on a stabilized amplifier. The difficulty is that in a stabilized amplifier such as that of Fig. 4.63 only one input is free to be used. If a power supply is available in which the positive, negative, and "common" lines are all able to be isolated from ground, the circuit of Fig. 4.71 can be used, with the normal output terminal grounded and the output signal appearing at the power-supply common terminal. There is usually considerable leakage and stray capacitance from the common lead to earth (some power supplies are specially built to minimize them), but with the follower configuration the output impedance is so low that this is not serious at low frequencies. Unfortunately the necessity of tying the positive input to the common lead in Fig. 4.63 makes it impossible to construct a stabilized version of the follower with gain in this way. Circuits

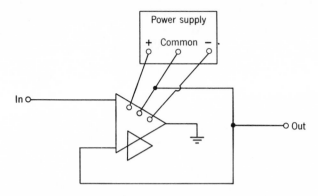

Fig. 4.71   Stabilized follower.

have been devised to overcome this problem by using a different stabilizing procedure; examples can be found in the references given at the end of this chapter.

The interesting circuit given in Fig. 4.72 is the converse of the current-to-voltage converter of Fig. 4.68. The action of the operational amplifier is to keep the voltage difference between the positive and negative inputs at a minimum; thus $I_{out} \cdot R$ differs from E_{in} only by the very small error signal $E_{in}/(1 + \beta A)$. This circuit can be regarded as a follower with gain in which the voltage at the amplifier output is governed by the amount of feedback through the variable load; hence if the load increases the voltage also increases and the current therefore remains constant. With a fixed input voltage this circuit becomes a constant-current generator.

Figure 4.73 shows some circuits for performing mathematical operations with operational amplifiers. In the first circuit, neglecting the small capacitor C_f, current that flows through the capacitor C is forced through the resistor

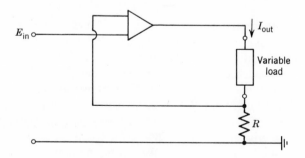

Fig. 4.72   Voltage-to-current converter.

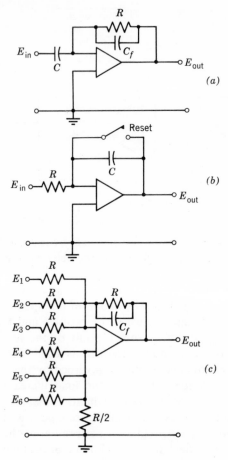

Fig. 4.73 Mathematical operations using operational amplifiers: (a) differentiator: $E_{out} = -RC(dE_{in}/dt)$; (b) integrator: $E_{out} = -1/RC \int_0^t E_{in} \, dt$; (c) adder and subtracter: $E_{out} = (E_1 + E_2 + E_3) - (E_4 + E_5 + E_6)$.

R, and since the differential of $q = CV$ is $i = C \cdot dV/dt$, where $E_{out} = -iR$ and $E_{in} = V$, we have $E_{out} = -RC \cdot dE_{in}/dt$. The capacitor C_f, which is required for high-frequency stability, may be augmented by a resistor in series with C between the input and the summing point. The Philbrick Applications manual includes a circuit of this sort in which R is 100 M and the capacitor C is 10 μF; thus RC is 1000 sec, and the output is 1 V when $dE_{in}/dt = 1$ mV/sec. The capacitors must be low-leakage polystyrene types (leakage resistance greater than 10^{12} Ω) and the complete circuit includes a bounds network and "reset" provision for setting the input at a convenient dc level in the absence of an input signal.

In the integrating circuit of Fig. 4.73b the input current that flows through R is forced to continue on through C, and we have $E_{out} = q/C = \int i \cdot dt/C = -\int E_{in} \cdot dt/RC$, where the upper and lower limits of integration are the time of observation and the time at which the reset switch was last opened. The circuit is basically stable because of the large amount of negative feedback through C at high frequencies. A complete circuit would again include a bounds network and probably a more elaborate arrangement, such as a relay, for resetting.

In the adding and subtracting circuit of Fig. 4.73c we have a combination of a unity-gain inverting amplifier with three inputs and a unity-gain non-inverting amplifier, also with three inputs. As usual it is necessary to have some capacitance in the feedback loop to ensure stability. The output impedances of the voltage sources are assumed to be very small in comparison with R.

For our last examples of operational amplifier circuits in this section we have the precise voltage sources of Fig. 4.74, in the first of which the inability

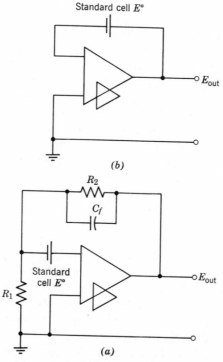

Fig. 4.74 Use of stabilized operational amplifiers to obtain precise voltage sources from which appreciable current may be drawn; (a) voltage standard, $E_{out} = E^\circ \times A_v/(1 + A_v)$; (b) reference voltage, $E_{out} = -E^\circ \times A_v/(1 + \beta A_v)$, where $\beta = R_1/(R_1 + R_2)$.

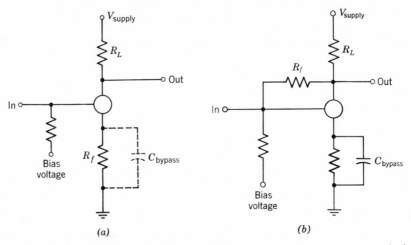

Fig. 4.75   Feedback in a single stage: (a) series feedback resulting from an un-bypassed cathode, emitter, or source resistor; (b) shunt feedback directly from anode, collector, or drain to the input. A small capacitor in series with R_f may be present for dc isolation.

of a standard cell to deliver more than a few microamperes safely is circumvented while an accuracy of 0.1 mV in the value of the standard is retained, and in the second of which the precision potential divider comprising resistors R_1 and R_2 enables the reference voltage to be multiplied to an extent limited only by the voltage available from the amplifier's power supply. Both circuits will operate as well with the cell polarity reversed. Other applications of operational amplifiers, notably to waveform generators and switching circuits, are discussed later in this chapter.

Before leaving this section we consider two other applications of negative feedback. The first, shown in Fig. 4.75a, is fairly trivial but worth mentioning because it often serves as a convenient method of stabilizing the voltage gain of a single amplifier stage. Also there are difficulties associated with the use of large amounts of negative feedback over several stages in a transistor amplifier, and it often helps to introduce added stability by the provision of local feedback in this way, especially if series feedback stages like Fig. 4.75a can be alternated with shunt feedback stages similar to Fig. 4.75b. In Fig. 4.75a the negative feedback is obtained by omitting the bypass capacitor which in the figure is shown as a dotted outline. The simplest way of looking at this circuit is to regard it as a follower, with the voltage signal at the top of R_f always being essentially equal to the input signal. Therefore, since the same signal current flows through both R_L and R_f, the voltage gain of the stage must be $-R_L/R_f$. The alternative approach via (4.42) uses the formula

$$A_v = -g \cdot R_L, \qquad (4.44)$$

where the nature of g is dependent on the nature of the active device, together with $\beta = -R_f/R_L$, to get

$$A_{v'} = \frac{-g \cdot R_L}{1 + g \cdot R_f}, \qquad (4.45)$$

which reduces to the simple result obtained before, provided $g \cdot R_f \gg 1$. It is to avoid the loss of gain resulting from this kind of feedback that the cathode, emitter, or source resistor is usually bypassed with a capacitor. If, however, R_f is small enough to make $g \cdot R_f$ negligible in comparison with unity, the result (4.45) shows that the bypass capacitor is not really necessary.

A different kind of application of negative feedback is shown in Fig. 4.76. This is a *servomechanism*, which in its simplest form is just a device for causing a mechanical system that requires a large amount of power to reproduce the precise behavior of a system operated at a low power level. Thus the diagram of Fig. 4.76 might represent the steering mechanism of an ocean liner, in which the input supplied by the helmsman is converted by a transducer to a voltage signal and added to a negative feedback signal derived from the angular position of the rudder. The resulting error signal is supplied to a *servoamplifier* whose output controls the *servoactuator*, that is, the motor that drives the rudder when the wheel is turned. The motor is connected so that the rudder is driven in the direction required to reduce the error signal to zero, that is, in the direction corresponding to negative feedback. In practice a finite amount of power is required to start the actuator moving; hence there is always a small "dead space" through which the wheel, in this example, can be moved before the rudder begins to respond. Further, a small delay invariably occurs between the application of power

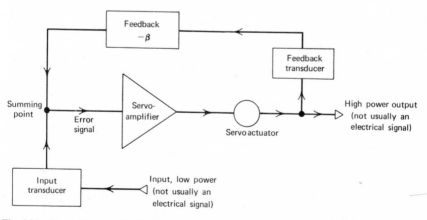

Fig. 4.76 Block diagram of a simple servomechanism. The combination of feedback transducer, feedback loop, and summing point is often termed a comparator circuit.

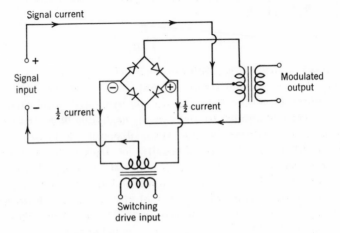

Fig. 4.77 Ring modulator.

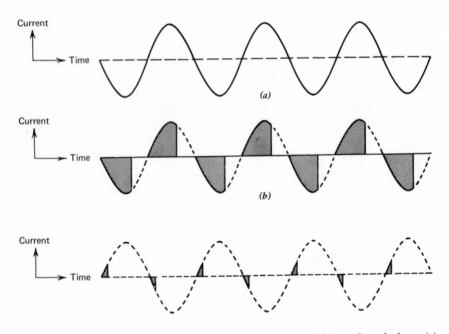

Fig. 4.78 Control of motor speed and direction by variation of duty cycle and phase: (*a*) reference waveform; (*b*) waveform (duty cycle shaded) for rapid clockwise rotation; (*c*) waveform (duty cycle shaded) for slow counterclockwise rotation.

and the beginning of motor response; therefore if the system were capable of responding to changes that occurred in a time comparable to this delay it would be possible for the feedback to change from negative to positive, with a consequent loss of control and the likelihood of dangerous oscillations building up. To avoid this sort of catastrophe the servoactuator is always damped to limit the loop gain at frequencies larger than the reciprocal of some minimum tolerable response time.

Servomechanisms can be seen to have a great deal in common with the operational amplifier circuits that we have previously considered. In particular, the servoamplifier is basically an operational amplifier with a relatively large power output. The details of the amplifier design are governed by the nature of the servomotor or other actuator required, but in general the amplifier need have no very remarkable properties, since the feedback system is basically insensitive to any foibles, such as departure from linearity or peculiarities of frequency response, it may possess. Many representative circuits can be found in the references given at the end of this chapter. Servomotors may use direct or alternating current, the direction of rotation in an ac motor being controlled by the relative phases of the amplified error signal and a reference signal. For high-power applications ac operation has the advantage that the servoamplifier may have a class B or class C output. The motor coils themselves present an inductive load to the amplifier, and it is a common practice to insert a capacitor in series or parallel with the motor windings so that they form part of a tuned circuit, in which case the load at the error-signal frequency is purely resistive. The error signal may be converted to alternating current with a mechanical or transistor chopper, as described before, or with a diode or "ring" modulator, as shown in Fig. 4.77. In the ring modulator the action of the switching drive is to cause the upper pair of diodes to conduct during half a switching cycle and the lower pair of diodes to conduct during the other half. Thus the direction of signal current flow through the primary of the output transformer is reversed twice during each cycle. The flow of signal current shown in Fig. 4.77 is for the period of conduction by the lower pair of diodes. Yet another mode of operation is to use pulse-width modulation, or other means of varying the *duty cycle* of the signal applied to the motor. Some waveforms that provide an elementary illustration of this method are given in Fig. 4.78 for the case of a motor driven by a sinusoidal waveform. The duty cycle is the fraction of the repetition period of the signal during which power is applied to the load. In the usual kind of ac servomotor (Fig. 4.79) the armature rotates at its maximum rate in one direction—say clockwise—when the power is supplied exactly in phase with the reference signal, and in the reverse direction when power is supplied out of phase with the reference signal. For this kind of operation it is an advantage to employ specialized switching devices, such

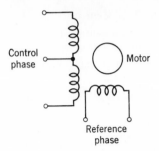

Control phase

Motor

Reference phase

Fig. 4.79   Circuit symbol for an ac servomotor showing windings for reference and control waveforms.

as the thyratrons and silicon-controlled rectifiers described in the next section. Servomechanisms are used in a huge variety of scientific instruments; the best known application is the potentiometric recorder. In this case error signal is equal to the difference between the input voltage and the voltage picked off by a contact on a circular slide-wire, and the servomotor rotates an arm which holds the contact on the slide-wire while simultaneously driving an endless cable which controls the position of the pen on the recorder chart. Another familiar example is the usual form of double-beam infrared spectrometer in which the error signal is provided by the difference in intensity of two light beams, one of which has traversed the sample whose spectrum is required. The action of the servomotor is to drive an attenuating optical wedge into the reference beam until the two signals are equalized and either the same servomotor or another translates the position of the atten-uator wedge into the position of a pen on a chart. For a full discussion of the different applications the reader is referred to other chapters and books in this series.

Bandwidth and Noise

We now discuss two basic limitations of amplifiers, namely their inability to respond to signals of frequency above or below a more-or-less narrow passband and their inability to distinguish arbitrarily small signals from random noise. We begin by considering bandwidth limitations.

At low frequencies it is possible to remove bandwidth limitations entirely by using dc amplifiers. Nevertheless it is still of interest to consider the nature of the low-frequency response of an ac amplifier. Referring to the equivalent circuit for the coupling of two stages of an ac amplifier in Fig. 4.80, we see that in general

$$\frac{dE_{in}}{dE_{out}} = \frac{R_{in}}{R_{in} + R_{out} - j/\omega C}, \tag{4.46}$$

whereas at "mid-band" frequencies, where the low frequency limitations are

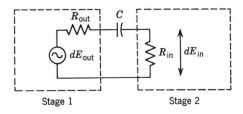

Fig. 4.80 Low-frequency equivalent circuit of an ac amplifier shows the coupling between the output of one stage and the input of the following one.

not significant,

$$\frac{dE_{in}}{dE_{out}} = \frac{R_{in}}{R_{in} + R_{out}}. \qquad (4.47)$$

Hence, if A_f is the amplifier gain at frequency f and A_m is the midband gain we have

$$\frac{A_f}{A_m} = \left(1 - \frac{j}{\omega CR}\right)^{-1} = \left(1 - \frac{j}{2\pi f CR}\right)^{-1}, \qquad (4.48)$$

where R is $(R_{in} + R_{out})$. In terms of measured voltages (Fig. 4.81) this becomes

$$\frac{|A_f|}{|A_m|} = (1 + 1/4\pi^2 f^2 C^2 R^2)^{-\frac{1}{2}}. \qquad (4.49)$$

The half-power frequency, at which the gain is 3 dB below the midband value, is therefore given by

$$f_1 = 1/2\pi CR \qquad (4.50)$$

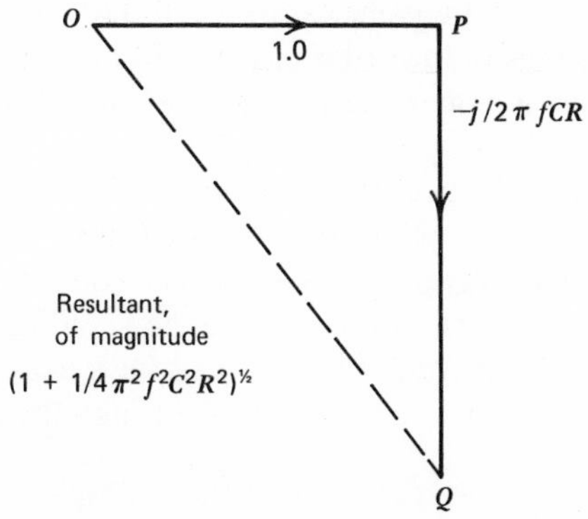

O
P
1.0
$-j/2\pi fCR$

Resultant,
of magnitude
$(1 + 1/4\pi^2 f^2 C^2 R^2)^{\frac{1}{2}}$

Q

Fig. 4.81 Vector diagram to obtain magnitude of $|A_f|/|A_m|$ in (4.46).

and in terms of the lower half-power frequency f_1 (4.49) becomes

$$\frac{|A_f|}{|A_m|} = \left(1 + \frac{f_1^2}{f^2}\right)^{-\frac{1}{2}}. \tag{4.51}$$

The form of the result in (4.48) shows that for best low-frequency performance the coupling capacitors, and also any bypass capacitors, should be as large as possible. This can lead to problems at high frequencies, for if the capacitors are physically large their residual inductance, and their stray capacitance to earth in the case of coupling capacitors, can cause attenuation of rapidly changing signals. To overcome the effects of inductance it is common practice in wideband amplifiers to bypass any large electrolytic decoupling or bypass capacitors with small ceramic capacitors. The stray capacitance associated with bulky coupling capacitors is minimized by using the lowest value of capacitance that is consistent with the required low-frequency performance.

The nature of the limitations that appear at high frequencies is different for tubes and transistors. In tubes, which must operate at fairly high impedance levels if reasonable gain is to be obtained, the main limitations are due to unwanted or "parasitic" capacitance, especially interelectrode capacitances in the devices themselves but also including stray wiring capacitance. In junction transistors, on the other hand, the main limitations develop from transit-time effects, that is, the finite time required for carriers to diffuse through the base region. Any rapidly changing input signal is effectively averaged over this transit time. Field-effect transistors are in this respect also more akin to tubes than to junction transistors. Transit-time effects do begin to appear in tubes at frequencies in excess of 100 MHz, when tube amplifiers generally have to employ the grounded-grid configuration in which the earthed grid serves as a shield against interactions between the input and output signals. The planar metal-ceramic "disk-seal" triodes designed to be used at frequencies above 100 MHz are constructed with interelectrode spacings of the order of 1 mm to make the time during which the electron stream is under the influence of the control grid as small as possible.

Interelectrode capacitance has two main effects on tube amplifiers at high frequencies, the first being to reduce the input impedance. The effect of a capacitance between two electrodes depends on the voltage gain between a signal applied at the first electrode and the resulting signal that appears at the second. This is illustrated in Fig. 4.82 for a capacitance C_{12} between the pair of electrodes 1 and 2. The current through the capacitance is

$$dI = (dE_1 - dE_2) \cdot j\omega C_{12}$$
$$= dE_1(1 - A) \cdot j\omega C_{12}, \tag{4.52}$$

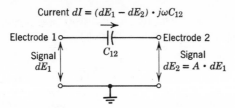

Fig. 4.82 Calculation of the effect of gain on interelectrode capacitance.

and from the point of view of the input signal the capacitance behaves as if it were equal to C_{12} multiplied by $(1 - A)$. Thus in a follower circuit the effective capacitance linking input and output is very small, since A is close to $+1$. The high input impedance of the follower is therefore retained at high frequencies; only the stray capacitance to ground is effective in reducing this impedance. In an ac amplifier in the form of a follower with gain (Fig. 4.83) the stray input capacitance can be effectively *neutralized* by connecting a small trimming capacitor C_N in the position corresponding to positive feedback. With this arrangement the input current that flows to earth through C_{in} is compensated by an equal current that flows from the output to the input through C_N.

In a grounded-cathode stage the voltage gain A between grid and anode is large and negative, and the effective size of this capacitance is thereby multiplied by a large factor. This is the *Miller effect*, which is largely responsible for the poor performance of an ordinary triode amplifier at high frequencies. To see its effect on the input impedance of some typical grounded-cathode stages we refer to Table 4.11. This table lists grid-anode and grid-cathode capacitances and total effective input capacitance for

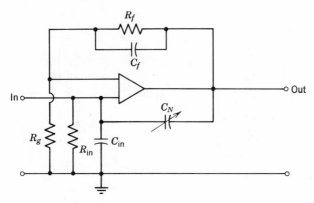

Fig. 4.83 Neutralization of capacitance at the input of an ac amplifier: $A_v = +(R_f + R_g)/R_g$; $C_N = C_{in}/A_v$.

Table 4.11 Input Impedances Due to Interelectrode Capacitances*
(capacitance values in picofarads)

Tube	R_L	Gain A	C_{ag}	$(1 - A)C_{ag}$	C_{gk}	C_{in}	Z_{in} (10 kHz)	Z_{in} (10 MHz)
12AU7	33 K	−16.5	1.5	25	1.6	27	590 K	590 Ω
12AT7	68 K	−55	1.5	84	2.2	86	185 K	185 Ω
12AX7	330 K	−80	2.0	162	2.2	164	97 K	97 Ω
6AU6	22 K	−100	0.0035	0.35	5.5	5.9	2.7 M	2.7 K
12AT7 cascode	33 K	−140	1.5	6.3	2.2	8.5	1.9 M	1.9 K
(gain = −3.2 to nearest anode)								

* Table from L. F. Phillips, *Electronics for Experimenters*, Wiley, New York, 1966.

amplifiers based on single sections of the 12AU7, 12AT7, and 12AX7 double triodes, on a 6AU6 pentode, and on a 12AT7 cascode stage. The last two columns of the table give the resulting input impedances due to interelectrode capacitance at 10 kHz and at 10 MHz. Even in the most favorable cases the input impedance at 10 MHz is seen to be quite low, and unless this low impedance is to be permitted to load the preceding amplifier stage to an undue extent it will be necessary for the preceding stage to have a similarly low value of output impedance, which in a grounded-cathode stage implies a low value of load resistance.

To calculate the dependence of gain on frequency for a tube amplifier at high frequencies we consider Fig. 4.84a. From the equivalent circuit (b) it follows, by using Kirchhoff's first equation, that

$$dI_L = dI_1 + dI_2 + dI_3, \tag{4.53}$$

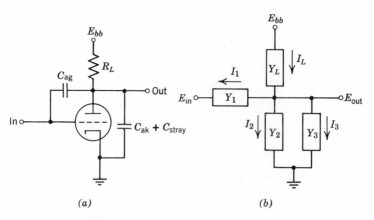

(a)   (b)

Fig. 4.84 (a) Tube amplifier at high frequencies (neglecting lead inductance); (b) equivalent circuit from viewpoint of load current I_L.

where

$$dI_1 = (dE_{\text{out}} - dE_{\text{in}}) \cdot Y_1 \qquad (4.54)$$

and

$$dI_2 = \frac{dE_{\text{out}}}{r_p} + g_m \cdot dE_{\text{in}}$$

$$= Y_2 \cdot dE_{\text{out}} + g_m \cdot dE_{\text{in}} \qquad (4.55)$$

and

$$dI_3 = Y_3 \cdot dE_{\text{out}} \qquad (4.56)$$

Hence

$$A = \frac{dE_{\text{out}}}{dE_{\text{in}}} = \frac{-(g_m - Y_1)}{Y_L + Y_1 + Y_2 + Y_3}. \qquad (4.57)$$

In general the effects of Y_1 and Y_3 in the denominator are apparent well below the frequency at which Y_1 becomes significant in comparison to g_m in the numerator of (4.57), and we can write

$$A = \frac{-g_m}{Y_L + Y_1 + Y_2 + Y_3}. \qquad (4.58)$$

If we now substitute $1/R$ for $(Y_L + Y_2)$ and $j\omega C$ for $(Y_1 + Y_3)$, we obtain

$$A = \frac{-g_m R}{1 + j\omega RC} \qquad (4.59a)$$

$$= \frac{-g_m R}{1 + 2\pi j f RC}. \qquad (4.59b)$$

Performing the vector addition in the denominator (cf. Fig. 4.81), we find that the magnitude of the gain at a frequency f is given by

$$|A_f| = \frac{-g_m R}{(1 + 4\pi^2 f^2 C^2 R^2)^{1/2}} \qquad (4.60)$$

and the upper half-power frequency is given by

$$f_2 = 1/2\pi RC. \qquad (4.61)$$

The midband gain A_m is simply $-g_m R$, so we have

$$\frac{|A_f|}{|A_m|} = \left(1 + \frac{f^2}{f_2^2}\right)^{-1/2}. \qquad (4.62)$$

This should be compared with the result (4.50) that describes the variation of gain with frequency at the low-frequency end of the passband. The total frequency response is shown in Fig. 4.85. We may note that the gain falls off at 6 dB per octave at both ends of the band. The bandwidth of the amplifier is equal to f_2 minus f_1, and in most practical cases is hardly different from

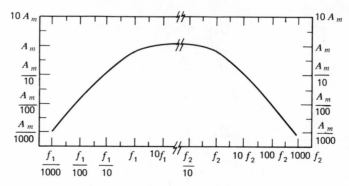

Fig. 4.85 Frequency response of an ideal ac amplifier, with upper and lower half-power frequencies f_i and f_2 at which $A = 0.707A_m$.

f_2. Thus the gain-bandwidth product is given by

$$f_T = A_m \cdot f_2 = \frac{-g_m \cdot R}{2\pi RC} = \frac{-g_m}{2\pi C}. \tag{4.63}$$

In a perfectly constructed amplifier the capacitance C consists only of the sum of the tube capacitances C_{ag} and C_{ak}, in which case the gain-bandwidth product is seen to be a constant characteristic of the amplifying tube itself, a large value of f_T being favored by a large value of g_m and small values of the interelectrode capacitances. To obtain a large bandwidth it is therefore necessary to sacrifice gain, either by using a small value of load resistance or by negative feedback. A definite improvement in f_2 can also be obtained by inductive compensation (Fig. 4.86).

For a field-effect transistor essentially similar considerations apply; the high-frequency figure of merit that is commonly stated for the device is the

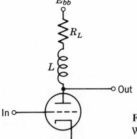

Fig. 4.86 Extension of bandwidth by inductive compensation. With $L = 0.414R^2C$ the optimum response $f_2' = 1.7f_2$ is obtained. See text for significance of R and C.

ratio of common-source forward-transfer admittance y_{fs} to common-source (short circuit) input capacitance C_{iss}. The common-source (short-circuit) reverse transfer capacitance C_{rss} is also relevant, though generally smaller than C_{iss}, since in the equation analogous to (4.62), with y_{fs} replacing g_m, C is the sum of C_{iss} and C_{rss}. (The qualification short-circuit is added to indicate that the capacitance is measured by observing a transient response at one electrode with the other electrodes bypassed for ac signals.) For the 6AU6 pentode f_T works out to be 900 MHz, for the 12AT7 cascode it is 2250 MHz, and for two typical high-frequency FET's, the Texas Instruments 2N3993 and the Motorola 2N4223, it is within the ranges 300–600 and 350–800 MHz, respectively.

With a junction transistor the necessity for carriers to diffuse through a base region of finite thickness and the low impedance levels at which transistor amplifiers normally operate conspire to make the effects of stray and interelectrode capacitance much less important, in comparison to transit-time effects, than they are for tubes. The internal high-frequency limitations of a transistor are generally expressed in terms of the value of f_α ($= f_{hfb}$) or f_1 ($= f_T$). The "α-cutoff frequency," f_α, is the frequency at which α ($= h_{fb}$) is reduced to 0.707 of its midband value and is thus essentially the same as f_2 for the transistor in a common-base amplifier stage. For the same transistor in the common-emitter configuration there is the useful approximate result that $f_2 = (1 - \alpha)f_\alpha$. The frequency f_1 or f_T is the frequency at which the current gain β ($= h_{fe}$) is equal to unity; that is, it is the current gain-bandwidth product. The quantity f_1 is easier to measure than f_α and is now stated by most manufacturers in preference to f_α. As a rough basis of comparison between the two cutoff frequencies we can say that f_1 is commonly about 1.2 times f_α. Junction transistors are available with values of f_T in excess of 1 GHz ($= 1000$ MHz); examples are the Texas Instruments types TIS71 (silicon) and 2N5043 (germanium) with $f_T = 2.4$ GHz and 1.5 GHz, respectively. Almost as important as f_T for this kind of transistor is the high-frequency *noise figure* whose significance is explained shortly.

With both tube and transistor amplifiers a considerable improvement in bandwidth can be obtained by a judicious combination of inductive compensation and feedback. Negative feedback alone cannot increase the gain-bandwidth product of an amplifier, but by applying negative feedback at midband frequencies and positive, or regenerative, feedback at the high frequency end of the passband a net increase in f_T may be obtained in principle. However, because of the lack of isolation between stages found with transistors, it is fact *necessary* to use feedback merely to achieve the limit f_T in a multistage amplifier. The design of such an amplifier is not a simple matter because of the need to avoid instability and to obtain a

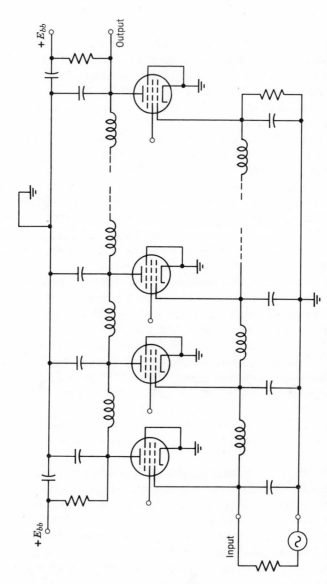

Fig. 4.87 A distributed amplifier stage. Note that the grid and plate circuits each constitute a transmission line which is properly terminated at both ends. The number of tubes per amplifier stage may be 12 or more; the over-all gain-bandwidth product is roughly equal to the sum of the products for the individual tubes.

frequency response as flat as possible at all frequencies below f_2. Some typical circuits are described in the references to this chapter, together with such elaborate devices for obtaining a large bandwidth as "distributed" amplifiers (cf. Fig. 4.87).

In evaluating the ideal gain-bandwidth products of different devices, we have so far ignored such factors as lead inductance and stray wiring capacitance. These factors are, in fact, never negligible at frequencies greater than a megacycle, but they can be minimized by careful attention to layout and "lead dress," that is, by arranging the leads to an active device to reduce the inductive and capacitive coupling between them and the stray capacitance to earth. Devices for use at very high frequencies (1000 MHz and above) are usually designed to fit directly into a coaxial or parallel-strip transmission line, or to insert into a waveguide, and are kept small in size so that lead inductance, stray capacitance, and transit-time are all small. At somewhat lower frequencies, at which tubes and transistors have a more recognizable appearance, inductances are minimized by keeping all signal-carrying leads as short as possible, effects of stray capacitance are similarly reduced by keeping high-impedance signal paths short, and interactions that could lead to instability are avoided by using a linear signal path such that the output of the amplifier is a maximum distance from the input consistent with the short lengths of the intermediate leads. Sensitive high-impedance input leads (to grid, base, or gate) need to be shielded, and impedance-matching, especially of transmission lines, is very important. Wherever possible, stray capacitance is "neutralized," as in Fig. 4.83.

Noise in electronic equipment constitutes all and any unwanted signals that are superimposed on the changing current or voltage that is to be measured. Noise sources that can be overcome by careful design and construction include the following:

1. Electromagnetic pickup due to poor shielding or the transmission of switching surges along power lines.

2. Mains hum due to incomplete smoothing of ripple on dc power supplies, poor shielding, or pickup from ac leads to tube filaments.

3. Instability due to unintentional positive feedback.

4. Intermittent signals due to noisy or defective components, badly soldered connections, or leaky insulation.

5. Microphonics, due to vibrations affecting interelectrode spacings in tubes.

6. Variations in tube gain due to lack of stabilization of filament power supplies or of transistor gain due to ambient temperature changes.

7. Drifts arising from the presence of offset voltages and currents or from the presence of varying background signals.

The methods of overcoming these noise sources, which include the provision of better shielding, use of higher quality power supplies or batteries, use of shock-absorber mountings for microphonic components, the avoidance of interactions which could give rise to positive feedback and reduction of high-frequency open-loop gain, and the minimizing of offset are self-evident or have already been discussed.

The following important sources of noise are fundamental in character and may be reduced but not eliminated by selecting the optimum values of circuit parameters and the best type of active device for a particular purpose:

1. Thermal noise due to the random motion of electrons in a resistor.

2. Shot noise due to statistical fluctuations in the flow of electrons to the anode of a tube or of carriers through depletion layers in a transistor.

3. $1/f$ 'flicker-effect noise' in tubes and 'excess noise' in transistors, due to variations in the nature of the cathode surface affecting the rate of emission of electrons in a tube, and to variations in the conductivity of the medium or of conditions on the crystal surface in a transistor.

4. Partition noise due to random fluctuations in the division of current between different electrodes in multigrid tubes.

The *thermal* or *Johnson* noise in a resistor R $(= 1/Y)$ is described by the formulas

$$v_{rms} = (4kTR\,\Delta f)^{\frac{1}{2}} \tag{4.64}$$

$$i_{rms} = (4kTY\,\Delta f)^{\frac{1}{2}}, \tag{4.65}$$

where v_{rms} is the root-mean-square output of the noise generator in the Thévenin equivalent circuit (Fig. 4.88a) and i_{rms} is similarly the root-mean-square output of the noise generator in the Norton equivalent circuit (Fig. 4.88b) in a bandwidth Δf at an absolute temperature T. Here k is the Boltzmann constant, equal to 1.38×10^{-23} J/°K. For an ideal 1-M resistor at 300°K and with $\Delta f = 10$ kHz we find v_{rms} to be 13 μV and i_{rms} to be 1.3×10^{-11} A.

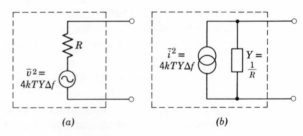

(a)   (b)

Fig. 4.88   Equivalent voltage (a) and current (b) noise generators due to the thermal motion of electrons in a resistance R.

Shot noise in tubes is described by the formula

$$i_{rms} = (2I\epsilon\Gamma^2 \, \Delta f)^{\frac{1}{2}}, \tag{4.66}$$

where I is the anode current, ϵ is the charge carried by one electron or by one shower of electrons in tubes in which secondary emission is important, the electronic charge being 1.60×10^{-19} C, Γ^2 is the "space-charge reduction factor" which is typically between 0.05 and 0.3 (it arises because the interaction with the space charge smooths out some of the random fluctuations in the electron stream), and Δf is the bandwidth as before. It can be shown to a good approximation that the shot noise in a tube can be represented by the thermal noise of an equivalent resistor R_s in series with the grid, where for a triode at an ambient temperature of 300°K

$$R_s = \frac{2.5}{g_m}. \tag{4.67}$$

Hence the shot noise is equivalent to the input from a signal generator

$$v_{rms} = 2 \times 10^{-10}\left(\frac{\Delta f}{g_m}\right)^{\frac{1}{2}}. \tag{4.68}$$

For the triode amplifier of Fig. 4.34 we should therefore have v_{rms} due to shot noise equal to 0.3 μV in a 10-kc bandwidth, compared with 13 μV due to the 1-M grid resistor with the input open-circuited. In practice the grid resistor would be in parallel with the output impedance of the preceding stage and its noise contribution would be somewhat reduced. In the presence of partition noise the equivalent resistor of (4.67) is multiplied by a factor $(1 + 8I_{c2}/g_m)I_b/I_k$, where I_{c2}, I_b, and I_k are the screen-grid, plate, and cathode currents, respectively. A cascode stage does not suffer from partition noise and therefore is often to be preferred to a pentode at the input stage of a low-noise, wideband amplifier.

With transistors the internal noise sources include both thermal and shot-noise generators and are difficult to treat theoretically. The experimentally observed noise properties of these devices are usually expressed in terms of an over-all *noise figure*.

Flicker-effect noise, or $1/f$ noise, is the predominant form in both tubes and transistors below 100 Hz. In most junction transistors it begins to be significant in comparison with other forms of noise at about 1 kHz. It has been found to obey equations of the form

$$v_{rms} = \text{constant} \times \left(\frac{\Delta f}{f}\right)^{\frac{1}{2}} \tag{4.69}$$

$$i_{rms} = \text{constant} \times \left(\frac{\Delta f}{f}\right)^{\frac{1}{2}} \tag{4.70}$$

with extremely good accuracy down to frequencies of a small fraction of 1 Hz. At direct current this form of noise is experimentally indistinguishable from the usual slow drifts of dc amplifiers.

The basic measure of the extent to which a signal can usefully be amplified and of the precision with which information can be extracted from it is the *signal-to-noise ratio S/N*, which is defined as the ratio of the power available in the form of the required information to the power present in the accompanying noise. The *noise figure F* of any device is the ratio of *S/N* in the input to *S/N* in the output and is usually expressed in decibels; that is,

$$F = 10 \log (S/N)_{\text{input}} - 10 \log (S/N)_{\text{output}}. \tag{4.71}$$

If the first stage of an amplifier possesses a large gain, the noise introduced by subsequent stages will be negligible in comparison to the amplified input noise, so that only the noise figure of the input stage will be important. This conclusion is embodied in the formula

$$F = F_1 + \frac{F_2 - 1}{A_1} + \frac{F_3 - 1}{A_1 \cdot A_2} + \cdots \tag{4.72}$$

for the over-all noise figure of a multistage amplifier with noise figures $F_1, F_2, F_3, \ldots$ and power gains $A_1, A_2, \ldots$ for successive stages 1, 2, 3, \ldots.

The noise figure of a particular device is a function of its own operating parameters, together with the signal frequency, the bandwidth, and the output impedance of the signal generator. For many purposes it is sufficient to know the maximum value of F at a given frequency, that is, the "spot noise figure," which is likely to be found with a device under optimum operating conditions and with the optimum generator resistance. Thus for a Texas Instruments 2N2865 transistor the optimum noise figure is guaranteed to be less than 4.5 dB at 200 MHz, while for a 2N2500 FET it is stated to be less than 5 dB at 10 Hz and less than 1 dB at 1 kHz, with specified operating conditions. A useful way of expressing information about the noise characteristics of a device is shown in Fig. 4.89, in which the noise figures of several related Texas Instruments FET's are plotted against frequency and generator resistance. Similar information is usually supplied by manufacturers of junction transistors intended for small signal applications. In general field-effect transistors are noticeably superior to junction transistors, especially at frequencies at which $1/f$ noise is important, while tubes, particularly high-mu triodes, are appreciably better than both kinds of transistor.

The noise figure is valuable for an individual device because it does not vary greatly with the amplifier configuration in which the device is used and

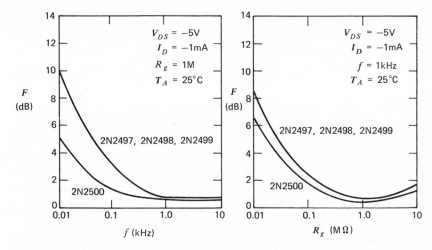

Fig. 4.89 Dependence of noise figure on frequency and generator resistance for some *p*-channel FET's.

because it provides a simple basis for comparison between different devices. The noise figure is also an important quantity to have specified for low-noise amplifiers and preamplifiers, especially if data are given in regard to its variation with frequency and generator resistance so that optimum conditions can be selected. For other purposes, however, the actual magnitude of the input noise associated with a device may be equally useful; for example, in the Philbrick operational amplifier catalog four actual values of internally generated noise are quoted; namely peak-to-peak voltage and current noise signals present in the form of flicker noise (0.016 to 1.6 Hz) and rms voltage and current signals in the form of broadband noise (160 Hz to 16 kHz). With the aid of these figures and the known square-root dependence of noise on bandwidth the noise performance of an operational amplifier in any particular configuration can be predicted without too much difficulty.

To conclude this section we note a few general results concerning the separation of signals from noise:

1. Thermal noise and pickup are both enhanced in high impedance circuits. Therefore for best signal-to-noise ratio it is advisable to operate at a low impedance level.

2. Because of $1/f$ noise, it is easier to measure small signals if the signals are modulated, that is, ac rather than dc, the modulation frequency preferably being above 100 Hz with tube or FET amplifiers and above 1000 Hz with amplifiers having junction transistors at the input.

3. The mean-square noise signal is always proportional to the bandwidth Δf. Therefore with a modulated signal the best signal-to-noise ratio will be obtained by making the amplifier bandwidth as narrow as possible.

4. If S/N is less than unity, the *phase* of the signal passed by a narrow-band amplifier will be governed mainly by the phase of the random noise and the signal will tend to be lost. In this situation the improvement expected from narrowing the amplifier bandwidth will not be realized—the signal is said to be below the "improvement threshold." The situation can be saved in this case if the phase of the buried signal is known, so a fixed amount of another signal of the same phase may be introduced to render the noise ineffective in deciding the phase of the signal passed by the amplifier. The added signal is to be subtracted later as a zero correction. The phase information can also be exploited at the end of the amplification process by using a phase-sensitive detector (cf. Chapter VI) to convert the modulated signal back to direct current and in the process reject signals of incorrect phase.

5. If the signal of interest is superimposed on a strong background signal the latter can be expected to contribute a proportionate amount of noise. Therefore when measuring very small signals, it is necessary to ensure that any background, for example, the background count in measurements of radioactivity, the stray light in a spectrometer, or the dark current in a photomultiplier, is reduced to the lowest possible level.

6. Noise is random in nature and over a sufficiently long period must average out to zero. Signals, by definition, are nonrandom and over a long period must average to a finite value. Therefore the greater the period of time for which a noisy signal is summed, or averaged, the greater the signal-to-noise ratio in the accumulated data. Thus, for example, in Mössbauer spectroscopy it is common practice to accumulate signal data for a day or more in a multichannel analyzer until a reasonable S/N is obtained; in *nmr* spectroscopy it is usual to improve the appearance and utility of a spectrum obtained with a dilute sample by computer averaging of a number of recorder traces. A variety of commercial signal-averaging devices is available to improve S/N ratios in measurements involving both fast and slow repetitive waveforms. The simplest electronic averaging procedure uses an output device with a long time constant, in other words a very narrow bandwidth near dc, for example, a meter or recorder whose input is derived from an integrating network. The result is necessarily to decrease the over-all bandwidth of the instrument in question so that fast processes may go unobserved and to increase the time required for each measurement; with very elusive signals, however, this may be the only alternative to obtaining no data at all.

3 WAVEFORM GENERATORS AND SWITCHING CIRCUITS

Sine-Wave Generators

In the preceding section we noted that in an amplifier with positive feedback the gain may become formally infinite; that is, an infinitesimal disturbance at the input builds up to a maximum signal at the output and the circuit then behaves as a self-sustaining oscillator. In general the output from such a circuit contains a range of oscillation frequencies and so appears distorted, but if a frequency-sensitive network is included in the feedback loop and the amount of feedback is made just sufficient to sustain oscillation, it is possible to confine the oscillations to a relatively narrow frequency range and the output is then a sine wave of well-defined frequency.

At low frequencies and up to about 100 kHz it is convenient to use one of the frequency-sensitive *RC* phase-shift networks in Figs. 3.27, 3.28, or 3.29 in one of the oscillator configurations in Fig. 4.90. If the amplifier has a low input impedance, the phase-shift network for current signals should be used, whereas, if it has a high input impedance the corresponding network for voltage signals should be used. The setting of the potentiometer across the output terminals is to be adjusted so that the fraction β multiplied by the attenuation of the network and the gain of the amplifier is just equal to unity. Obviously the passband of the amplifier must include the oscillator

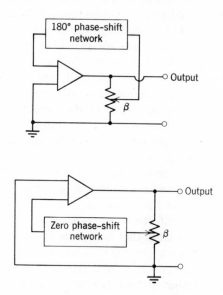

Fig. 4.90 Basic configurations for an audiofrequency oscillator.

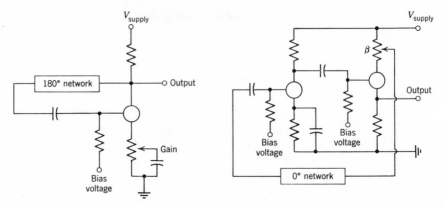

Fig. 4.91   Simple one-device and two-device audio oscillators.

frequency. It is not necessary to use a high-gain amplifier to generate the oscillations; Fig. 4.91 shows two simple one-device and two-device oscillators, in the first of which the onset of oscillation is controlled by adjusting the amplifier gain, while in the second the fraction β is adjusted for the same purpose. In these circuits the load resistors and coupling capacitors may form part of the phase-shift network. Still another approach uses a tuned amplifier, as in Fig. 4.66, and returns a controlled amount of the output to the positive input via a potential divider.

An ideal audio oscillator should include a means of stabilizing the amplitude and frequency of the output against variations in temperature and aging of active components, a facility for switching resistors or capacitors in the phase-shift network to vary the oscillation frequency, an amplifier with stabilized gain so that the onset of oscillation is reproducible and the gain or β-control may be preset, and a variable-gain follower at the output to allow variation of the amplitude of the output signal and to isolate the feedback loop from a load across the output terminals. The effects of temperature on transistor parameters in circuits such as Fig. 4.91 can be partly compensated by including a thermistor in series with the feedback loop. The resistance of a thermistor increases rapidly with increasing temperature, and one may be chosen so that the increased attenuation of the feedback signal compensates for the increased gain of the amplifier. The thermistor also has a stabilizing effect on the amplitude of the feedback signal, as has a small incandescent lamp that is operated just below the region in which its filament is beginning to glow. A more easily predictable method of stabilizing the amplitude at a predetermined value is to apply a bounds circuit at an intermediate point in the amplifier. Many conveniently packaged and reasonably inexpensive signal generators are available commercially,

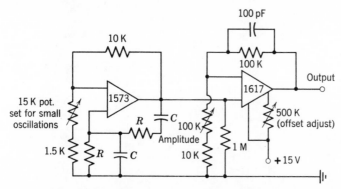

Fig. 4.92 Wien-bridge oscillator, $f = 1/2\pi RC$, $R > 5$ K. Operational amplifiers Melcor types 1573 and 1617.

with all the amenities listed in the first sentence of this paragraph so that the occasion to design and build such a circuit should seldom occur. The circuit in Fig. 4.92 is intended mainly as an illustration of the type of oscillator that can be constructed with relatively inexpensive operational amplifiers should the need arise. This circuit depends for its amplitude stability on the feedback stabilization of the amplifier gain. More positive control of the amplitude can be obtained by using part of the output signal to control one element in the feedback loop, as in Fig. 4.93, in which use is made of the fact that at low drain-source voltages a field-effect transistor behaves as a resistor whose value is controlled by the gate-source voltage. In this example a dc-control voltage is obtained by rectifying and integrating some of the output signal with a small diode. The 0.1-μF capacitor and 100-K resistor that integrate the rectified signal have a time constant of 0.01 sec. If the period of oscillation

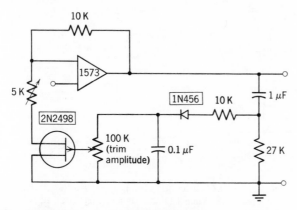

Fig. 4.93 Use of an FET as a voltage-controlled resistor to stabilize the amplitude of the oscillator of Fig. 4.92.

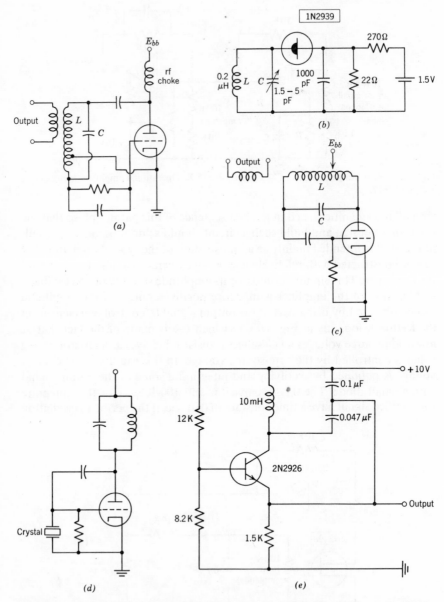

Fig. 4.94 Some representative *LC* oscillators: (*a*) tuned-grid Hartley oscillator; (*b*) 100-Mc tunnel diode oscillator (from G.E. Tunnel Diode Manual); (*c*) series-fed Hartley oscillator; (*d*) crystal-controlled oscillator; (*e*) 10 kc Colpitts oscillator (from G.E. Transistor Manual).

is more than about 10% of this value, the capacitance should be increased correspondingly.

Radiofrequency oscillators invariably incorporate an LC tuned circuit as the frequency-sensitive element. We recall that at resonance a tuned circuit has zero phase shift. Some typical oscillator configurations are shown in Fig. 4.94. Here, even more than in the case of audio oscillators, it is recommended that for stable amplitude and frequency control, and to obtain such refinements as the provision of interchangeable piezo-electric quartz crystals for frequency stability, it is better and usually cheaper to buy rather than to build. When a considerable output of radiofrequency power is required it is advisable first to check the availability of obsolescent transmitters in the stock lists of military surplus stores. At low power levels some extremely elegant circuits can be built by using tunnel diodes; one such circuit is shown in Fig. 4.94 and further examples may be found in the references given at the end of this chapter.

Square-Wave Generators

A square-wave generator is a circuit in which the active devices are switched almost instantaneously between a highly conducting ON state and a slightly conducting or nonconducting OFF state. The simplest square-wave generator is an amplifier stage overloaded to the extent that the tube or transistor is completely cut off during half a cycle and "bottomed" or saturated during the other half. The resulting waveform is shown in Fig. 4.95a, and the corresponding circuit conditions in a tube or npn transistor are shown in Fig. 4.95b. If a transistor is saturated during the ON part of the cycle, this confers the advantage that the output signal is almost independent of transistor characteristics such as current gain. During the saturation period, however, a certain amount of charge becomes "stored" in the base region and when the switching cycle is reversed this charge takes a finite time to diffuse out again, thereby increasing the delay time and fall time. Therefore in very fast switching circuits which use transistors it is often necessary to prevent saturation by some means (e.g., with a diode clamp as shown in Fig. 4.96).

A useful form of self-sustaining square-wave generator is the *astable multivibrator* whose basic circuit is shown in Fig. 4.97a; representative tube and transistor circuits are given in Figs. 4.97b and c, respectively. The mode of operation of the basic circuit is as follows: suppose that when the power supply (which for the sake of argument we assume to be positive) is first turned on device 1 tends to conduct slightly more than device 2. As device 1 begins to conduct strongly the bottom of R_{L1} is driven toward ground and the resulting negative-going signal is transmitted through C_2 to the control element of device 2, turning it off and thus exaggerating the imbalance of

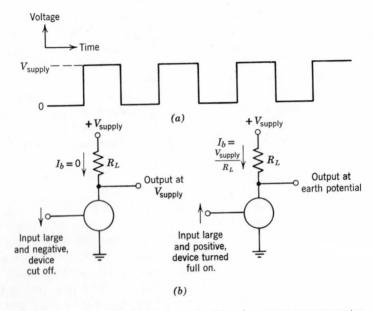

(a)

(b)

Fig. 4.95 Output waveform and circuit conditions in a square-wave generator.

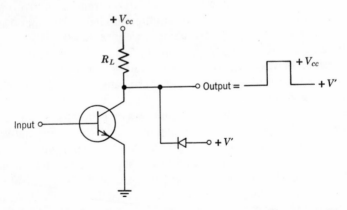

Fig. 4.96 Use of a clamping diode to prevent saturation of an ON transistor.

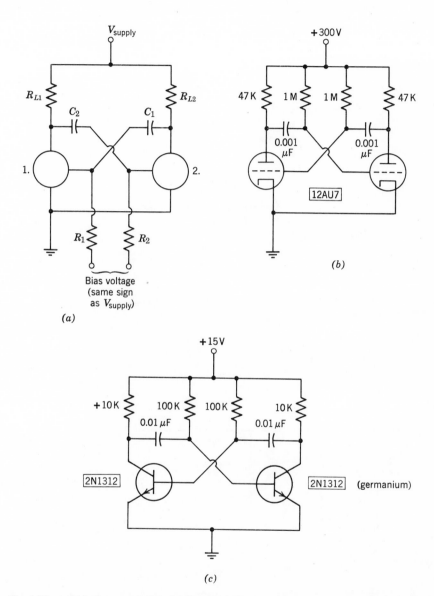

Fig. 4.97 Astable (free-running) multivibrator: (*a*) basic circuit; (*b*) representative tube circuit (note that the 12AU7 is rated to withstand negative grid voltages to -660 V in short pulses); (*c*) representative transistor circuit with the same repetition frequency as (*b*). (Note that most silicon transistors have quite low values of the base-emitter breakdown voltages BV_{EBO}.)

271

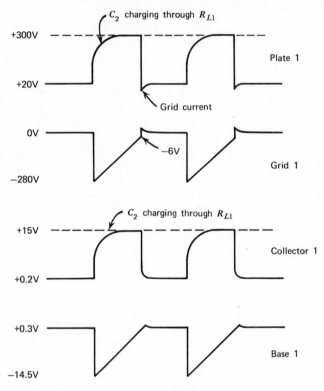

Fig. 4.98   Waveforms in astable multivibrators.

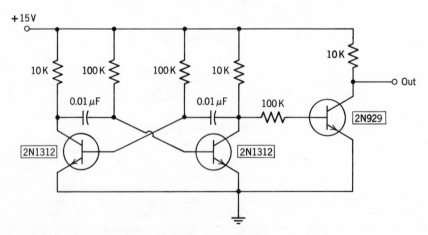

Fig. 4.99   Complete free-running square-wave generator.

the current through the two devices. Consequently the circuit settles into a state in which device 1 is saturated and device 2 is OFF. The effectiveness of this switching action can be enhanced, if necessary, by inserting a resistor in the common ground lead, so that while the control element of 2 is driven negative the source element is driven positive by the increasing current through device 1. The state of the circuit arrived at by the initial switching action is metastable, since the control element of 2, having been driven negative, immediately begins to rise toward the bias voltage as a result of capacitor C_2 charging up through R_2. After a period governed by the time constant R_2C_2 device 2 begins to conduct, the resulting negative-going signal from the bottom of R_{L2} is transferred through C_1 to the control element of device 1, turning it OFF while device 2 is turning ON, and the whole process is repeated. If $R_1C_1 = R_2C_2$, the durations of the OFF and ON states are equal. If the bias voltage is, in fact, the supply voltage, as in (b) and (c) of Fig. 4.97, the duration of the metastable state of device 1 is $0.7R_1C_1$ and therefore in the symmetrical case the repetition frequency of the signal across either load resistor is $0.7/R_1C_1$.

The waveforms observed with the circuits (b) and (c) are given in Fig. 4.98. In the top curve it is seen first that the saturation voltage for the tube is not zero, but of the order of 20 V, and second that the plate potential does not rise sharply to the supply voltage because of the time required to charge the plate capacitance C_2 up to the supply voltage with the current flowing through R_{L1}. Another departure from an ideal square wave occurs during the switching ON process as a result of grid current flowing into C_1. At grid 1 the voltage falls sharply as a result of the switching on of tube 2 and then begins to rise exponentially towards $+300$ V as C_1 charges through R_1. At about -6 V the tube begins to conduct and the regenerative switching process takes over; the small amount of overshoot, and consequent grid-current flow, results from the positive-going waveform transferred from plate 2 via the capacitor C_1. In the lower two curves the same general behavior is observed, but in this case the saturation voltage is only about 0.2 V and the transistor begins to conduct when the base is at about $+0.3$ V. The effect of C_2 charging through R_{L1} is still apparent, but the effect that was due to grid current is absent. To obtain a perfectly square output signal the multivibrator may be followed by a saturating amplifier stage as in Fig. 4.99. The 100-K base resistor is to prevent the multivibrator from being loaded significantly by the amplifier. An astable multivibrator can be triggered, or "synchronized," by a repetitive pulse signal of frequency greater than its natural repetition frequency applied to an anode or a collector.

As a contrast to the astable multivibrator we next consider the *bistable multivibrator*. or "flip-flop," of which the basic circuit is shown in Fig. 4.100a and representative tube and transistor circuits are given in 4.100b

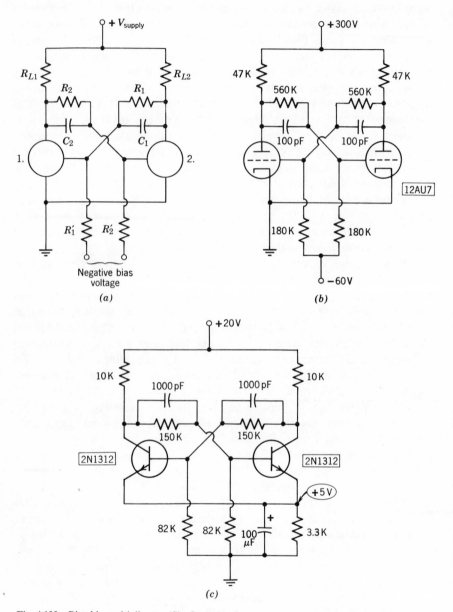

Fig. 4.100 Bistable multivibrator (flip-flop) circuits.

274

and *c*. Here in place of the capacitors coupling devices 1 and 2 we have potential dividers R_1, R_1' and R_2, R_2'. The small capacitors C_1 and C_2 are there merely to provide an easy path for high-frequency signals and thus promote a more rapid switching action. The resistors in the potential divider are chosen so that if device 1 is in the ON state the control element of device 2 is held sufficiently negative to ensure that 2 is in the OFF state, whereas with 2 OFF the control element of 1 is sufficiently above earth potential to ensure that this device is turned ON. In a practical circuit a negative bias voltage may be used as in Fig. 4.100*a* and *b* or the source elements may be held at an intermediate voltage as in *c*. The circuit can be switched between its two stable states by means of pulses that are large enough to initiate the regenerative switching action, a positive pulse at the bottom of the load resistor of the ON device or the control element of the OFF device or a negative pulse at the load of the OFF device or the control element of the ON device being in the correct sense to bring about the change. It is usually best to bring triggering pulses into the anode or collector because the switching action may be disturbed if a coupling capacitor is attached to a grid or base. The correct destination for a switching pulse can be ensured by using pulse-steering diodes, as in Fig. 4.101. The bistable multivibrator is

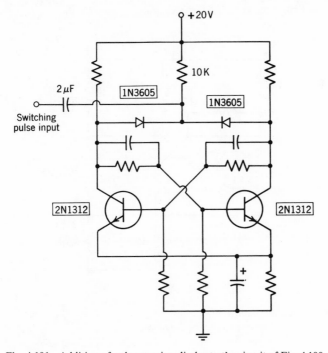

Fig. 4.101   Addition of pulse-steering diodes to the circuit of Fig. 4.100c.

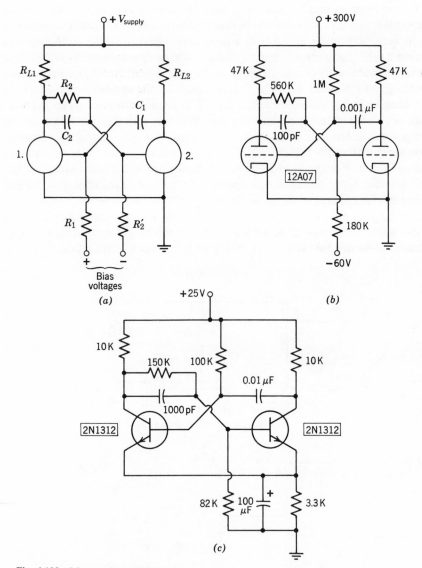

Fig. 4.102 Monostable multivibrators.

276

the basic element of binary logic circuits and is also an essential part of pulse-counting circuits and of most instruments concerned with information carried in the form of discrete pulses.

If we compromise between the astable and bistable multivibrators to the extent of building a circuit with a coupling capacitor on one side and a potential divider on the other, the result is an entity with one stable and one metastable state and known variously as a *monostable multivibrator, one-shot multivibrator,* or *univibrator.* The basic circuit, plus tube and transistor examples, is given in Fig. 4.102. As in the free-running circuit, the duration of the metastable state is $0.7R_1C_1$ when R_1 is connected to the supply voltage. The circuit normally remains in its stable state, with device 1 ON and 2 OFF, but, for example, a positive pulse applied to the anode or collector of device 1 will cause the circuit to switch into the metastable state from which it returns after a predetermined time. The univibrator can serve as a *pulse-shaper,* since it gives a standard output pulse whatever the shape of the input pulse, and also as a *pulse-delay circuit,* if a subsequent circuit is triggered by a pulse derived from the trailing edge of the output waveform. A simple circuit for this purpose is shown in Fig. 4.103. With appropriate component values the delay period may be anywhere between a few microseconds and a few minutes.

The forms of astable and monostable multivibrator we have considered so far have the disadvantage that both devices in the circuit have their control elements fully involved with the switching action and for triggering it is usually necessary to apply a rather large pulse to the bottom end of one of the load resistors; a further point is that the presence of capacitors attached to the load resistors tends to produce square waves with distorted leading

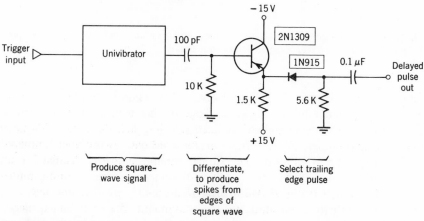

Fig. 4.103 Use of a univibrator as a pulse-delay circuit.

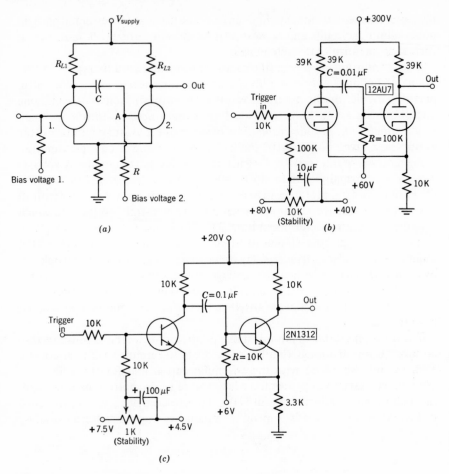

Fig. 4.104   Cathode-coupled and emitter-coupled multivibrators: (*a*) basic circuit; (*b*) representative tube circuit; (*c*) representative transistor circuit.

edges, as in Fig. 4.98. The cathode-coupled or emitter-coupled circuit of Fig. 4.104 is better in both respects, since the use of the common cathode or emitter resistor to complete the feedback loop (cf. the long-tailed pair) leaves one grid or base free for triggering and one load resistor unencumbered with capacitance. With both bias voltages equal the positive feedback loop is sufficient to ensure that the circuit will behave as a free-running multivibrator. Point *A* in Fig. 4.104*a* is driven alternately positive and negative, recovering with time constant *RC* to recommence the switching process. If the bias voltages are unequal, the time required for switching when *A* has been driven negative is different from that required when A has been driven positive and an unsymmetrical square wave results; that is, the mark-space ratio is able to be varied by the controls labeled "stability" in Fig. 4.104b and c. If the stability control is adjusted to the point at which the bias voltages are very different, the circuit settles into a stable state in which one of the devices is permanently conducting and the other is cut off. In this condition a trigger pulse of correct polarity applied to the spare grid or base of device 1 will initiate a single switching cycle and the circuit will then behave as a univibrator.

Univibrators and binary "flip-flops" are among the variety of digital circuits available in integrated form. We shall have more to say about some of these circuits shortly. Failing the use of integrated circuitry, compact multivibrator circuits can be constructed by using dual transistors, in which close matching of characteristics is an advantage if low-level switching signals are to be used, or even integrated operational amplifiers. The latter allow circuits to be obtained with very precise and predictable behavior. A group of simple operational amplifier multivibrators is illustrated in Fig. 4.105. The essential feature of each of these circuits is that feedback to the positive input causes the amplifier to become saturated with a small differential input. In the astable form the voltage at the negative input recovers gradually from each excursion of the output to the point at which the amplifier is no longer saturated, whereupon the circuit immediately switches to the other saturated state. In the monostable form the presence of the diode prevents switching to the other saturated state, and therefore the circuit responds only once to a triggering pulse. In the bistable form the positive feedback causes the amplifier to remain in one of its stable states until the situation is disturbed by a trigger pulse. The input to which the pulse-steering diodes direct the trigger pulse is governed by the polarity of the output voltage.

If an ordinary dc amplifier has its gain increased by positive feedback, there comes a point at which the output is always saturated, and the sign of the output is governed by whether the input voltage is above or below some predetermined level. If the input changes from one side of this level to the other the amplifier switches rapidly from one state to the other, intermediate states being unstable. The resulting circuit is known as a *Schmitt trigger*. Its usual form is shown in Fig. 4.106. If the gain around the loop from the input via the bottom of R_{L1} to the top of R_3 and back to the input is less than unity, the circuit is merely an amplifier with positive feedback; if the gain around this loop is just unity, the circuit will trigger with a signal that is infinitesimally above or below the sensitive level, while if the gain exceeds unity the circuit shows *hysteresis;* that is, if device 1 is OFF, a voltage somewhat higher than the predetermined level is needed to turn it ON and

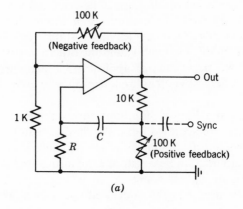

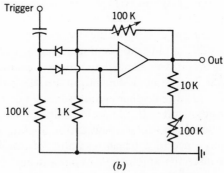

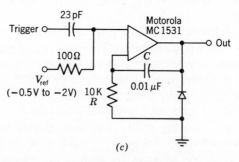

Fig. 4.105 Multivibrators based on operational amplifiers: (*a*) astable; (*b*) bistable; (*c*) mono-stable, pulse length controlled by reference voltage.

280

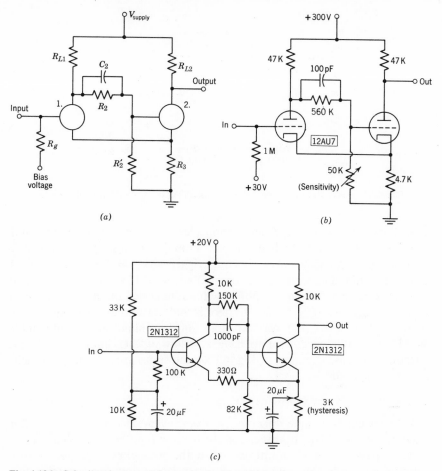

Fig. 4.106 Schmitt triggers: (*a*) basic circuit; (*b*) and (*c*), tube and transistor examples. The latter may also include a sensitivity control similar to that in (*b*).

if it is ON a voltage lower than that level is needed to turn it OFF. The ability of the circuit to act as a voltage discriminator is diminished by hysteresis, so it is desirable to be able to reduce the loop gain to the point at which the hysteresis is just tolerable. With care it is possible to build circuits in which the hysteresis is of the order of millivolts. A Schmitt trigger can be a useful pulse-height discriminator, since it switches only with pulses that are above the predetermined switching level. Two Schmitt triggers with slightly different switching levels can be used as a "window discriminator" by providing for a succeeding "anticoincidence" circuit to respond only when one is triggered and the other is not. An anticoincidence circuit is one

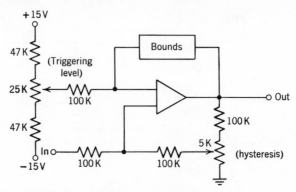

Fig.4.107 Level discriminator (Schmitt trigger) based on an operational amplifier.

of the forms of gating circuit that we consider later in connection with digital logic. A chopper-stabilized operational amplifier of high gain behaves in almost the same fashion as a Schmitt trigger, since with a gain of 10^6 or more the amplifier can be saturated by a signal of 10 μV or less! A circuit that uses an operational amplifier with differential input to produce a Schmitt trigger with controlled hysteresis and adjustable triggering level is shown in Fig. 4.107. For best sensitivity of discrimination the differential amplifier should be chosen to have very low offset; similarly, with the orthodox transistor circuit of Fig. 4.106c the transistors should preferably be a matched pair.

Other Waveform Generators

A particularly simple form of sawtooth generator is the *relaxation oscillator* in Fig. 4.108. In this circuit the resistor R is chosen so that it is too large to pass all of the current needed by the neon glow tube. Such a tube has a minimum burning current requirement and below this current it goes out. Once the tube is out the voltage at A rises exponentially toward the supply voltage as the capacitor C charges through R. Before the supply voltage is reached, however, the "striking voltage" of the tube is exceeded and it begins to conduct, discharges capacitor C, and goes out, whereupon the whole process is repeated. By suitable choice of R and C the repetition time of the relaxation process can be fixed anywhere between a few milliseconds and a few minutes.

A precise, high-speed sawtooth wave is essential in many applications, the most important being the time base of an oscilloscope. The waveform in Fig. 4.108 is not an ideal sawtooth because of the curvature that results from the exponential charging rate. To obtain a perfectly linear ramp or sawtooth voltage it is necessary to charge a capacitor with a current that is essentially constant. A circuit that achieves this is the *Miller sweep circuit* in Fig. 4.109. Here the 6GY6 pentode is cut off by the −10 V bias of the suppressor grid, and a current 300/R amperes flows to earth through the control grid. When the tube is turned on by a positive gate signal, the capacitor C begins to charge up through R and at the same time the anode potential begins to fall from the 250-V level at which it was formerly held by the diode clamp. The initial rapid fall of anode potential is transmitted through C to grid 1 and almost cuts the tube current off. The gain of the tube in this circuit is −59, and the capacitor C is effectively multiplied by a factor of 60. Also, for a 60-V change at the anode the voltage change at the grid is only 1 V; therefore the voltage drop across R, which governs the charging current of C, changes only from about 305 to 304 V when the anode potential falls by 60 V. When the tube is cut off again by the gate, there is an initial rapid change of the grid and plate potentials and then a more gradual change as the anode end of C charges towards +300 V through the 18-K resistor. The anode never reaches 300 V because it is caught at 250 V by the "catching diode." The slope of the linear or "ramp" portion in volts per second is given to a good approximation by $-AV/RC(1 - A)$ where V is the supply voltage (= E_{bb}) and $-A$ is the gain of the amplifier. A simple operational amplifier version of this circuit, for use at relatively low sweep frequencies (depending on the choice of amplifier), is

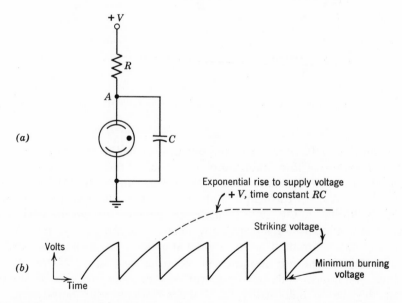

Fig. 4.108 (*a*) Relaxation oscillator based on a neon glow tube; (*b*) typical wave forms at A.

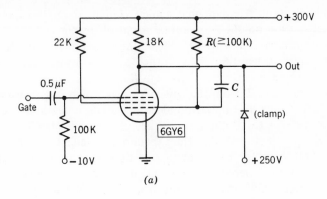

(a)

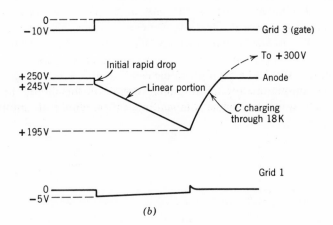

(b)

Fig. 4.109 (a) Miller sweep circuit; (b) waveforms during a sweep.

given in Fig. 4.110. Here the gating signal is applied to the gate of a field-effect transistor of low drain-source resistance in the ON state and very high drain-source resistance in the OFF state. During the OFF state the capacitor C charges through R and the output is slowly driven negative, whereas during the ON state C discharges quickly through the FET. The device is essentially an integrator with an arrangement that provides a constant input current. The operational amplifier is used in a single-ended configuration, and for applications requiring very slow, steady sweep voltages a chopper-stabilized type can be used. The capacitor C should preferably be a high-quality low-leakage variety, with polystyrene or comparable insulation.

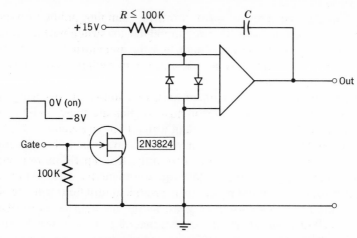

Fig. 4.110 Gated Miller integrator based on an operational amplifier.

If the Miller circuit is driven by a source of sharp current pulses it becomes a staircase-wave generator. One circuit of this type is shown in Fig. 4.111. When a positive pulse arrives it flows to earth through D_1 and does not affect the potential of C. A negative pulse, on the other hand, adds a small amount of charge to C and causes the output voltage to rise one step. Another way to produce a staircase output would be to insert an FET between R and the power supply in Fig. 4.110 and drive the gate of the FET with a pulse train.

A useful form of *ratemeter* circuit can be constructed by inserting a resistor R' between the summing point of the integrator and ground. The summing point is driven negative by an amount proportional to the number of negative pulses that arrive in unit time and inversely proportional to the

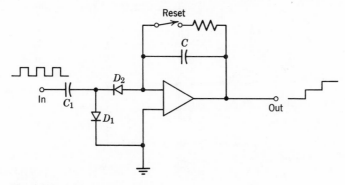

Fig. 4.111 Miller integrator used as a staircase generator.

rate at which charge can leak away from the summing point through R'. Different counting rates can be accommodated by switching the value of R'. For this purpose the pulses should first be standardized, for example, by applying the input pulses to a univibrator and feeding the output of the univibrator to the ratemeter circuit.

For many purposes it is convenient to have a source of fast-rising pulse signals, and the question therefore is how to generate these pulses. Sharp test pulses with rise times shorter than 1 nsec (1 nanosecond $= 10^{-9}$ sec) can be generated by using a mercury switch; however, pulse generators based on mercury switches are limited to rather low repetition frequencies, typically below a few kilocycles, and large pulse lengths. An obvious non-mechanical source of square pulses is the astable multivibrator in Fig. 4.97, with the time constants chosen to give a large mark-space ratio, that is, chosen so that the output has the appearance of a train of well-separated short pulses. The circuit in Fig. 4.97 is limited to mark-space ratios less than about 50:1, so that if very short pulses are being produced the repetition frequency may have to be inconveniently high. Mark-space ratios up to about 1000:1 can be obtained by using Scarrott's oscillator, whose basic circuit is shown in Fig. 4.112. In this circuit, which is a derivative of the cathode-coupled multivibrator, the time constant $R'C'$ is made large so that

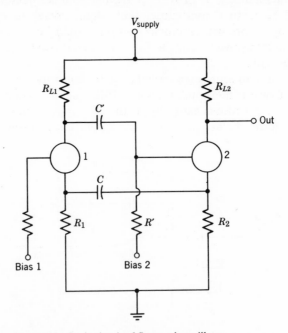

Fig. 4.112 Basic circuit of Scarrott's oscillator.

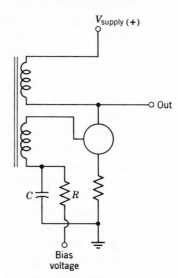

Fig. 4.113   Basic circuit of a blocking oscillator.

the potential of the control element of device 2 remains essentially constant after 2 has been switched ON by the positive square-wave signal from the load resistor of 1. Because of follower action the potential at the junction of R_2 and C is also constant, and the subsequent change of potential at the junction of R_1 and C, which has been driven positive by feedback through C, is governed by the time constant R_1C. When the potential at the cathode or emitter of device 1 has fallen sufficiently, the switching action is initiated again and 1 turns ON, switching 2 OFF. When 2 is turned hard OFF, there is no follower action at R_2, and the capacitor C can charge through R_2, but the junction of R_1 and C is held at a constant potential by follower action from device 1. The mark-space ratio is thus controlled by the ratio of R_1 to R_2. Because of the large difference in current through the devices implied by a large ratio of R_1 to R_2, it is usually necessary to specify two different types of device in transistorized versions of this circuit.

The blocking oscillator in Fig. 4.113 is an interesting circuit for producing very sharp high-current pulses of controlled mark-space ratio. In this circuit the transformer coil which forms the load is not tuned but is strongly coupled via the iron or ferrite core to the coil in the circuit of the control element in such a way that a positive-going output voltage results in a negative-going voltage at the control element. Suppose, initially, that the device is in a quiescent OFF state with the control element driven well negative. The control voltage will recover as C charges through R to the point at which the device begins to conduct. Positive feedback through the transformer then causes a very rapid transition to a fully conducting state. Once the device is ON the rate of current change is momentarily zero and so, therefore, is the voltage across the coil attached to the control element. The control element suddenly finds itself at a voltage corresponding to much less than full conduction and the switching process begins again, this time turning the device full OFF and driving the control element voltage negative once more. The duration of the ON state, which may be as short as 10 nsec, is governed mainly by the properties of the transformer, with the capacitor C having only a very small effect, and it is not easy to vary the duration once the transformer itself has been specified. The circuit has the basic virtue that the output pulse is produced by turning the active device hard ON, so that the leading edge in particular is not readily distorted by stray capacitance at the output. A further point for this arrangement is that it is economical of power, since nothing is drawn from the supply except during the very small duty cycle corresponding to delivery of a pulse. If required to deliver single pulses, the circuit can be biased off permanently and triggered into a conduction by a signal applied at the output terminal or through an auxiliary transformer winding. A blocking oscillator with a transistor as the active device should be equipped with diode clamps on collector and base to prevent the breakdown voltages from being exceeded.

Pulse Amplifiers

An amplifier that is intended to transmit fast-rising pulses faithfully must be able to respond to all the Fourier components of a pulse, that is, all the individual sine or cosine terms that must be added together as a Fourier series to reproduce the observed voltage or current as a function of time. Hence a pulse amplifier is necessarily a wideband amplifier. The response of the amplifier at low frequencies need not be particularly good, provided only that the low-frequency cutoff f_1 is considerably less than the repetition frequency of the pulses. The different effects of limited high- and low-frequency response are shown for pulses of various lengths in Fig. 4.114. A very limited high-frequency response produces effects analogous to integration, whereas a very limited low-frequency response gives effects analogous to differentiation. When the low-frequency response is a limiting factor, each stage of amplification adds a negative voltage excursion to any positive excursion already present in the input and a similar positive excursion at the end of any existing negative excursion. Consequently, after progressing through several such stages each pulse is followed by a train of ripples (Fig. 4.115) which interferes with subsequent pulses and in extreme cases may cause "paralysis" by overloading subsequent amplifier stages.

We noted in connection with the blocking oscillator that circuits for handling large pulses should be arranged so that the active devices are turned ON, rather than OFF, by each pulse. This implies that we should

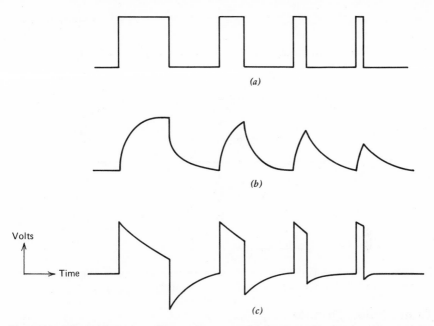

Fig. 4.114 Effect of limited amplifier response on pulse signals: (*a*) input pulses; (*b*) output of one stage with limited high-frequency response; (*c*) output of one stage with limited low-frequency response.

have an emitter follower based on an *npn* transistor as the output stage of a transistor amplifier for large positive pulses, whereas if the output stage is to produce negative pulses the emitter-follower should be based on a *pnp* transistor. If both positive-going and negative-going signals are to be handled faithfully, the output stage should be a dual emitter-follower as in Fig. 4.116. For tubes the absence of an analog to the *pnp* transistor has necessitated the design of a variety of "turn-on" stages for handling negative-going wave-fronts (e.g., the anode-follower and the White cathode-follower). Details of these and related circuits may be found in the references listed at the end of the chapter.

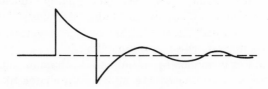

Fig. 4.115 Effect of several stages with limited low-frequency response.

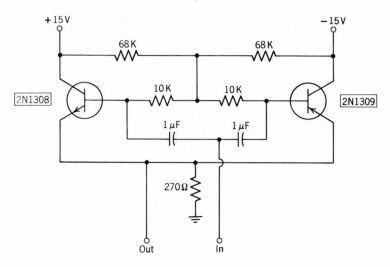

Fig. 4.116   Dual emitter-follower for both positive-going and negative-going wavefronts.

Diode Pulse Circuits

The basic function of a diode is that it conducts readily in one direction but not in the other. Thus a diode can be used to discriminate against pulses of one sign, as in the pulse-delay circuit of Fig. 4.103, which we now recall. Waveforms showing the operation of this circuit are given in Fig. 4.117. The initial trigger pulse (*a*) causes the univibrator to produce the square-wave (*b*). This square-wave is passed through a differentiating network made up of R and C which generates voltage spikes from the leading and trailing edges, as shown at (*c*). The spikes are taken through an emitter-follower and then to the diode, which transmits the negative-going spike almost unchanged but attenuates the positive-going spike in the ratio of R' to the diode's reverse resistance, which is about 10 M. The resulting output waveform, with the positive-going spike somewhat exaggerated, is shown at (*d*).

If the output side of the diode is connected not to ground but to a voltage V, as in Fig. 4.118, pulses are not transmitted unless their height exceeds V and the diode behaves as a pulse-height discriminator. If, however, the resistor R' is omitted, as in Fig. 4.119*a*, signals that go outside the voltage range between $+ V_1$ and $- V_2$ are lost, as indicated in Fig. 4.119*b*. The result is a diode clipper, so called because it clips the top or bottom off any waveform that exceeds the prescribed amplitude limits.

If a train of pulses is applied to a diode in the clipping configuration, as in Fig. 4.120, the action of successive pulses is to charge the capacitor C gradually up to the voltage V_1, at which point the pulses are no longer

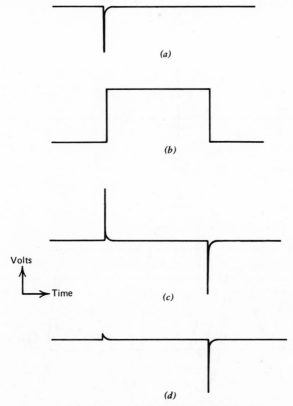

Fig. 4.117 Waveforms in pulse-delay circuit of Fig. 4.103: (a) trigger pulse; (b) univibrator output; (c) input and output of emitter-follower; (d) output from diode.

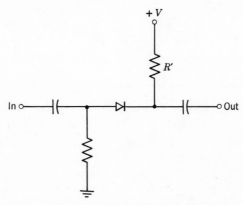

Fig. 4.118 Diode used as a pulse-height discriminator.

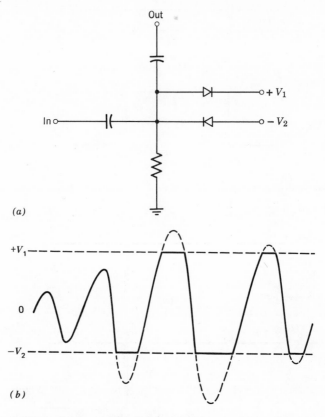

(a)

(b)

Fig. 4.119 (a) Diode clipping circuit; (b) input waveforms (dotted) and output waveforms (solid), showing clipping action.

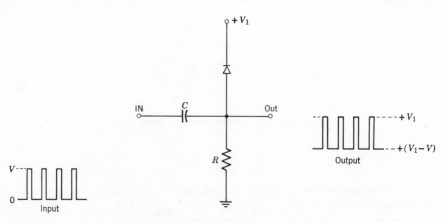

Fig. 4.120 Action of a diode as a dc restorer.

292

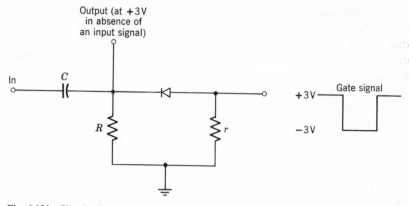

Fig. 4.121   Simple diode gate.

conducted through the diode and the top of the pulse train is clamped at V_1 in the output signal. For this to be effective the time constant RC should be much greater than the interval between pulses. If the diode is reversed, the bottom of the pulse train is clamped at V_1. This circuit is commonly used for dc restoration; that is, the conversion of a pulse train from some intermediate voltage level into an identical train with the tops or bottoms of the pulses fixed at ground potential.

Diodes also play a part in various kinds of *gate* circuit, many of which have important applications in digital logic, as described shortly. The simplest form of diode gate is shown in Fig. 4.121. In this circuit, when the gate signal swings negative, the diode behaves as a very high resistance and the input signal appears across the resistor R. When the gate signal swings positive, the diode becomes a short circuit and the input signal flows to earth through the small resistance r which represents the internal resistance of the gate-signal generator. The time constant RC needs to be large enough so that the output voltage does not change appreciably as a result of C charging through R while the gate signal is negative.

Digital Logic

Although most chemists with an interest in electronics are likely to have better things to do than building digital computers, nevertheless it is an advantage to have some understanding of the elements of digital logic. This is, first, because of its potential usefulness in situations in which the results of experiment appear in digital form, and, second, because of the variety of relatively inexpensive digital integrated circuits now available for use by people who can appreciate and exploit their properties.

Digital logic circuitry can be realized in a variety of ways; for example, RTL (resistor-transistor logic), DCTL (direct-coupled transistor logic), DL (diode logic), CML (current-mode = nonsaturated transistor logic), DTL (diode-transistor logic), TTL (transistor-transistor logic), and TDL (tunnel diode logic). The name in each case reflects the manner in which a basic gate element is constructed. Digital integrated circuits most often use diode-transistor logic but other forms are common also. The word "digital" implies a system of numbers based only on integers; in practice the system is even more limited than that, being restricted to the binary integers 0 and 1. Digital logic circuits are such that the input and output voltages are necessarily at one of two discrete levels that correspond to the two binary integers; for example, we might choose ground to correspond to logical 0 and $+3$ V to be logical 1. From each output the signal level may "fan out" to a number of other logic circuits and each individual circuit may receive a number of inputs from other circuits. To begin with the simplest possibility, suppose that we have a circuit whose output is responsive to one input alone and is such that when the input $A = 0$ the output $B = 1$ and when $A = 1$ the output $B = 0$. We should describe this as a NOT circuit, which performs the logical operation $B = not$ A, or $B = \overline{A}$. (The operation $B = A$ or "B is A" would be a simpler example still, but no circuit is required for this.) The more complex circuit with two inputs has several alternative ways of responding. First, if the output C is logical 0, except when both inputs A and B are 1, we have an AND circuit, which performs the logical operation $C = A$ and B, or in the notation of Boolean algebra, $C = A \cdot B$. A second kind of response would have the output C at the level 1 whenever input A or input B was at the level 1, but if both A and B were 0 then the output C would be 0 also. This would be an OR circuit, which performs the logical operation $C = A$ or B, represented as $C = A + B$. If the output of the AND circuit were inverted so that C was 0 only when A and B were both 1, the result would be the not-and, or NAND, circuit, which performs the operation $C = not$ (A and B), or in algebraic form $C = \overline{A \cdot B}$. Finally, if the output of the OR circuit were inverted so that C was zero whenever A or B was 1, the result would be a not-or, or NOR, circuit, with the operation $C = not$ (A or B), which in algebraic form is $C = \overline{A + B}$. The logical relations embodied in the algebraic statements can be visualized readily with the aid of the Venn diagrams in Fig. 4.122. Beside each Venn diagram is shown a generalized circuit symbol for the operation. The number of inputs to each kind of circuit can be increased to give statements of the type $E = \overline{A + B + C + D}$ and so on.

The circuit symbols shown at the right of Fig. 4.122 are not universal; Fig. 4.123 shows some alternative forms that are used, for example, by Texas

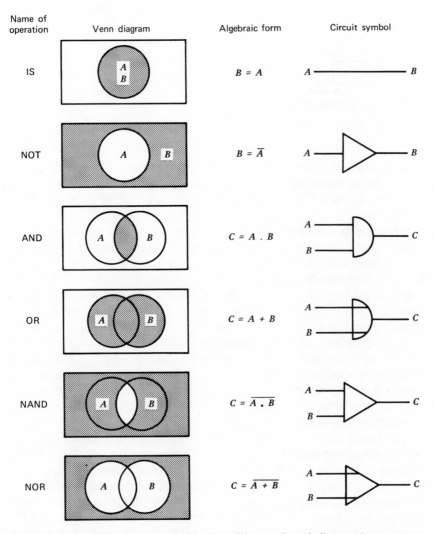

Name of operation	Venn diagram	Algebraic form	Circuit symbol

Fig. 4.122 Logic operations represented by Venn diagrams. In each diagram the areas corresponding to the right-hand side of the algebraic equation are represented by circles; the area corresponding to the left-hand side of the equation is shaded.

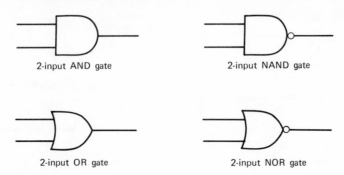

2-input AND gate   2-input NAND gate

2-input OR gate   2-input NOR gate

Fig. 4.123 Alternative representations of noninverting and inverting gates.

Instruments and Motorola for describing their digital integrated circuits. A slight disadvantage of these forms is that they take longer to draw by hand than those in Fig. 4.122. A point to observe is the use of the small open circle to indicate an inverted signal.

It is now time for some definitions. The form of logic used is described as *positive logic* if a circuit's low voltage state (or most negative voltage) is defined as logical 0 and its high voltage state (or most positive voltage) as logical 1. For *negative logic* the low voltage is logical 1 and the high voltage logical 0. We have already noted the use of the term fan out to describe the number of succeeding logic circuits that can be driven by a single output. When the situation requires more circuits to be driven than the single output can supply current for, it is necessary to insert a *buffer*, which is essentially a power amplifier, between the output and the group of circuits to be driven. Similarly, if a multiple input device is required to have more inputs than there are leads available, that is, if the *fan in* needs to be increased, an *expander* can be used to bring several inputs together before they reach the main circuit. (It would not do simply to bring more than one output directly to the same input because the current-carrying capability of an input may be limited and because the *noise-margin* might become too small for reliable operation; that is, the likelihood of obtaining a spurious input signal through the superposition of random noise signals from different outputs would be increased.) The *propagation delay* is a measure of the time required for an input signal to produce a response at the output. For simple TTL or DTL gates this delay is of the order of 30 nsec with currently available integrated circuits. The propagation delay is usually somewhat shorter than the rise time and fall time for a square pulse output. Nonsaturated CML gates commonly have propagation delays of the order of 10 nsec.

Two practical realizations of a positive logic NAND gate are shown in Fig. 4.124, the first being an example of TTL and the second DTL. In the

TTL form the inputs are taken to emitter leads of a multiple-emitter transistor. If all of these inputs are at $+3$ V (logical 1), the collector-base diode of the input transistor behaves as a short circuit, the second transistor is turned on, and the transistor between Y and ground behaves as a short circuit, so that the output Y is at ground (logical 0); but if one or more of the input leads is connected to ground (logical 0) the input transistor conducts, its collector-base diode is reverse-biased, the second transistor is turned off, and the transistor between Y and ground is no longer a short circuit. Simultaneously the transistor between Y and the $+5$ V line begins to conduct and the potential of Y rises to about $+3$ V (logical 1). In the DTL form the transistor is turned off when any one of the three inputs is at or near ground, since the base is then fixed at earth potential or slightly below. If, however, all of the inputs are at $+3$ V or thereabouts, the diodes in the base lead are forward-biased and the transistor is turned hard on. With the transistor on the output is at about $+0.5$ V, whereas with the transistor off the output is $+5$ V unless a diode clamp is used to keep the output below some fixed level, say $+3.5$ V. The caption for the DTL gate points out that in terms of positive logic this is a NAND gate, since the output is 0 only when all three inputs are at 1, but in terms of negative logic it is a NOR gate, with the output at 1 only when all three inputs are at 0. An AND or NAND gate can also serve as a *pulse coincidence detector*, for if two positive-going pulses are applied simultaneously to a 2-input gate the result is an output pulse that is positive-going with the AND gate and negative-going with the

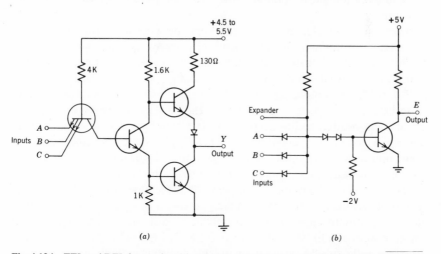

(a) (b)

Fig. 4.124 TTL and DTL forms of positive NAND gate: (a) 3-input NAND gate, $Y = \overline{A \cdot B \cdot C}$, positive logic (one section of Texas Instruments SN5410); (b) 3-input NAND-NOR gate, $E = \overline{ABC}$, positive logic; $E = \overline{A + B + C}$, negative logic (Motorola MC252 e.g.).

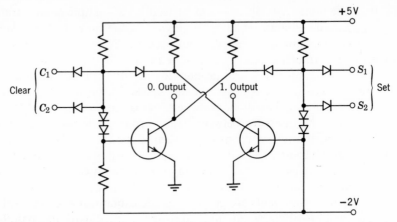

Fig. 4.125   Flip-flop made from two DTL 3-input NAND gates.

NAND gate. If the input pulses should arrive separately, however, there would be no output pulse. The time-resolution of the coincidence detector for sharp input pulses is approximately equal to the sum of the gate rise time and fall time. To make an *anticoincidence detector* it is necessary only to use the pulse from the coincidence detector to operate gates that will prevent the input pulses from entering subsequent pulse-handling circuits. For this purpose the input pulses need to be slightly delayed so that they will arrive at their separate gates simultaneously with the pulse from the coincidence detector.

The other main element of a digital logic network is the flip-flop, binary, or bistable multivibrator, which generally serves as a short-term storage device for digital information. (Magnetic devices with no power consumption are preferred for long-term storage.) A flip-flop can be made, as shown in Fig. 4.125, by connecting two NAND gates back-to-back; if one output is at the 0 level, the other is necessarily at the 1 level, and vice-versa, and there is sufficient positive feedback to ensure fast switching. The flip-flop has two states, labeled 0 and 1, such that after a SET command it is always in the 1 state, and after a CLEAR (= RESET) command it is always in the 0 state. In Fig. 4.125, when the flip-flop is in the 1 state, the output 1 is at the logical 1 level. A CLEAR command consists of bringing the CLEAR input to ground potential and thereby switching output 1 into the 0 state if the flip-flop were initially in its 1 state or leaving the situation unchanged if the flip-flop were initially in the 0 state. A COMPLEMENT command switches the state of the flip-flop, regardless of what the state actually is.

Many more or less elaborate versions of the flip-flop are available as integrated circuits. In the simple "*R-S* flip-flop" circuit of Fig. 4.125 it is not certain what the outcome will be if identical input signals are applied simultaneously to the set and clear terminals. In a *J-K* flip-flop this ambiguity is absent; simultaneous SET and CLEAR inputs at one logic level cause the state to reverse and simultaneous inputs at the other level leaving the state unaltered. In many applications it is convenient to have a train of *clock pulses*, typically of repetition frequency near 10 MHz and duration 20 to 100 nsec, which are used to synchronize the various logical operations taking place in a group of interconnected circuits. The arrival of a clock pulse triggers a flip-flop into a state governed by its SET and CLEAR inputs; in the absence of a clock pulse the state of the flip-flop does not change. A clock-pulse input for the circuit of Fig. 4.125 could be arranged as follows. Suppose that inputs S'_1, S'_2, S'_3 are taken to S_1 through a NAND gate and inputs C'_1, C'_2, C'_3 to C_1, through another NAND gate. If S'_1 and C'_1 are now connected and held at the 0 level, then S_1 and C_1 must both be at the 1 level and the state of the flip-flop is governed by the states of S_2 and C_2 or by the most recent input if S_2 and C_2 also are both at the 1 level. When the combined S'_1 and C'_1 inputs are held at the 1 level the NAND gates are free to respond to the inputs S'_2, S'_3, C'_2, C'_3. Thus S'_1 and C'_1 together form the clock pulse input and the flip-flop can change its state in response to S'_2, S'_3, C'_2, C'_3 only while this input is at the 1 level. The inputs S_2 and C_2 not affected by the clock pulse can serve as *direct set* and *direct clear* inputs, respectively.

Figure 4.126 shows a circuit symbol for a flip-flop controlled by clock pulses as far as the C_1, C_2, S_1, and S_2 inputs are concerned and which may also be set or cleared with the S_D and C_D inputs independently of the clock. This figure is copied from the data sheet for a Texas Instruments type

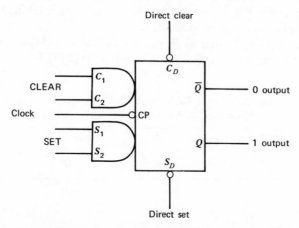

Fig. 4.126 Symbol for a flip-flop with gated SET and CLEAR, and direct SET and CLEAR, with clock pulse operation.

Table 4.12 Truth Table for the Flip-Flop
of Fig. 4.126 in the R-S Mode

State of Inputs at t_n				Output at t_{n+1}
S_1	S_2	C_1	C_2	Q
0	X	0	X	Q_n
0	X	X	0	Q_n
X	0	0	X	Q_n
X	0	X	0	Q_n
0	X	1	1	0
X	0	1	1	0
1	1	0	X	1
1	1	X	0	1
1	1	1	1	Indeterminate

SN15 848, as is the *truth table* for the R-S mode (Table 4.12), which shows
how the state of this flip-flop at time t_{n+1}, after a clock pulse, is dependent
on the state of the inputs at t_n, before the pulse. The symbol Q_n means that
the state is unchanged; a symbol $\bar{Q}_n$ would mean that the state had changed
either from 1 to 0 or from 0 to 1. The symbol X means that either a logical
1 or a logical 0 may be present at the input.

In the last line of this table we see that with a simultaneous 1 level applied
to all inputs the state of the output after the clock pulse is indeterminate.
To use this circuit in the J-K mode it is necessary only to connect S_2 to $\bar{Q}$
and C_2 to Q, since $\bar{Q}$ and Q can never be the same and the possibility of all
inputs being at the 1 level is therefore eliminated. The resulting truth table
for the J-K mode is given in Table 4.13.

A "D-type flip-flop," such as Texas Instruments SN5474, has a single
data input D, corresponding to S_1 in the truth table (4.13). In a "master-slave

Table 4.13 Truth Table for the Flip-Flop of
Fig. 4.126 in the J-K Mode

Time: t_n		Time: t_{n+1}
$S_1 = J$	$C_1 = K$	Q
0	0	Q_n
0	1	0
1	0	1
1	1	$\bar{Q}_n$

flip-flop" two flip-flops are connected and the clock pulse brings about the sequence of operations: (*a*) isolate slave from master; (*b*) enter information from gates to master; (*c*) disconnect gates; (*d*) transfer information from master to slave. With this arrangement information can be read from the slave at the same time that new information is being read into the master, with a significant over-all saving of time.

Included in the list of references to this chapter is a *Scientific American* article that describes how digital logic elements can be combined to produce circuits for converting numbers from decimal to binary form and back again and for carrying out arithmetic operations such as addition and multiplication on the binary numbers so obtained. Probably of more interest to the chemist, however, are the applications of digital logic to pulse counting, to a digital clock, to analog-to-digital conversion, and, by the use of stepping motors, to digital control of mechanical systems.

A block diagram of a basic *pulse counter* is given in Fig. 4.127. The first block contains the source of pulses, which is typically a Geiger tube or a photomultiplier; these devices are included among the transducers discussed in Chapter VI. The succeeding boxes, from the amplifier to the bistable multivibrator, represent elements whose operation we have already considered. The output of the "scale of 2" is in either the logical 0 or the logical 1 state, and the state changes each time a pulse is received, a complete cycle of the output requiring two pulses to be received at the input. This initial scale of 2 can, if desired, be regarded as the first element of the decade scaler by which the number of pulses received up to a given time is totaled and converted into decimal notation for supply to the bank of "nixie" or "dekatron" tubes, group of electromechanical relays, or other visual readout system. The scaler will include devices for starting and stopping a count and for returning the recorded count to zero. The main question to be considered now is how a group of flip-flops can be used to record the total count in binary or decimal form.

There are a number of ways of combining flip-flops into counters, two extreme cases giving rise to the types known as *serial*, or *ripple*, counters and *clocked* counters. In a serial counter the output from one flip-flop is immediately used to drive the next flip-flop, so that in the absence of feedback, for example, the first would undergo one complete cycle for every two input pulses, the second one cycle for every four, the third one cycle for every eight, and so on. This method is very useful for high-speed counting systems in which the main function is one of frequency division or in which the total count is to be read out only after the counter is stopped. In a long chain of flip-flops it is likely that successive input pulses may arrive in less time than it takes for one pulse to propagate or "ripple" along the chain so that while counting is in progress the state of the system is not a simple measure of the

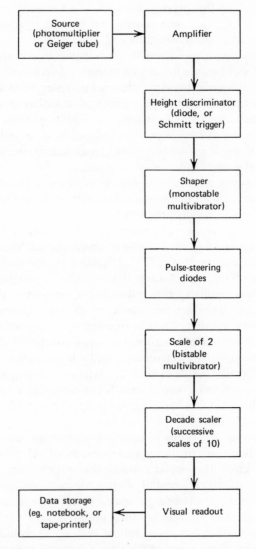

Fig. 4.127 Block diagram of a basic pulse-counting experiment. (Ground reference connections to each block not shown.)

number of counts accumulated. In a clocked counter, on the other hand, the flip-flops undergo transitions simultaneously on the arrival of each clock pulse (master-slave flip-flops are ideal for this application) and the state of the system can be read out at any time without interrupting the count. This type of counter is commonly used in decoding systems (e.g., for converting binary numbers into decimal form). The decade scaler of Fig. 4.127 would normally use serial counting.

Serial or ripple counters are of two types, namely *straight binary* and *feedback*. In a straight binary ripple counter containing n flip-flops the input frequency is divided by 2^n and the states of the successive counters represent the total counts in the form of a binary number; for example, if successive states were 01011, the total number would be $2^1 + 2^3 + 2^4 = 26$. This is illustrated in Fig. 4.128. In one form of feedback ripple counter the

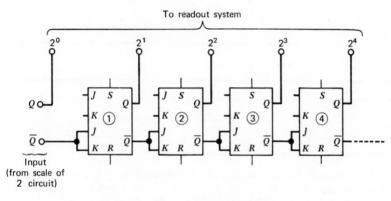

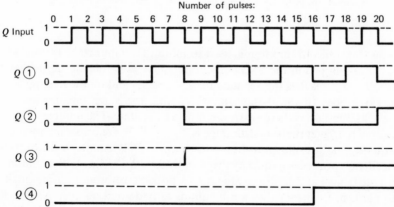

Fig. 4.128 Interconnections and waveforms in a straight binary ripple counter using J-K flip-flops. Note that the over-all zero state is chosen as having all $Q = 0$ and all $\bar{Q} = 1$ and that the flip-flop transitions occur when both J and K inputs go from the 0 state to the 1 state.

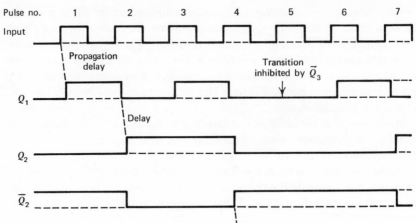

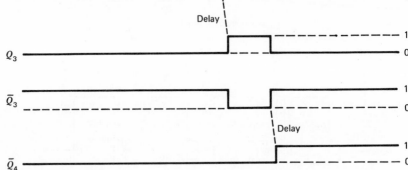

Fig. 4.129 Waveforms in a feedback counter with $n = 3$. An extra binary (4) is added to produce a scale of 10. Note that when pulse 5 causes the input level to go from $0 \rightarrow 1$ the level of $\bar{Q}_3$ is still 0 because of the propagation delay, and so Q_1 is prevented from responding.

output from the nth flip-flop is used to inhibit the input stage so that while the nth flip-flop is in the 1 stage the input stage must remain in the 0 state. The nth stage reaches the 1 state after 2^{n-1} pulses and on the next pulse the nth stage goes to the 0 state, in which the first stage remains, and the $(n + 1)$th flip-flop is thereby triggered into the 1 state. The number of pulses required to trigger the $(n + 1)$th stage is $2^{n-1} + 1$. Waveforms corresponding to the process are shown in Fig. 4.129 for $n = 3$. A counter with this type of feedback produces frequency division by 3, 5, 9, 17, 33, etc. By combining straight binary and feedback stages it is possible to produce a circuit that will perform frequency division by almost any desired number. Within the feedback loop the stages are linked as in Fig. 4.128. To apply the feedback in such a way that, when $Q_n = 1$, the $(J + K)$ input of stage 1 cannot make the transition from 0 to 1, it is necessary only to take the $\bar{Q}_n$ output back to a J or K input which shares an AND gate with one of the two inputs that make up the $J + K$ input of stage 1. In a flip-flop with more than one J or K input, such as those in Fig. 4.128, it is the usual practice to take the several inputs of the same kind through an AND gate so that the effective inputs are $J = J_1 \cdot J_2 \cdot J_3$ etc., and $K = K_1 \cdot K_2 \cdot K_3$ etc. This kind of feedback is therefore easy to arrange. It remains to ensure that on the 0 to 1 transition of the input signal, to which the first flip-flop is prevented from responding, the nth stage will undergo the required transition into the 0 state. To do this we note first that when the nth stage undergoes its transition into the 1 state both the input to stage 1 and $\bar{Q}_{n-1}$ are changing from the 0 state to the 1 state and that the expected transition in the nth stage will still occur if one part of its $(J + K)$ input is connected to $\bar{Q}_{n-1}$ as usual and the other part is connected to the input of stage 1. Then, when the nth stage is to go back to the 0 state, the input from $\bar{Q}_{n-1}$ is stationary at the 1 level, and, according to the truth table (Table 4.13), with either J or K at the 1 level we can expect a transition of the nth stage when the other one of the J-K pair undergoes a transition into the 1 level. Therefore to achieve the desired behavior we can connect K_n to $\bar{Q}_{n-1}$ and J_n to the input, or vice-versa. Fig. 4.130 gives the resulting circuit for $n = 3$, with the AND gates for J and K specifically indicated. Several other useful ways of connecting flip-flops to make scales of 10 and other numbers have been devised and may be found, for example, in the application notes supplied by manufacturers of digital integrated circuits.

A straightforward application of digital scalers occurs in a mains-operated *digital clock*, of which a block diagram is given in Fig. 4.131. The mains voltage at either 50 or 60 Hz is broken down with a tube-filament transformer and a 1-K potentiometer to the point at which it will operate a Schmitt trigger, whose output becomes a 50- or 60-Hz square wave. The *seconds*, *minutes*, *hours*, and *days* counts are obtained by dividing the mains frequency by 50 or 60, 60, 60, and 24, in that order. A manual reset button, which returns

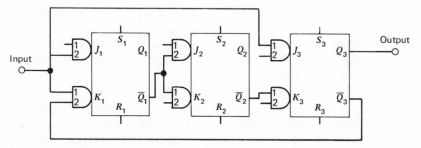

Fig. 4.130   Use of three flip-flops with feedback to produce a scale of 5.

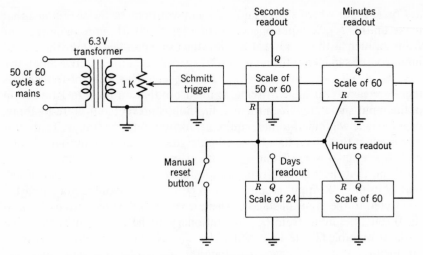

Fig. 4.131   Block diagram of a mains-operated digital clock.

all flip-flops to the zero state and sets the readout units to zero, is normally provided to allow starting the clock at an arbitrary zero time. Methods of constructing scales of 50, 60, and 24 are shown in Fig. 4.132.

The subject of *analog-to-digital* and *digital-to-analog converters* is a large one and we can do no more than consider the basic elements here. First, in digital-to-analog the heart of the converter is a flip-flop register in which the digital information is stored and a potential divider network constructed so that the output of each flip-flop will contribute its correct relative amount to the output voltage from the whole network. Level amplifiers are used to ensure that the output produced from each flip-flop is sharply defined— commonly at ground for the 0 state and -10 V for the 1 state. The contributions from the separate flip-flops are finally combined with a summing amplifier, as in Fig. 4.133. With this arrangement an analog voltage can be made to follow a continuously rising digital count, or, if a second flip-flop register for negative pulses can be used to subtract from the output, the analog voltage will follow a digital input arising from a measured quantity that can vary up or down with time. We assume here that the input pulses are widely enough spaced that the effects of propagation delay in the serial register can be neglected.

The basic element of any analog-to-digital conversion system is the *comparator*, which is a device whose properties are similar to those of a Schmitt trigger; that is, if the input is below a certain voltage level the output is in the 0 state and if the input is above this level the output is in the 1 state. With the range of the input divided into 2^N subranges it is possible to express the analog information in digital form with a precision of N binary digits, or "bits." For low-precision and high-speed conversion it is satisfactory to use a separate comparator for each range simultaneously, in which case $2^N - 1$ comparators are required for N bits of information. An example of a 3-bit simultaneous converter is provided by the digital thermometer discussed in the first section of this chapter. When moderately high precision is required, however, the simultaneous method becomes expensive because of the large number of comparators required.

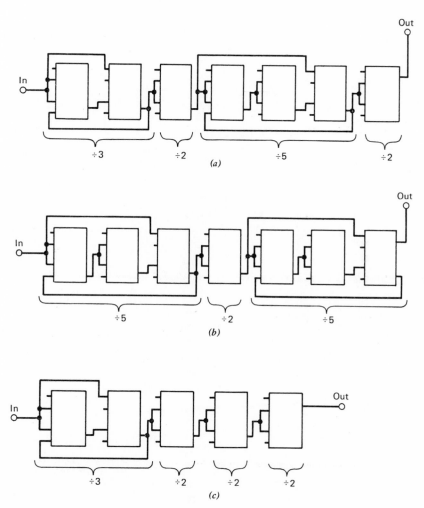

Fig. 4.132 Scales of (a) 60, (b) 50, and (c) 24 for use in the circuit of Fig. 4.131.

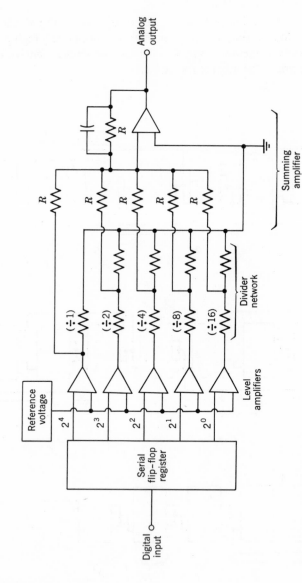

Fig. 4.133 Digital to analog converter.

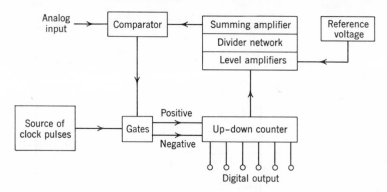

Fig. 4.134 Block diagram of a continuous analog to digital converter.

Figure 4.134 illustrates an analog-to-digital converter with continuous feedback. Many digital voltmeters operate in this manner. Here the analog voltage is compared with a voltage obtained by digital-to-analog conversion of the contents of a flip-flop register. The flip-flop register itself is driven upward by one increment if the comparator output shows that the analog input is too high and down by one increment if the comparator shows that the analog input is too low, a comparison being made each time the clock-pulse source goes through a cycle. This type of conversion is capable of excellent precision with analog inputs that do not change too rapidly in comparison to the product of the clock frequency and the size of the increments. When this form of continuous conversion is too slow, it is both preferable and convenient to use a successive approximation procedure in which the register is set first at half the maximum voltage, then at three-quarters or a quarter, depending on comparator response, then at the half-way point in the remaining voltage range, and so on. For N bits of information only N steps are required. A control gate is required to direct pulses first to the largest power of 2 in the register, then to the second largest, and so on; otherwise the circuitry is basically the same as in Fig. 4.134. For a fuller discussion of conversion methods and sources of error the reader should consult the references given at the end of this chapter.

In the case of analog signals a convenient device for converting an electrical signal into a proportional linear or rotary displacement is available in the form of the servomotor, of which numerous types exist. With digital signals a similar conversion is made possible by the use of a *stepping motor*. Like servomotors, stepping motors are of many types (cf. Chapter II), but most precision types have four leads plus a common lead, and stepping, that is, rotation through a small angle, is brought about by a prescribed sequence of pulses applied to the four signal leads. For linear motion

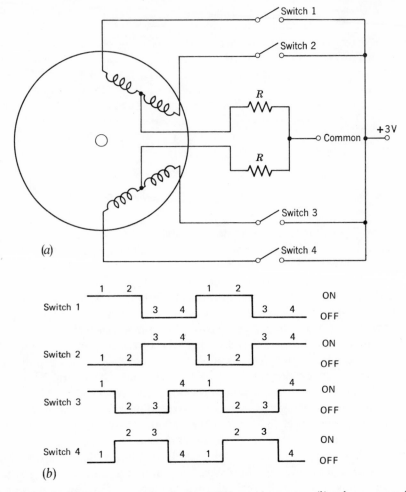

Fig. 4.135 (*a*) Wiring diagram of a Slo-Syn HS50 stepping motor; (*b*) pulse sequence for clockwise rotation.

translators that operate on the same principle are available. A preset *indexer* can be used to provide a switching sequence to drive a motor or translator through a controlled number of steps. Commonly used stepping motors, such as the Superior Electric Slo-Syn or United Shoe Machinery Responsyn, can be obtained to operate at speeds up to about 800 rpm, with an angular resolution between $\frac{1}{100}$ and $\frac{1}{1000}$ of a revolution, depending on the particular model. A typical motor wiring diagram and a switching sequence graph for clockwise rotation are given in Fig. 4.135. For counterclockwise rotation the sequence of steps is reversed. The details of the motor switching sequence generally differ from one model to another. Motors are available to operate from supplies up to 100 V dc, with currents of the order of 100 mA per winding, but for the kind of switching circuits that we have been considering it is preferable to use a low-voltage motor such as the Slo-Syn HS50, for which the windings are rated at 3 V and 4 A. This current requirement is too high for the output of an ordinary logic circuit but might be obtained by the use of an emitter-follower or Darlington booster. Since the stepping speed of this particular motor is limited to about 1000 steps per second, it would not be necessary for the booster to be capable of a particularly fast response. Stepping motors have many applications in automatic control equipment, including star-tracking devices for telescopes, preprogrammed machine tools, and automatic tape and card feeds for computers. Undoubtedly a great many potential applications have yet to be realized.

Thyratrons and Silicon-Controlled Rectifiers

We conclude this section by discussing the specialized power-switching devices whose circuit symbols are given in Fig. 4.136. Both devices have the property of allowing the flow of a large anode current to be initiated by a small signal in the form of a voltage applied to the grid of the thyratron or current applied to the gate of the silicon controlled rectifier (SCR). Further, once the flow of anode current has been initiated, it continues to flow in both cases until the anode supply voltage is removed from the thyratron or until the anode current supply drops below a minimum "holding current" through the SCR. Small, rugged SCR's and "thyristors" are at present available with current ratings of about 300 mA to 500 A and inverse voltage ratings of 20 to more than 1000 V rms. The thyratron's days are numbered,

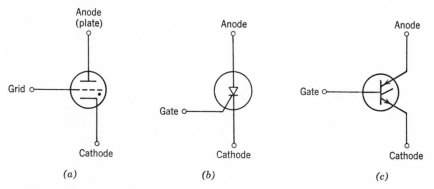

Fig. 4.136 (a) Circuit symbol for a thyratron; (b) and (c), alternative symbols for a silicon-controlled rectifier or thyristor.

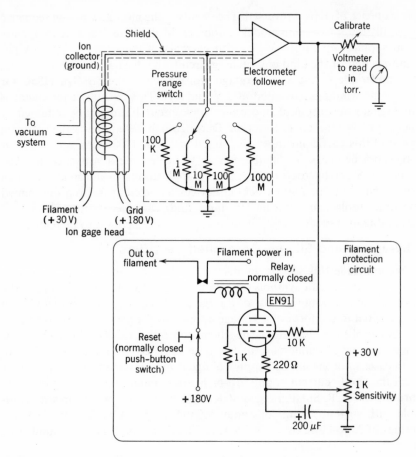

Fig. 4.137   Ion gage filament protection circuit using a small thyratron.

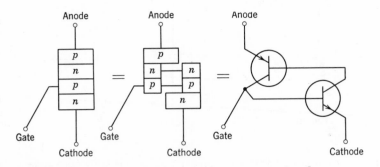

Fig. 4.138   Two-transistor equivalent of SCR.

nevertheless thyratrons are still being manufactured and occur in many pieces of equipment in current use. Therefore it is worthwhile to give them brief attention.

The circuit symbol of Fig. 4.136a differs from that of a triode tube only by the presence of the dot which indicates that the tube is gas-filled. The internal construction of a thyratron is very different from that of an ordinary triode; in particular the control grid usually takes the form of a plate with a single hole through the middle. If the anode voltage is applied to the thyratron while the grid is at a negative potential, the electrons emitted by the cathode cannot pass through the hole and the tube is cut off. Then, once the grid potential has been allowed to rise, conduction sets in, the gas (commonly hydrogen) is ionized, and a continuous discharge capable of carrying a large current forms between cathode and anode. In this condition the grid has no further control over the anode current, which can be cut off again only by removing the anode voltage. When a thyratron is operated from an ac source such as the mains, the anode voltage drops below zero once during each cycle, thereby turning off the current, and the grid regains its control in time for the next positive anode voltage excursion. The output is pulsed direct current, since the tube conducts only when the anode is positive. Figure 4.137 shows the application of a thyratron to a protective relay system for an ionization gage. When the gage pressure rises to a level chosen by the setting of the sensitivity control, the thyratron fires and a relay in series with the gage filament opens. Other pressure-sensitive circuits may be protected by pairs of contacts on the same relay. The "reset" button serves to interrupt the anode current and return control to the grid when the pressure rise has subsided or the position of the range switch has been altered. Other applications of thyratrons include the operation of electro-magnetic valves in such devices as automatic titrators, and ac power controls for motors, heaters, and lighting systems. Thyratrons have also been used a good deal in the past in time-base circuits for use at sweep repetition frequencies below about 10 kHz.

The SCR is a four-layer *pnpn* device which, as shown in Fig. 4.138, may be regarded as equivalent to a combination of a *pnp* and an *npn* transistor. We see that if the gate is at the same potential as the cathode, or slightly negative, the *npn* transistor is cut off and no current can flow from the anode. Then, if the gate is made sufficiently positive to allow a small base current to flow through the *npn* transistor, this in turn supplies a base current for the *pnp* transistor. The *pnp* base current is amplified and appears as a collector current that adds to the *npn* base current. Thus there is a positive feedback loop, and a small gate pulse can cause a regenerative switching action so that the device ends in a highly conducting ON state. The current flow from anode to cathode has to be above a minimum "holding current" level in order for the positive feedback to be able to maintain the ON state; this is because the α-parameters of the transistors, which give the probability that a carrier will penetrate the base region before being lost by recombination, fall off sharply at low collector currents. If the forward voltage on the SCR is very large, it may trigger ON, even in the absence of any gate current, through breakdown caused by acceleration of minority carriers. The *peak forward blocking voltage* is the maximum value of anode potential at which it can be certain that this type of triggering will not occur. Triggering can be brought about intentionally either by turning on a steady gate current or by injecting a brief current pulse. In the second mode of operation it is often convenient to use a triggering pulse derived from a *unijunction transistor* (UJT; Fig. 4.139), which is a device that can deliver a current pulse when the emitter reaches a predetermined potential. In the circuit of Fig. 4.139c the current will suddenly begin to flow from emitter to base 2 when the emitter potential has risen to $\eta \cdot V_{BB}$, where the parameter η is known as the "intrinsic standoff ratio" of the unijunction transistor and is commonly in the range 0.5 to 0.6. This emitter potential corresponds to the point at which the junction between the p-type emitter region and the n-type base region just becomes forward-biased. When the emitter potential is less than $\eta \cdot V_{BB}$, the junction is reverse-biased and the impedance between emitter and base 2 is very high. Many ingenious applications have been

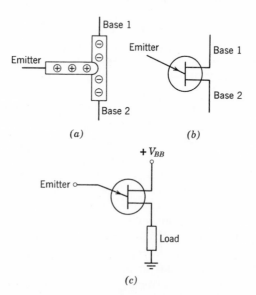

Fig. 4.139 Unijunction transistor: (*a*) construction; (*b*) circuit symbol; (*c*) usual biasing arrangement.

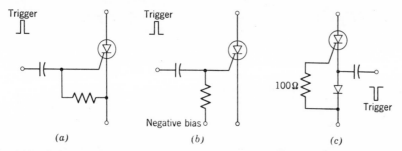

Fig. 4.140 Pulse triggering circuits for an SCR: (*a*) and (*b*) for positive-going pulses; (*c*) for negative-going pulses. In (*b*) the OFF state in absence of triggering is reinforced by applying a *small* amount of negative bias to the gate. The gate may be clamped with a diode to prevent the negative gate voltage rating from being exceeded.

found for both the SCR and the UJT. Here we consider a few basic kinds of circuit; for further discussion and advanced applications the reader should consult the appropriate references in the list at the end of this chapter.

In Fig. 4.140 are shown some circuits for applying triggering pulses to an SCR. The amplitude of such a pulse need be only as great as the minimum dc voltage and current triggering requirements (e.g., 3 V and 80 mA for a General Electric 35-A SCR, type 2N683), whereas the necessary duration of the pulse is governed by the time required for the load current to build up and so is greater for an inductive than for a resistive load. Switching times are typically of the order of microseconds or less for turning ON; the time required for an SCR to regain its forward-blocking voltage capability after the anode voltage is removed is considerably greater, being in the range of 12 to 50 μsec or more, larger devices in general having longer turn-off times. The rated gate dissipation can be exceeded momentarily during pulse triggering, provided the product of maximum dissipation and duty cycle does not exceed the power rating.

Figure 4.141*a* and *b* show two ways of using a small switch carrying a few milliamperes in conjunction with an SCR to control a pulsed dc current that may be several hundred amperes. With two such circuits in parallel, and using a double-pole switch, an ac current can be controlled (see Fig. 4.141*c*). In these circuits the ac signal applied to the gate is in phase with the ac voltage on the anode, and simple on/off control is obtained. In the more elaborate circuit of Fig. 4.142 the phase of the gate signal, hence the turn-off time, is delayed by an amount dependent on the setting of the 50-K potentiometer, and the power delivered to the load during the period that the SCR is forward-biased is varied accordingly. During each negative half-cycle the capacitor C is reset at a negative voltage. This type of circuit is often used for motor-speed and light-dimming controls. If the load requires an ac

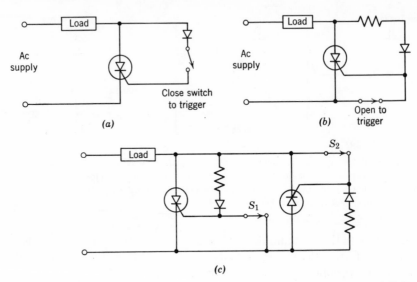

Fig. 4.141 Use of an on/off switch to control the current through an SCR: (*a*) and (*b*) for a rectified current; (*c*) for an alternating current through the load. (S_1 and S_2 are sections of one double-pole switch).

supply, the full-wave phase control circuit of Fig. 4.143 can be used. The negative voltage to which the capacitor C_1 is reset when SCR1 is not conducting is related here to the negative voltage across the load in such a way that if SCR2 is turned off the voltage across C_1 will never rise high enough to trigger SCR1. If SCR2 is on during the complete half-cycle in which SCR1 is reverse-biased, then SCR1 is fully on during the other half-cycle. Thus a single phase-control will serve for both SCR's.

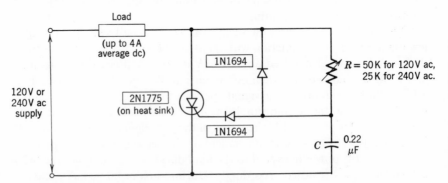

Fig. 4.142 SCR phase-control circuit for controlling the amount of dc power delivered to a load. (Adapted from the General Electric SCR Manual.)

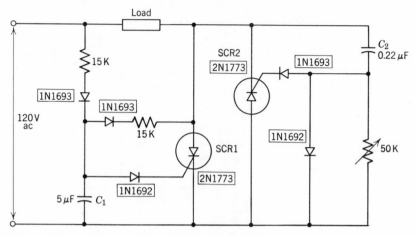

Fig. 4.143 Circuit for full-wave phase control. (Adapted from the General Electric SCR Manual.)

Many triggering circuits for SCR's can be based on the unijunction transistor relaxation oscillator, whose basic circuit is given in Fig. 4.144. In this circuit the capacitor C_1 charges through R_1 until the emitter junction becomes forward-biased. The original reverse-biased condition was maintained by the flow of a small current through R_{B1}, the interbase resistance (typically 5 K), and R_{B2}. The much greater flow of current as C_1 discharges through the emitter and R_{B1} (and any parallel load) is sufficient to keep the emitter junction forward-biased for the duration of a short current pulse, after which C_1 begins to charge again. The pulse repetition frequency is given, to a good approximation, by

$$\frac{1}{f} = -2 \cdot 3 R_1 C_1 \log (1 - \eta), \qquad (4.73)$$

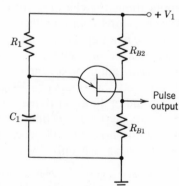

Fig. 4.144 *UJT* relaxation oscillator, frequency given by equation 4.73.

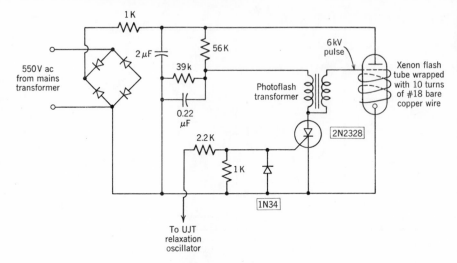

Fig. 4.145 Stroboscope for 100-μsec flashes, based on an SCR and a UJT relaxation oscillator with variable repetition frequency. (Adapted from Reference 6.)

where η is the intrinsic standoff ratio. Usually R_{B1} is 100 Ω or less, V_1 is between 10 and 35 V, and R_1 is between 3 K and 3 M. If the output pulses are taken directly to the SCR gate rather than through a capacitor, the voltage across R_{B1} while C is charging must be less than the minimum voltage required to turn on the SCR. The main purpose of R_{B2} is to protect the UJT from thermal runaway; the absolute minimum value recommended is 100 Ω for the G.E. type 2N2646 and 2N2647 UJT's. The General Electric SCR manual gives details of the design procedure for obtaining the optimum relaxation oscillator for a particular purpose. The oscillator can be synchronized with an ac supply by using a signal derived from the supply to reduce either the supply voltage or the interbase voltage. In more elaborate applications the charging current of capacitor C_1 may be controlled by a transistor or by an amplifier containing several transistors. An interesting example of an application in which an SCR is triggered by a low-frequency UJT relaxation oscillator is provided by the stroboscope of Fig. 4.145, which is an adaption of a circuit given in Reference 6 at the end of this chapter. The circuit was originally designed to be triggered by a pulse of 3 V and 5 mA and of duration 10 μsec, as obtained from a photodiode. The number of flashes per second is limited to a maximum of about 25, but the duration of each flash is only 100 μsec, so that precise timing is possible if the UJT oscillator is synchronized with a signal of accurately known frequency.*

* For another interesting application of SCR's to the production of timed high-current pulses see J. T. Clarke and B. R. Fox, *J. Chem. Phys.*, **46**, 827 (1967).

4   POWER SUPPLIES

General Considerations

Power supplies for the operation of electronic circuits or for the supply of known currents or voltages to experimental equipment can be graded in terms of cost, type of output, size or convenience, and stability. The first point to be considered in connection with a new power supply is always the type of output required—whether alternating or direct current, regulated or unregulated, high voltage or low.

For an ac supply it is normally convenient to take current from the mains with a transformer or variable transformer, although for equipment to be used away from civilized amenities or in the event of mains failure it is possible to use an *inverter* to convert the output of a battery from direct to alternating current. A number of inverters based on SCR's are discussed in the General Electric SCR manual. If the amplitude of an ac supply voltage is required to be constant, it is often convenient to use a self-regulating transformer. With the commonest type the output waveform is badly distorted, but, if a sinusoidal waveform is essential, special versions with low distortion are available. The efficiency of this type of regulator is low, being approximately 50% at the rated load. Both efficiency and regulation suffer if the load is much less than the rated value, and therefore, the regulator should be selected to have a load rating not greater than twice the power to be drawn from it.

In another type of regulator, which supplies an undistorted sine-wave output and operates at much higher efficiency, a servomechanism is used to drive a variable autotransformer whose output is added to or subtracted from the input in such a way that the output voltage is held constant. Because of the mechanical movement involved, the response of this type of regulator to a sudden change in input voltage is much slower than that of the preceding type. Transformers, variable transformers, self-regulating transformers, and ac voltage regulators are available commercially in a wide variety of voltage and current ratings.

For a low-current, low-voltage dc supply the ordinary dry-cell battery has advantages which are widely exploited in portable radios and hearing aids. In applications in which the magnitude of the supply voltage is important it is advisable to use mercury-cell batteries, rather than batteries composed of the usual Leclanché (zinc-carbon) cells, since the output of a mercury cell remains essentially constant during the battery's useful working life, whereas the output of a new Leclanché cell may be 20% greater than that of a similar cell near the end of its life. All batteries have a finite shelf-life, due to chemical effects occurring in the absence of external current flow; with small hearing-aid batteries the shelf-life can be the main limiting factor. Generally the power obtained from a dry cell is expensive in comparison with that available from the mains, but the virtues of small size, absence of connecting cords, and lack of superimposed ac "ripple" can often outweigh the cost factor. The lack of ac ripple may sometimes justify the use of batteries in situations in which a steady *high* voltage and relatively small current are required (e.g., in supplies for photomultipliers and ion chambers). The use of batteries is also favored when the circuit to be energized is "floating" at some large potential with respect to earth, and the use of any other kind of power supply would give rise to problems with the insulation of connecting wires. The ordinary lead-acid accumulator has many advantages in battery-power supplies in which small size and weight are not essential. In particular, the output voltage falls only very slowly as discharging proceeds, a lead-acid battery can be recharged easily with commercially available and inexpensive equipment, and the output resistance of the battery is typically a small fraction of an ohm so that large currents may be drawn if necessary. It is possible to obtain an extremely stable dc supply for critical applications by using a lead-acid battery in parallel with a battery charger, with the charger adjusted so that its output is almost sufficient to compensate for the current being drawn continuously from the battery.

For many purposes the voltage or current level of the output of batteries is too low, too inconstant, or too inconvenient, and it is preferable to use a mains-operated dc supply. In critical applications it is usually best to buy a power supply to fit the required specifications, but when the application is less critical it may be more convenient, as well as much less expensive, to build one. The operation of such a supply covers two problems, namely the conversion of alternating current to direct current and the stabilization, or regulation, of the resulting power. We deal with these problems separately in the two subsections that follow.

Rectifiers and Smoothing Networks

We have already noted that one function of a diode, based on its ability to conduct electricity in one direction only, is to act as a rectifier and convert alternating current to direct current. Figure 4.146 shows some typical rectifier circuits that use silicon and vacuum diodes with appropriate waveforms. The half-wave rectifier circuits (*a*) and (*b*) eliminate the negative-going portion of the transformer output waveform (*e*) to give the succession of rounded pulses (*f*). This kind of circuit is commonly used in applications in which only small currents are required. In the circuit (*c*) one anode of the full-wave rectifier tube is positive with respect to the center-tap on the transformer secondary and the other is negative. Consequently half the voltage across the secondary appears at the anode during each half-cycle

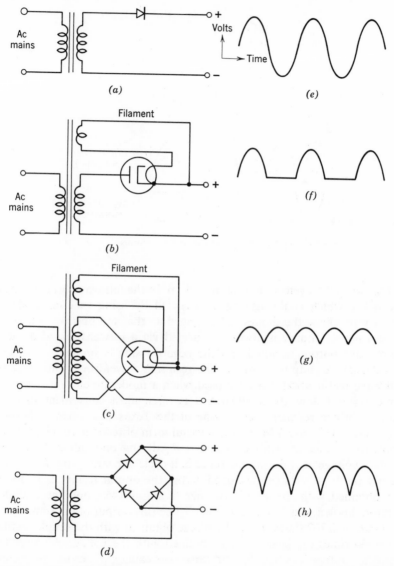

Fig. 4.146 Rectifier circuits and waveforms. *Circuits*, reading from the top: (*a*) silicon diode half-wave rectifier; (*b*) vacuum diode half-wave rectifier; (*c*) vacuum double-anode full-wave rectifier; (*d*) silicon diode full-wave bridge rectifier. *Waveforms*, reading from the top: (*e*) waveform across transformer secondary; (*f*) output of half-wave rectifiers; (*g*) output of vacuum double-anode full-wave rectifier; (*h*) output of bridge rectifier. Note that the transformer secondary in (*c*) is center-tapped.

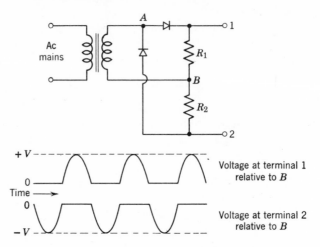

Fig. 4.147   Voltage doubler circuit and waveforms.

and the output waveform is as shown at (g). In the full-wave bridge rectifier circuit (d), which could also be constructed by using vacuum diodes or mercury rectifiers, the diodes are arranged so that the positive side of the transformer secondary is always connected via a forward-biased diode to the positive output terminal and the negative side is similarly connected to the negative output terminal. The resulting waveform is shown at (h). Full-wave rectification is always used when a moderate current is needed. For currents below about 500 mA it is often most convenient to use a "potted" bridge rectifier such as one of the Texas Instruments 1N3183–1N3188 series. Figure 4.147 shows a useful form of rectifier circuit in which a positive voltage at A appears across R_1 during one half-cycle and the negative voltage at A during the other half-cycle appears across R_2. Consequently the total voltage developed across the output terminals is double that obtained with the simple rectifier of Fig. 4.146a, and the circuit is therefore known as a "voltage doubler." The rms output of the transformer secondary is 0.707 times the peak voltage obtained with the simple rectifier and 0.354 times the peak voltage obtained with the voltage doubler. The complete voltage doubler has at least one capacitor across the output terminals for smoothing. Circuits that multiply the rms input voltage by 3, 4, or more can be constructed on the basis of the dc restorer circuit of Fig. 4.120. A quadrupler is shown in Fig. 4.148. This type of circuit is often a convenient and inexpensive means of obtaining a high voltage supply from a low voltage source in situations in which the output current is not required to be greater than about 5 mA.

Although the output voltages of the rectifier circuits we have considered are nominally direct current, the waveforms obtained would not be suitable for supplying power to most dc equipment. To obtain a steady dc output with a minimum of superimposed ac ripple it is necessary to employ a smoothing network such as those shown in Fig. 4.149. The inexpensive RC network (a) is suitable for smoothing in applications in which only a small current is to be drawn and in which the circuit can afford the voltage drop that occurs across the smoothing resistor R. (The small resistor r is normally included to prevent the current rating of the rectifier from being exceeded during charging of the capacitor C_1). The LC network (b) is convenient when larger currents have to be drawn, and in this form, that is, with "capacitor input," it has the advantage of giving "peak rectifier action" and the output of the filter is close to the peak value of the input voltage. The choke-input form of LC filter (c) has the advantage of evening out the demand for current from the rectifier, so that a rectifier with a lower surge current rating may be used, but the peak rectifier action is lacking and the output voltage is correspondingly smaller in relation to the peak input voltage. For currents larger than about 500 mA filter chokes become inconveniently heavy and bulky, and in this situation the smoothing network usually degenerates into a single large capacitor of 500–10,000 μF. A voltage regulator circuit is then relied on for any further smoothing that is necessary.

One way of viewing the filter networks of Fig. 4.149 is to regard them simply as circuits that provide an easy path to ground for ac signals and a

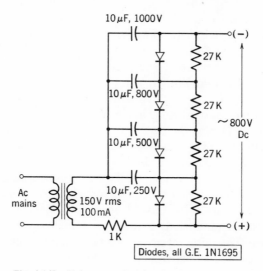

Fig. 4.148 Voltage quadrupler circuit.

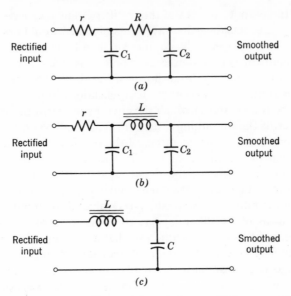

Fig. 4.149   Some basic forms of smoothing network: (a) RC smoothing, useful for currents of less than 10 mA, especially with high voltages. Typical input 1800-V peak, output 1400 V at 1 mA, $r = 100$ K, $C_1 = 0.5$ μF, $R = 330$ K, $C_2 = 4$ μF; (b) LC smoothing (capacitor input filter). Typical input 600-V peak, output 550 V at 200 mA, $r = 180$ Ω, $C_1 = 10$ μF, $L = 10$ H, $C_2 = 100$ μF; (c) LC smoothing (choke input filter). Typical input 700-V peak, output 530 V at 200 mA, $L = 10$ H, $C = 100$ μF.

difficult path to ground for direct current. A more instructive approach, however, is to consider the waveforms for the RC smoothing network, as illustrated in Fig. 4.150. At (a) is shown the voltage output from the rectifier as a function of time, and the corresponding voltage on the capacitor C_1 in Fig. 149a is shown at (b). The capacitor initially charges to the peak input voltage by drawing current from the rectifier, then discharges through resistor R with time constant RC_1, in the process charging C_2 to nearly the peak input voltage. During the slow discharge of C_1 the rectifier is reverse-biased and no current flows. This is shown in the rectifier current waveforms at (c). Capacitor C_1 continues to discharge through R until the next time that the output voltage from the rectifier exceeds the voltage on C_1, at which point another pulse of current is delivered to C_1 and the whole process is repeated. A large current is drawn from the rectifier during the cycle in which C_1 receives its initial charge, but in subsequent cycles a much smaller current is drawn. The initial cycle is sometimes termed the "hot switching transient." It is easy to see that smoothing is less of a problem with full-wave rectifiers, since the period during which the voltage falls with time constant

RC_1 in (b) would be less than half as long if the current pulse from the other half-cycle were available. The ripple that remains in the waveform (b) at capacitor C_1 is reduced further by the smoothing action of capacitor C_2 with a characteristic time constant given by the product of C_2 and the load resistance across the output terminals of the network.

Regulated Direct-Current Supplies

A regulated dc supply is a feedback system that operates to minimize the difference between its own output and an internal voltage standard. For low voltages, especially, and in the range from 2 to about 200 V, the voltage standard is commonly a zener diode (cf. Figs. 4.14 and 4.64b). Zener diodes have an appreciable temperature coefficient of breakdown voltage which must be allowed for in critical applications. The magnitude of the temperature coefficient is typically $+0.1\%/°C$ at zener voltages between 50 and 200 V, falling to almost zero near 5 V, and in some cases becoming negative below 5 V. Thus in the Texas Instruments 1N746 series the 1N751 with a nominal zener voltage of 5.1 V at 20 mA has a typical temperature coefficient of $-0.008\%/°C$, whereas the 1N752, with zener voltage nominally 5.6 V at 20 mA, has a typical temperature coefficient of $+0.006\%/°C$. The

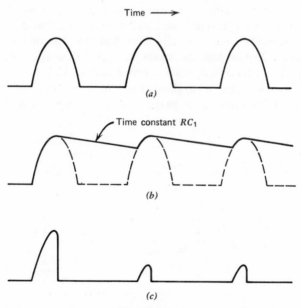

Fig. 4.150   Waveforms in an RC smoothing network: (a) output voltage waveform of half-wave rectifier; (b) voltage on capacitor C_1 (solid line); (c) current drawn from the rectifier to charge C_1.

same manufacturer's 1N821 series of temperature-compensated voltage reference diodes have a nominal zener voltage of 6.2 V, with maximum temperature coefficients that range from 0.01% per degree for the 1N821 to 0.001% per degree for the 1N827. The temperature coefficient of the 1N827 is seen to be essentially the same as that of a Weston unsaturated cadmium cell and less by a factor of 4 than that of a Weston normal cell. For applications that require a relatively high reference voltage it is possible to arrange for the temperature coefficients of two zener diodes to cancel one another, as in the circuit of Fig. 4.151.

For reference voltages greater than 50 V it is generally convenient to use a voltage reference tube, of which the commonest type relies on a cold-cathode discharge through a gas such as neon at low pressure (typically 0.1 torr) to produce a device whose burning voltage is almost independent of current over an appreciable range. As an example we consider the 85A2, which supplies a reference voltage nominally 85 V over the current range of 1 to 10 mA, the maximum variation from tube to tube being ± 2 V. As with an ordinary neon bulb, the tube requires an ignition voltage, which is usually about 30 V greater than the steady burning voltage, to start the discharge. For the 85A2 the maximum ignition voltage is stated to be 115 V in the presence of some ambient light; in complete darkness the discharge may not start immediately, even at this voltage. When the discharge has started, the voltage across the tube falls to the steady burning voltage, which is typically 83.3 V at 1 mA, 85.0 V at 6 mA, and 86.2 V at 10 mA. The burning voltage is extremely reproducible, especially when the tube has operated for a few hundred hours. The typical maximum voltage drift is 0.2% in 100 hr and 0.01% in 8 hr after an initial 3-min warmup period. Voltage reference tubes are not usually connected in parallel because of the difficulty of ensuring that the same current will pass through each tube, but they may be connected in

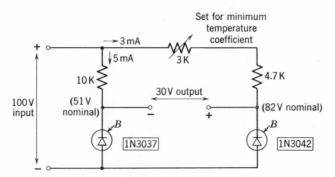

Fig. 4.151 Circuit for obtaining a temperature-compensated reference voltage. (Typical temperature coefficient 0.003% per °C.)

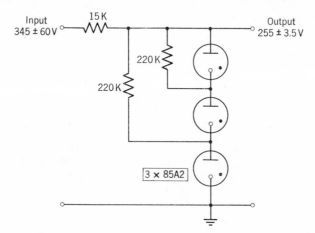

Fig. 4.152   Method of connecting voltage regulator tubes in series.

series, as in Fig. 4.152. The purpose of the pair of 220-K resistors is to ensure that the tubes ignite one at a time, starting from the bottom, so that the excess ignition voltage is not multiplied by the number of tubes in the series.

For voltages between 300 V and 30 kV voltage reference tubes which employ a corona discharge rather than a glow discharge are available, a good example being the Victoreen "Corotron." These tubes have no excess ignition voltage, and can be used at very low currents provided an *RC* filter network is used to reduce the electrical noise that accompanies the steady voltage output.

The simplest form of regulated power supply is the emitter-follower circuit of Fig. 4.153, in which the output voltage is equal to the zener diode voltage less the base-emitter voltage of the power transistor. Similar circuits using Corotron voltage regulator tubes and high-voltage triodes or pentodes have proved quite successful at voltages above 2 kV.*

The emitter-follower type of circuit can also be used for a constant-current power supply, such as would be required for a moving boundary experiment to measure the transport number of an ion in solution. The basic circuit is shown in Fig. 4.72 and a practical example is given in Fig. 4.154. For the tube version of this circuit it would be preferable to use a pentode rather than a triode, because the anode current of the pentode is relatively independent of anode voltage.

A further application of the follower circuit is shown in Fig. 4.155, in which a 12AX7 cascode amplifier is used to drive a constant current of 1 mA through a load of 1 M; the result is a constant-voltage supply suitable for

* See, for example, D. O. Ward, *Electronic Industries*, May and June issues, 1962.

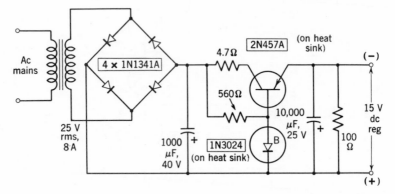

Fig. 4.153 Emitter-follower type of regulated power supply. (This circuit will deliver up to 2 A without losing its regulation and withstand having the output terminals short-circuited for brief periods.)

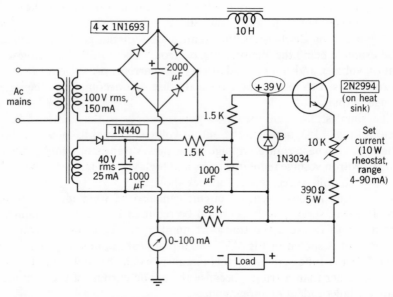

Fig. 4.154 Constant current power supply based on an emitter-follower. The voltage across the load can vary from zero to about 100 V in order to maintain the constant current. Either side of the load may be grounded; the meter should preferably be connected to the ground side.

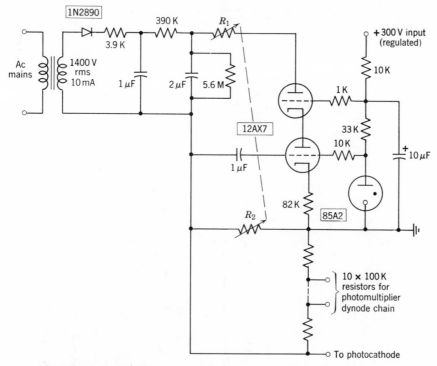

Fig. 4.155 Photomultiplier power supply based on a constant current source.

R_1	R_2	*Typical Output*
0	∞	−1040 V
180K	4.7M	−855 V
330K	2.2M	−715 V
390K	1.5M	−625 V
470K	1.2M	−565 V
560K	1.0M	−500 V

operating a 1P21, 1P28, or similar type of photomultiplier tube. Voltage steps are provided by inserting the resistor R_2 in parallel with the 1-M load, the total voltage across the 12AX7 sections being kept constant by a simultaneous adjustment of R_1. The 1-μF capacitor attached to the grid of the lower 12AX7 section provides a direct negative feedback path between ac ripple on the output and the control element of the constant-current source.

The basic circuit of a *series regulated power supply* is shown in Fig. 4.156a, and tube and transistor examples are given in Fig. 4.156b and c, respectively.

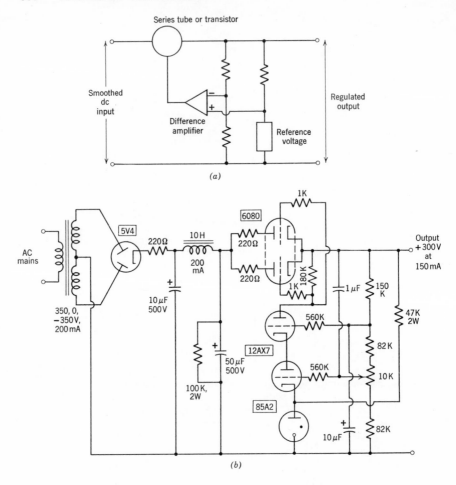

Series tube or transistor

Smoothed
dc
input

Difference
amplifier

Reference
voltage

Regulated
output

(a)

AC
mains

350, 0,
−350 V,
200 mA

5V4

220 Ω   10 H

200
mA

10 μF
500 V

+

100 K,
2W

50 μF
500 V

+

6080

1 K

220 Ω

220 Ω

1 K

180 K

12AX7

560 K

85A2

560 K

1 μF

10 μF

+

Output
+ 300 V
at
150 mA

150
K

47 K
2W

82 K

10 K

82 K

(b)

A regulated power supply is characterized first of all by its line regulation
factor, which may be stated either as the percentage change of output
voltage due to a fixed (commonly 10%) change of input voltage, or alter-
natively as the ratio of the change ΔV_{out} to a small change ΔV_{in} at constant
load. We use the second form here. For the tube circuit of Fig. 4.156b it can
be shown that to a good approximation $\Delta V_{\text{out}}/\Delta V_{\text{in}}$ is equal to $1/(k\,\mu A)$,
where k is the fraction of the output voltage fed back to the difference
amplifier, μ is the amplification factor of the series tube, and A is the voltage
gain of the difference amplifier. A second important parameter is the load
regulation factor, directly related to the output resistance of the supply,
which is defined as the ratio $\Delta V_{\text{out}}/\Delta I_{\text{out}}$, as measured with constant input
voltage. For the tube circuit this quantity is given by $-r_p/(k\,\mu A)$, where

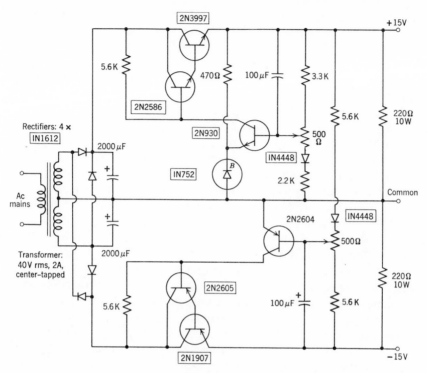

Fig. 4.156 Series-regulated power supplies: (*a*) basic series regulator; (*b*) 300-V, 150-ma supply, using tubes; (*c*) ± 15-V, 1-A supply, using transistors.

r_p is the plate resistance of the series tube, plus any series resistance in its plate circuit, and the other symbols have the same significance as before. The present tube circuit is a standard type, the choice of a 12AX7 cascode rather than a pentode for the difference amplifier being the only slightly unusual feature. The 1-μF capacitor provides a direct negative feedback path for ac ripple from the output to the difference amplifier. For greater stability of the output voltage a two-stage dc amplifier based on the long-tailed pair or even a high-voltage operational amplifier might usefully be substituted. With the present arrangement the gain of the difference amplifier is -225, the regulation factor as defined above works out to be $\frac{1}{125}$, and the output resistance is 5 Ω.

The circuit of Fig. 4.156*c* illustrates the use of the Darlington configuration to increase the effective current gain of a series transistor. In this circuit the 2N930 difference amplifier compares a portion of the $+15$ V output with the voltage across the 1N752 zener diode, and the output of this difference amplifier is used to control the *npn* Darlington pair. At the same time the 2N2604 difference amplifier compares the midpoint of the $+15$ V and -15 V terminals with the voltage on the "common" terminal (this is usually grounded), and the output of the amplifier controls the *pnp* Darlington pair. The voltage gains of the differential amplifiers are both in excess of 200, the actual value depending on the h_{fe} of the particular transistor used. For the Darlington pairs the term corresponding to r_p is of the order of 100 Ω, and the term corresponding to μ is of the order of 400. Hence, taking $k = 0.5$, we find that for each output the regulation factor is of the order of 40,000, and the output resistance is of the order of $\frac{1}{400}$ Ω. It appears that the most significant parameter describing the performance of this supply is likely to be its temperature coefficient, which develops from thermal drifts of the output due to the variation with temperature of the base-emitter voltages of the 2N930 and 2N2604. These drifts are largely compensated by the insertion of the forward-biased silicon diodes between one 500-Ω potentiometer and the 2.2-K resistor and between the other 500-Ω potentiometer and the $+15$ V line. The effect of temperature on the voltage supplied by the 1N752 is virtually negligible (typically $+0.006\%$ per degree), and its effect on the base-emitter voltages in the Darlington pairs should be adequately taken care of by the action of the voltage regulator circuits.

The basic circuit of a *shunt-regulated power supply* is given in Fig. 4.157*a* and tube and transistor examples are given in (*b*) and (*c*). The main advantages of a shunt-regulated supply are that nothing disastrous is likely to happen to the regulating tube or transistor if the output terminals are accidentally shorted together and that the dropping resistor R limits the amount of current that can flow. The second is a desirable safety factor in power supplies for voltages above 1 kV. Neither of the practical circuits in Fig. 4.157 contains a difference amplifier, a reasonable degree of regulation being obtained by simply applying the reference voltage direct to the grid of the

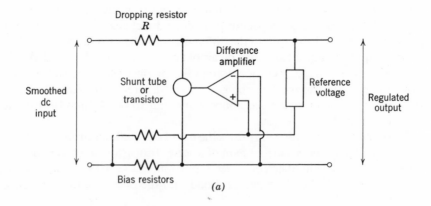

(*a*)

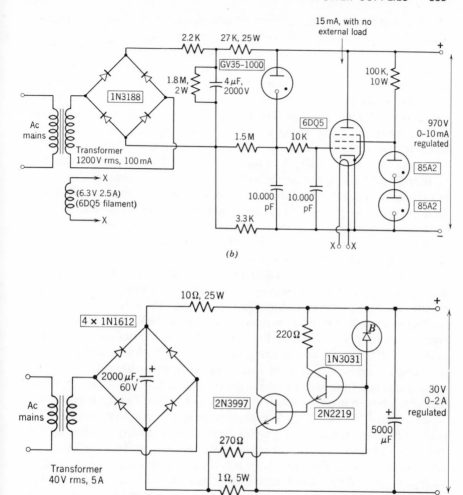

Fig. 4.157 Shunt-regulated power supplies: (*a*) basic regulator circuit; (*b*) high voltage supply, using tubes; (*c*) low voltage supply, using transistors.

6DQ5 in (*b*) and to the base of the Darlington pair in (*c*). To estimate the characteristics of these supplies we note that the change in the output voltage when current is drawn from the power supply appears directly as an input to a grounded-cathode or a grounded-emitter voltage amplifier that constitutes the shunt device itself and the dropping resistor. For both of the present circuits this voltage gain is of the order of 100. Thus a change of 1 V in the output of the tube circuit corresponds to a change of approximately 100 V across the 27-K dropping resistor and therefore to a change of 100 V/27 K $\sim$ 4 mA in the output current. Similarly, a change of 0.1 V in the output of the transistor circuit corresponds to a change of about 10 V across the 10 Ω resistor, and to a change of about 1 A in the output current. The tube circuit (b) is an example of the use of a Victoreen Corotron as a source of a reference voltage. The two 10,000-pF capacitors and the 10-K resistor make up a smoothing network whose purpose is to eliminate the noise that appears in the output voltage of a corona discharge tube at currents of the order of 10 μA or less. In this case the current is expected to be near 20 μA; it is not possible to be definite about operating conditions in this circuit because the 6DQ5 beam power tube is being operated in a manner that was probably not envisaged by its manufacturers, and the control grid potential needed to maintain the "no-load" plate current of 15 mA, when the plate is at nearly 1000 V with respect to the cathode, can be expected to vary from tube to tube.

In addition to series-regulated and shunt-regulated supplies, there is one other main type of power supply that is often encountered in scientific equipment, namely the rf (radiofrequency) supply, which is commonly used to deliver a small current at voltages in excess of 2 kV. The elements of a typical rf supply are shown in Fig. 4.158. The 100-kc oscillator at the left of the circuit is loosely coupled to power amplifier 1 whose output is taken to a control element, which in this instance is an n-channel FET. After passing through the control element the rf signal is taken to a second power amplifier whose output is fed into the primary of a tuned step-up transformer, where a signal of perhaps 20 V peak-to-peak is converted into one of 4 kV peak-to-peak or more. The high-voltage rf signal is finally rectified by the diode D and smoothed by capacitor C which need be only 10,000 pF or less because of the high frequency involved. A portion of the dc output voltage is selected by the potential divider made up of R_1 and R_2 and fed to the difference amplifier along with any output ripple that comes directly via capacitor C'. The output of the difference amplifier is returned to the series control element as a negative feedback signal; in this example, if the output voltage begins to rise, a negative signal is applied to the gate of the FET, thereby increasing its source-to-drain resistance and so reducing the size of the signal applied to power amplifier 2. The rf portion of the circuit is normally contained in a metal box to shield nearby circuits from pickup.

An rf power supply is relatively safe, from the point of view of the operator, because of the small size of the smoothing capacitor C and because the step-up transformer is incapable of delivering a large current. With other types of power supply the stored charge that persists on smoothing capacitors after the power is supposedly turned off can be a major hazard. For this

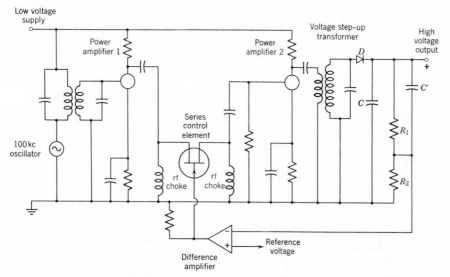

Fig. 4.158   Elements of a radiofrequency power supply for high dc voltages and low currents.

reason it is always good practice to insert resistors in parallel with any large smoothing capacitors that are required to operate above 60 V to provide a path for the capacitors to discharge after the power is turned off. This has been done for the high-voltage supplies in Figs. 4.155, 4.156, and 4.157.

A number of manufacturers have begun to produce complete voltage regulator units, each constituting a series or shunt transistor together with a voltage reference and differential amplifier in one compact package. Some of these devices are now available as integrated circuits; for high-current applications the voltage regulator can be used to supply the base current of a large power transistor. These units promise to greatly simplify the task of building a power supply with an output tailored to a particular application.

References

1. *Amplifier Handbook*, Richard F. Shea, Ed., McGraw-Hill, New York, 1966. (Contains 31 long articles, written by experts, which cover most applications of amplifiers and amplifying devices. Many of the authors are inclined to become very technical; nevertheless this is an extremely useful source of information on a wide variety of topics.)

2. *RCA Receiving Tube Manual*, Radio Corporation of America, Harrison, New Jersey, latest edition. (Contains, in addition to data on tube characteristics, a useful discussion of tube properties and applications.)

3. *G.E. Transistor Manual*, General Electric Company, Syracuse, New York, latest edition. (Covers the theory and applications of transistors in discrete-component circuits. The characteristics of JEDEC-registered transistors and diodes are summarized in tables at the end of the book.)

4. *The Semiconductor Data Book*, with supplements, Motorola Semiconductor Products Inc., Phoenix, Arizona, latest edition. (Contains useful application notes in addition to listing the characteristics of Motorola devices. Other application notes can be obtained separately from Motorola.)

5. *Linear Integrated Circuit Fundamentals*, Radio Corporation of America, Harrison, New Jersey, 1966. (Discusses the design, fabrication, and characteristics of linear integrated circuit amplifiers, including operational amplifiers.)

6. *Electronics Casebook of Circuit Design*, Electronics, McGraw-Hill, New York, latest edition. (The first (1967) edition of this publication contains more than 100 short articles, which describe interesting solutions to particular design problems, selected from previous issues of *Electronics* magazine.)

7. *Philbrick Applications Manual for Computing Amplifiers*, George A. Philbrick Researches, Dedham, Massachusetts, 2nd ed., 1966. (An authoritative and agreeably light-hearted discussion of the nature and applications of operational amplifiers. Anyone who works with operational amplifiers should have a copy.)

8. *Generalized Instrumentation for Research and Teaching*, Charles F. Morrison, Jr., Washington State University, Pullman, 1964. (An interesting account of operational amplifiers and their applications. Slightly dated in that it deals only with high-voltage amplifiers based on tubes.)

9. "Computer Logic and Memory," David C. Evans, *Scientific American*, **215,** 86 (1966). (Useful discussion, at an easy level, of digital logic, methods of performing arithmetic operations, and information storage devices.)

10. *The Digital Logic Handbook*, Digital Equipment Corporation, Maynard, Massachusetts, latest edition. (Contains discussions of the operation of gates and flip-flops and some valuable application notes concerned with analog-digital conversion.)

11. *G.E. Tunnel Diode Manual*, General Electric Company, Liverpool, New York, latest edition.

12. *G.E. Silicon Controlled Rectifier Manual*, General Electric Company, Auburn, New York, latest edition. (Both this manual and Reference 11 are primarily informative accounts of the applications of the devices, with tables of device characteristics taking a secondary place.)

13. *Electronics World*, **79,** Number 4 (April 1968). Ziff-Davis, Chicago. (This issue has a special section on power supplies.)

14. *Transistor Circuit Design*, by the engineering staff of Texas Instruments Incorporated, McGraw-Hill, New York, 1963.

15. *Field-effect Transistors*, L. J. Sevin, McGraw-Hill, New York, 1965. (This book and Reference 14 are part of the series of authoritative *TI Microlibrary* books.)

16. *Introduction to Chemical Instrumentation*, E. J. Bair, McGraw-Hill, New York, 1962.
17. *Electronics for Scientists*, H. V. Malmstadt, C. G. Enke, and E. C. Toren, Benjamin, New York, 1963.
18. *Electronics for Experimenters*, L. F. Phillips, John Wiley, New York, 1966.
19. *Introduction to Electronics*, V. A. Suprynowicz, Addison-Wesley, Reading, Massachusetts, 1966. (References 16 to 19 are books designed to provide scientists in physical or biological fields with a working knowledge of electronics. References 16, 17, and 18 give some attention to the practical problems of building, testing, and trouble-shooting with electronic equipment. Reference 17 incorporates a laboratory course for which the necessary equipment is available from the Heath Company, Benton Harbour, Michigan.)

APPENDIX IV.1: INTERCONVERSION TABLE FOR TRANSISTOR HYBRID PARAMETERS

Parameter	Relation to Other Configurations	Physical Significance of Parameter
h_{ie}	$h_{ib}/(1 + h_{fb}), h_{ic}$	r_{be}, base input resistance
h_{re}	$h_{ib}h_{ob}/(1 + h_{fb}) - h_{rb}, 1 - h_{rc}$	μ, early feedback factor
h_{fe}	$-h_{fb}/(1 + h_{fb}), -(1 + h_{fc})$	β, current gain
h_{oe}	$h_{ob}/(1 + h_{fb}), h_{oc}$	$1/r_{ce}$, collector output admittance
h_{ib}	$h_{ie}/(1 + h_{fe}), -h_{ic}/h_{fc}$	r_e, forward resistance of emitter-base diode
h_{rb}	$h_{ie}h_{oe}/(1 + h_{fe}) - h_{re},$ $(h_{rc} - 1) - h_{ic}h_{oc}/h_{fc}$	Common-base feedback factor
h_{fb}	$-h_{fe}/(1 + h_{fe}), -(1 + h_{fc})/h_{fc}$	$-\alpha$, negative ratio of collector and emitter currents
h_{ob}	$h_{oe}/(1 + h_{fe}), h_{oc}/h_{fc}$	r_c, reverse resistance of collector-base diode
h_{ic}	$h_{ie}, h_{ib}/(1 + h_{fb})$	r_{be}, base input resistance
h_{rc}	$1 - h_{re}, \sim 1$	Feedback term for emitter follower
h_{fc}	$-(1 + h_{fe}), -1/(1 + h_{fb})$	$-(1 + \beta)$, negative current gain
h_{oc}	$h_{oe}, h_{ob}/(1 + h_{fb})$	$1/r_{ce}$, collector output admittance

With a load resistor R the voltage gain is given by

$$A_v = -h_{fx} \cdot R/(h_{ix} + R[h_{ix}h_{ox} - h_{fx}h_{rx}])$$

APPENDIX IV.2: COMMONLY USED SYMBOLS AND ABBREVIATIONS (PREFERRED SYMBOLS UNDERLINED)

Admittance	$\underline{Y}, g$
Ambient temperature	T_a
Amplification factor	μ

Amplitude modulation	am
Anode current	$I_a, \underline{I}_b$
Anode dissipation	$P_a, \underline{P}_p, W_a$
Anode load	$R_a, \underline{R}_L$
Anode resistance (plate resistance)	$r_a, \underline{r}_p, \rho$
Anode supply voltage	$\underline{E}_{bb}, V_{a(b)}, V_{ba}$
Anode voltage	$\underline{E}_b, V_a$
Anode voltage peak	$\underline{E}_{bm}, V_{a(pk)}, V_{ap}$
Audiofrequency	af
Automatic gain control	agc
Bandwidth	$B, \Delta f, f_2$
Breakdown voltages	$BV_{CEO}, \underline{BV}_{CBO}, V_{(BR)CBO}$, etc.
Collector dissipation	P_c
Collector supply voltage	$\underline{V}_{cc}, E_{cc}$
Current gain of transistor	$\beta, \underline{h}_{fe}$
Cycles per second (hertz)	cps, $\underline{Hz}$
Decibel	db
Femto- $(= 10^{-15} \times)$	f-
Field-effect transistor	FET
Filament (heater) current	$\underline{I}_f, I_h$
Filament voltage	$\underline{E}_f, V_f, V_h$
Forward current transfer ratio, common base	$-\alpha, \underline{h}_{fb}$
Forward current transfer ratio, common emitter	β, h_{fe}
Gain-bandwidth product	f_T
Giga- $(= 10^9 \times)$	G-
Grid current	I_c, I_g
Grid voltage	$\underline{E}_c, V_g$
Impedance	Z
Intermediate frequency	if
Joint Electron Device Engineering Council	JEDEC
Kilo- $(= 10^3 \times)$	k-
Kilohm	K
Large-signal parameters	$\underline{h}_{FE}, \underline{h}_{FB}$, etc., $\bar{\alpha}, \bar{\beta}$
Mega- $(= 10^6 \times)$	M-
Micro- $(= 10^{-6} \times)$	μ-
Milli- $(= 10^{-3} \times)$	m-
Mutual conductance (transconductance)	$\underline{g}_m, S$
Nano- $(= 10^{-9} \times)$	n
Negative temperature coefficient	NTC
Noise figure	$\underline{F}$, NF
Peak inverse voltage (of a diode)	PIV
Pico- $(= 10^{-12} \times)$	p-
Radiofrequency	rf
Root-mean-square	rms
Silicon-controlled rectifier	SCR
Storage temperature	T_s
Tera- $(= 10^{12} \times)$	T-
Thermal resistance (°C/watt)	$K, \underline{\theta}$
Vacuum-tube voltmeter	VTVM

Chapter **V**

SOURCES AND MODULATION OF ELECTROMAGNETIC AND SONIC ENERGY

Leroy L. Blackmer

---

1   INTRODUCTION

Sonic energy is associated with mechanical vibrations of a rigid body or of a portion of an elastic material; electromagnetic energy develops from accelerated motions of electric charges on conductors or in atomic and molecular orbits. In either case the basic generator can be considered as a set of one or more harmonic oscillators from which energy propagates by wave motion. By a wave, in the most general sense, is meant a space-time dependent disturbance, not necessarily periodic, that progresses with a finite velocity. The disturbance may appear in such widely diverse forms, for example, as localized density variations in a liquid or a gas, the deformation of a solid, a pulse of electric current confined to a wire, or the electric-field intensity of a radio wave in free space. All such wave disturbances have the common attribute of conveying energy from one region to another much in the fashion of a ripple that traverses an otherwise still body of water.

The concept of waves is fundamental not only to propagation but also to the phenomena encountered in their generation and modulation. All harmonic oscillators have one feature in common. The vibratory mechanisms are described by periodic functions of time that involve three parameters, namely, amplitude, frequency, and phase, subject to certain boundary conditions. In particular, the allowable frequencies are limited by constraints imposed by physical structures and geometry. Under suitable conditions any one of the parameters may be varied to alter the instantaneous content and thus impose information on a wave. This process is called modulation and may, at least in principle, take place by interactions in the generator, in the transmission path, or in the output coupling arrangement. The optimum point of application depends primarily on the type of wave and on the characteristics and geometry of specific devices. In a broader sense modulation may also be considered as a means of protecting the informational content from the deleterious effects of noise.

Electromagnetic and sonic waves differ in quite fundamental ways. The former are described in terms of electric and magnetic field quantities that can exist in free space and in dielectric materials; the latter are essentially mechanical and require a physical medium for their propagation. Despite these differences, the mathematical formulations are strikingly similar. Moreover, certain interactions between sonic and electromagnetic fields depend on the wavelike character of each. At low frequencies the circuits and analogies pointed out in Chapter II, Section 2, are valid. However, as the frequency is increased, the wavelength of the disturbance becomes comparable to the dimensions of physical devices, and the lumped constants of the electrical circuit, or its equivalent, must be replaced by parameters distributed throughout the circuit. Impedance is still an important concept, but Q (see Chapter IV) and resonant frequency take on added significance. At still higher frequencies, particularly in the electromagnetic domain, emitted energy takes on particlelike aspects and is said to be quantized.

A complete treatment of any of the topics that fall under the headings of electromagnetic or sonic generation and modulation would require volumes rather than pages. Indeed, there are many excellent books that treat various aspects of both subjects in depth. The aim of this chapter is to outline the basic principles involved and to describe briefly the operation of a few devices that have practical importance in the design of instruments for measurement and control. For details on specific devices and their operating characteristics the reader is referred to pertinent treatises.

2 PROPERTIES OF WAVES

Wave Motion

The simplest analytical representation of a wave is one in which the disturbance moves with a constant velocity, v, along a straight line, as illustrated in Fig. 5.1. At some instant of time t the disturbance is represented by an arbitrary function $f(z, 0)$. At a later time $t = t_1$ the disturbance, without having changed shape, has moved to the new position at $z = z_1$. Since the velocity is assumed to be constant, the function $f(z - vt)$ represents the profile of a single disturbance propagating in the positive z-direction. The argument of the function is called the phase. Conceptually, the function $f(z + vt)$ represents a wave traveling in the negative z-direction, as would occur, for example, in the reflection of the original wave by a mirror located at some positive value of z. Both functions are solutions of the general wave equations in one dimension:

$$\frac{\partial^2 f}{\partial z^2} = \frac{1}{v^2} \frac{\partial^2 f}{\partial t^2}. \tag{5.1}$$

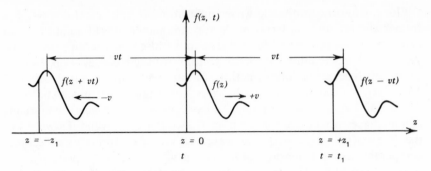

Fig. 5.1 An arbitrary one-dimensional wave disturbance moving with constant velocity.

In this expression f represents the quantity of interest—the displacement of a vibrating string, the electric-field intensity of a radio wave, or the density in a compressional acoustic wave. Since it has directional properties, the function is frequently called a wave vector.

As a matter of practical interest, simple periodic or harmonic functions not only occur in many physical processes but are also most amenable to analysis. Waves of almost any shape can be obtained by linear superposition of a suitable number of harmonic functions by the methods of Fourier analysis. Although no completely undamped waves are found in nature, the motions in an undamped oscillator form a good first-order approximation to the motions in many physical systems. A one-dimensional wave function moving in the positive z-direction that satisfies (5.1) is

$$f(z - vt) = a \exp\left[j(\omega t - kz \pm \theta)\right] = A \exp\left[j(\omega t - kz)\right] \tag{5.2a}$$

$$= A \cos(\omega t - kz) + jA \sin(\omega t - kz), \tag{5.2b}$$

where $j = \sqrt{-1}$ and θ is an arbitrary phase angle absorbed in the complex amplitude term $A = a \exp(\pm j\theta)$. Either the real or the imaginary parts of (5.2), which differ in phase by $\pi/2$, can be taken as the representation of a harmonic wave; $\omega/2\pi = v$ is the frequency and the spatial period $2\pi/k = \lambda$ is the wavelength, as indicated in Fig. 5.2. The wavenumber or propagation constant $k = \omega/v$ is in general complex (i.e., $k = k_r - jk_i$). The real part is always $2\pi/\lambda$; the imaginary part is the reciprocal of the distance over which the wave amplitude is attenuated by a factor of e, the natural logarithmic base, in its passage through a given medium.

Typical wave disturbances, including those that are nearly monochromatic, are made up of many waves with different angular frequencies that vary around a mean frequency $\bar{\omega}$. Together they constitute a wave group or packet. To each frequency component there is also assigned a wavenumber and a velocity that vary around their respective mean values. In the simplest case the summation of two harmonic waves of the same amplitude but differing in frequency by $\Delta\omega$ gives rise to the phenomenon of beats illustrated in Fig. 5.2. The resultant amplitude varies with both time and position and the maxima are propagated at the group velocity

$$v_g = \frac{\Delta\omega}{\Delta k} = v - \lambda\frac{\Delta v}{\Delta\lambda}. \tag{5.3}$$

This relation is quite general and holds for any group whatever [1].

Another particularly important aspect of wave motion in interferometric measurements relates to a quantity known as coherence. Lack of coherence appears in a random succession of wave trains of too short duration to

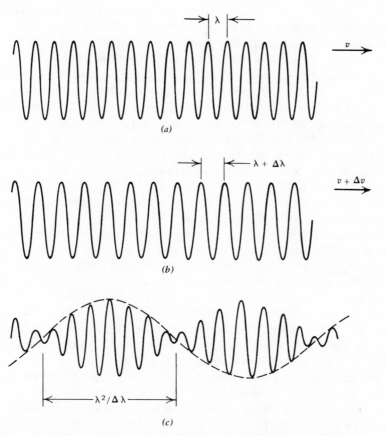

Fig. 5.2 (a) and (b). One-dimensional sinusoidal waves of slightly different velocities and frequencies; (c) beat frequency arising from summation of waves (a) and (b).

overlap in time or in a superposition of monochromatic components distributed over a range of frequencies. For practical purposes the two conditions are equivalent; for example, a very long wave train corresponds to a narrow frequency range such as is emitted by a stable radio transmitter operating at a single frequency. If a group of wave trains centered about a mean frequency v_0 all have the same duration Δt, it can be shown by Fourier methods [1] that the frequency spectrum is represented by a term of the form sin x/x and that Δv is proportional to $1/\Delta t$; Δt is defined as the coherence time. The coherence length is $\Delta l = c \, \Delta t = \lambda_0^2/\Delta\lambda$, where c is the phase velocity, λ_0 is the mean wavelength, and $\Delta\lambda$ is the wavelength spread.

In simple harmonic oscillators without losses energy passes back and forth between potential and kinetic energy states. The total energy remains constant and the power involved is proportional to the square of the amplitude of oscillation. Energy extracted from the oscillator may be considered as dissipation that is replaced from a supply reservoir. Energy in a traveling wave is carried by the component periodic variations of the disturbance and is likewise proportional to the square of the amplitude terms; that is, to $|A|^2$. However, flux, or intensity, is the quantity most readily measured. It is defined as the time-averaged rate of energy transmission through a unit cross-sectional area perpendicular to the direction of propagation or, alternatively, as the product of energy density per unit volume and wave velocity. For other than simple harmonic waves the group velocity $v_g = \Delta\omega/\Delta k$ must be used rather than the phase velocity $v = \omega/k$. Variations in intensity in the acoustic and radiofrequency domains are commonly expressed on the decibel scale, or $10 \log_{10} (I_2/I_1)$, where I_1 and I_2 are two values of intensity. In terms of the corresponding amplitudes A_1 and A_2 the variation is expressed as $20 \log_{10} (A_2/A_1)$.

A complete description of wave interactions in generators and modulators requires explicit knowledge of the behavior of the wave vectors. Acoustic waves are generally classified as either compressional (longitudinal) or shear (transverse), depending on whether the vibration is in the same direction or transverse to the direction of propagation. Either class may be accompanied by surface, or Rayleigh, waves. The latter are roughly analogous to water waves in which small volume elements describe elliptical orbits through a cross section a few wavelengths in depth. Except in special cases, shear waves can exist only in solids. Compressional waves may exist in solids, liquids, or gases, but not in vacuum. The most important quantities are particle displacement, particle velocity, acoustic pressure, and condensation. If the wave vectors at any given instant of time have the same value at all points in a plane normal to the direction of propagation, the disturbance is said to be a plane wave. Plane acoustic waves obey the well-known optical laws of reflection, refraction, diffraction, and interference.

Electromagnetic waves are described by two wave vectors that are always coexistent. They are the electric and magnetic field intensities **E** and **H**, respectively, related to each other through Maxwell's equations [1, 2]. In fact, a simultaneous solution of Maxwell's equations yields the wave equation (5.1). One important class of electromagnetic waves is the transverse plane wave in which the **E** and **H** vectors are mutually perpendicular to each other and both lie in planes normal to the direction of propagation, as shown in Fig. 5.3. This condition exists in free space and in ideal dielectrics at points removed many wavelengths from the source. Energy is shared equally between the two vector fields, and the rate of energy flow through unit area is given by the vector cross product **E** × **H**. The latter quantity, called the Poynting vector [2], points in the direction of propagation.

In general a plane electromagnetic wave disturbance of a single frequency is comprised of many wave trains, each of finite length, with the electric (or magnetic) vectors randomly oriented in phase from one train to the next. Under certain conditions, as in radiation from dipole arrays and many gas lasers, the electric (or magnetic) vectors can be made to fall completely, or at least chiefly, parallel to a given direction. Such waves are said to be plane polarized and the plane containing the direction of propagation and the electric vector is called the plane of vibration. Any set of plane wave trains can always be resolved into two components with polarizations that are mutually orthogonal, even when many frequencies are present. This feature is employed in some optical modulating methods. A longitudinal wave, by its nature, does not exhibit polarization.

Another important class of electromagnetic waves arises from a consideration of the boundary conditions imposed by walls of cavities and guide

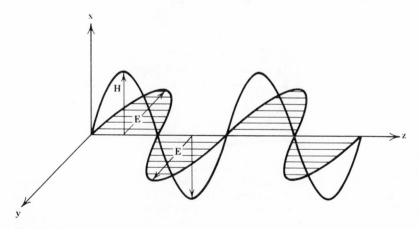

Fig. 5.3   The plane electromagnetic wave.

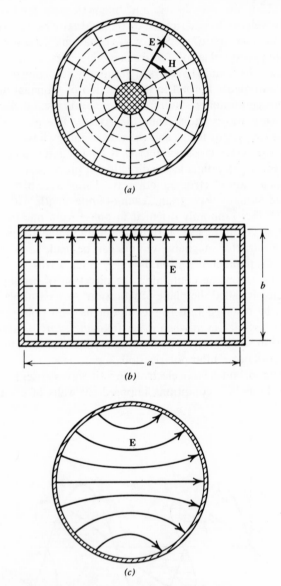

Fig. 5.4 Field directions in typical transmission lines (—— electric vector, – – – magnetic vector): (a) TEM wave in a coaxial line; (b) TE_{01} mode in a waveguide of rectangular cross section; (c) TE_{11} mode in a waveguide of circular cross section.

346

structures. In a coaxial line a transverse wave is propagated in the annular region between two rigid coaxial cylindrical conductors. Since both the electric and magnetic vectors (Fig. 5.4a) are transverse to the direction of propagation along the line, it is called a TEM wave. The wavelength is the same as that for a plane wave in an extended medium and the velocity of propagation is the same for all frequencies if the line has infinite conductivity. In practice there are always some losses, and the velocity does depend somewhat on frequency. Other modes that have longitudinal components of E and H are also permitted, but they are more complex and seldom used in practice. The average power transmitted in the TEM mode is given by

$$P = \frac{C^2}{120} \ln\left(\frac{b}{a}\right), \tag{5.4}$$

where C is a constant depending on the dielectric breakdown of the annular space, b is the inner radius of the outer cylinder, and a is the radius of the inner conductor [3].

Hollow conducting tubes of rectangular and circular cross sections are extensively used as cavity resonators and wave guides [3]. Such tubes, if made of perfectly conducting material, will not propagate TEM modes. They will, however, support either transverse electric fields (TE waves) which have no component of E in the direction of propagation or transverse magnetic fields (TM waves) which have no longitudinal component of H. In either case the wavelength of the guided wave is different from that of a plane wave and dependent on the guide dimensions. One of the simplest and most practically useful of guided waves is the TE mode that arises in an air-filled pipe of rectangular cross section having dimensions b and a. The wave is simply the superposition of a pair of plane electromagnetic waves with their E vectors oriented parallel to the narrow side of length b. In their passage down the guide the waves are reflected back and forth from the narrows sides as illustrated in Fig. 5.5 for one of the waves. Thus the electric field is always transverse, but a longitudinal magnetic component is permitted. Application of the appropriate boundary conditions yields the three vector components of the wave function for a guided wave progressing along the pipe in the positive z-direction:

$$E_z = 0 \tag{5.5a}$$

$$E_x = B\frac{\omega_m \lambda_c^2}{4\pi b} \sin\frac{m\pi y}{b} \cos\frac{n\pi x}{a} \sin(\omega t - kz), \tag{5.5b}$$

with a similar expression for E_y and three related expressions for the vector components of H [2]. The wavenumber is given by $k = 2\pi/\lambda$, where the

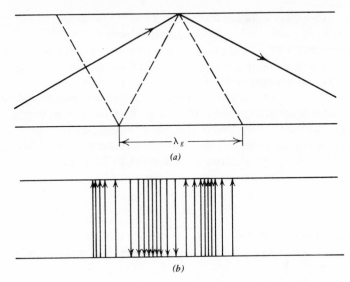

Fig. 5.5 Transmission of plane wavefronts in a rectangular waveguide: (a) top view (——— wave normals, – – – wavefronts); (b) side view showing direction and intensity distribution of the electric field.

guided wavelength is

$$\lambda_g = \lambda_0 \left[1 - \left(\frac{\lambda_0}{\lambda_c} \right)^2 \right]^{-1/2}. \tag{5.6}$$

In this expression λ_0 is the wavelength of a corresponding unguided wave and

$$\lambda_c = 2 \left(\frac{m^2}{b^2} + \frac{n^2}{a^2} \right)^{-1/2} \tag{5.7}$$

is called the cutoff wavelength; m and n are integers which, used as subscripts in TE_{mn}, denote the number of half-wave variations in transverse field intensity parallel to b and a, respectively. The lowest order, or dominant mode, in rectangular pipes occurs for $m = 0$ and $n = 1$. This is called the TE_{01} mode. The directions of the electric and magnetic field vectors are illustrated in Fig. 5.4b. Waves of free space wavelength greater than $\lambda_c = 2a$ are attenuated at an extremely rapid rate; the waveguide acts like a high pass filter, independent of the dimension b. Except at the cutoff wavelength, λ_g is always greater than λ_0. The next higher mode TE_{02} occurs for $m = 0$, $n = 2$ and can exist only if the unguided wavelength is less than $\lambda_c = a$. It is evident that other modes represent highly complex waves. Fortunately the dominant mode is not only the simplest wave but also the easiest to excite.

Similar analyses of circular-section waveguides in cylindrical coordinates show that the cutoff wavelengths are related to roots of Bessel functions. In the TE_{mn} and TM_{mn} mode designations the first subscript indicates the number of full-period variations of the radial component of field in the angular coordinate direction and the second subscript indicates the number of half-period variations of the angular component in the radial coordinate direction. The field configuration of the dominant TE_{11} mode, which has the highest cutoff wavelength, is illustrated in Fig. 5.4c.

Losses in waveguides due to finite conductivity of wall materials depend on geometry, mode, and frequency. Propagation modes in pipes of rectangular and circular cross section are well known. An extensive bibliography exists on the subject of other configurations such as single- and double-ridged guides, periodic structures, and those containing dielectrics.

Standing Waves

In an extended medium at rest the frequency is established by the source and remains constant, regardless of the properties of the medium. Except for possible dispersive effects (i.e., variations of velocity with frequency), there are apparently no other restrictions on the frequency. However, any physical device, such as a resonant cavity, is finitely bounded, and solutions of the wave equation must satisfy conditions that exist at the boundary. As a simple illustration, a taut string rigidly fixed at the points $z = 0$ and $z = l$ is a realistic model of both sonic and electromagnetic wave resonators [4]. The standing waves illustrated in Fig. 5.6 are the resultants of two one-dimensional waves traveling in opposite directions. A harmonic wave of amplitude A_1 progressing in the positive z-direction is reflected at $z = l$ with a reversal of phase and returns on itself with amplitude A_2 to repeat the process at $z = 0$ and so on. Phase shift and attenuation that occur on reflection are included in the complex amplitude terms. Since the ends are fixed, the net amplitudes at $z = 0$ and $z = l$ must reduce to zero. Thus from (5.2a)

$$A_1 e^{j\omega t} + A_2 e^{j\omega t} = 0 \qquad (5.8a)$$

and

$$A_1 e^{j(\omega t - kl)} + A_2 e^{j(\omega t + kl)} = 0. \qquad (5.8b)$$

The solutions are independent of time and it is readily shown that $\sin(kl) = 0$ or $k = n\pi/l$, where n is an integer. The allowable, or characteristic, angular frequencies are given by $\omega_n = n(\pi v/l)$. The lowest frequency occurs for $n = 1$ and is called the fundamental. Higher frequencies corresponding to $n = 2, 3$, etc., are called second, third, and higher order harmonics, respectively. The complete description of the disturbance is given by the superposition of terms of the form

$$A_n \left[e^{j(\omega_n t - kz)} - e^{j(\omega_n t + kz)} \right]$$

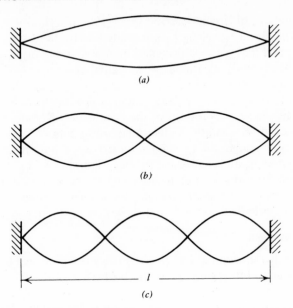

Fig. 5.6   Simple one-dimensional standing waves: (a) $l = \lambda/2$; (b) $l = \lambda$; (c) $l = 3\lambda/2$.

or, taking the real part,

$$f = \sum (a_n \sin \omega_n t + b_n \cos \omega_n t) \sin \frac{n\pi z}{l}$$

$$= \sum c_n \sin (\omega_n t + \alpha_n) \sin \frac{n\pi z}{l}, \qquad (5.9)$$

where

$$c_n = (a_n{}^2 + b_n{}^2)^{1/2} \qquad \text{and} \qquad \alpha_n = \tan^{-1} \frac{b_n}{a_n}.$$

The coefficients a_n and b_n are constants that must be evaluated from the initial conditions.

A standing wave is characterized by points of zero disturbance, called nodes, which are spaced $\lambda/2$ apart. In the example of a vibrating string the two ends are nodes by definition. Thus the shortest possible one-dimensional resonator is one that operates in its fundamental mode and has length $\lambda/2$. It can be shown that the number of interior nodes is always one less than the order of the harmonic [4]. Midway between the nodes the disturbance attains maximum amplitude with a temporal period $2\pi/\omega_n$. These regions, called loops or antinodes, are the only points at which efficient energy transfer can take place.

Analogous results which obtain for three-dimensional structures are extremely important in the design and operation of high-Q resonant wave cavities. The standard method of solution employs a separation of variables in which it is assumed that the wavefunction can be expressed as a product of functions, each of which depends on only one variable. Thus for the case of a rectangular parallelepiped of sides a, b, and c

$$f(x, y, z, t) = X(x)\, Y(y)\, Z(z)\, T(t) \tag{5.10}$$

must satisfy (5.1). It is shown in works on applied mathematics [5, 6] that the resulting second-order linear equations have solutions of the form

$$X(x) = A_1 e^{-jkx} + A_2 e^{jkx}, \tag{5.11}$$

with similar expressions for $Y(y)$ and $Z(z)$. Applying the boundary conditions that require the disturbance to have zero amplitude at the faces of the cavity, the allowable angular frequencies are given by

$$\omega_n = \pi v \left[\left(\frac{l}{a}\right)^2 + \left(\frac{m}{b}\right)^2 + \left(\frac{n}{c}\right)^2 \right]^{1/2}, \tag{5.12}$$

where l, m, and n are integers. Solutions for cylindrical and spherical shapes, though more complicated, follow similar procedures.

In essence, oscillations of only specific frequencies can be maintained in a given device, and these are determined by the material and geometry of the cavity. A cavity behaves much like a resonant electrical circuit and can be described in terms of equivalent inductance, capacitance, or impedance. The resonant frequency and equivalent Q, however, are generally more useful. Unlike the resonant circuit, a cavity can support an infinite number of harmonics.

A resonant cavity forms an integral part of many ultrahigh radiofrequency generators [3, 7–9]. Since the more useful ones resemble and can be derived from truncated waveguide structures, a similar mode designation is commonly used. Thus, if l, m, and n are the number of half-period variations along the respective a-, b-, and c-directions of a rectangular parallelepiped, the allowable transverse modes are designated by TE_{lmn} and TM_{lmn}. In this nomenclature there is no component of electric field along the c-direction for the TE_{lmn} mode and no component of magnetic field along the c-direction for the TM_{lmn} mode. Similar designations apply to cavities of other shapes.

3 THE MODULATION PROCESS

Amplitude Modulation

In modern optical as well as radio engineering parlance a progressive harmonic wave of constant frequency is referred to as a carrier [10]. It is evident that one way to modulate such a wave is to vary the amplitude parameter in the desired fashion [11]; for example, the amplitude can be alternated between minimum and maximum values in accordance with the dots and dashes of the telegraph or some other code. The general character of an amplitude-modulated wave can be deduced by letting the amplitude term A of (5.2) be a signal that varies sinusoidally in time. Thus

$$A = A_0(1 + M \cos \omega_m t), \tag{5.13}$$

where ω_m is the modulating frequency and A_0 and M are constants. The wavefunction then becomes

$$f = A_0(1 + M \cos \omega_m t) \cos (\omega t - kz)$$
$$= A_0 \cos (\omega t - kz) + A_0 M \cos (\omega t - kz) \cos \omega_m t. \tag{5.14}$$

With the help of a simple trigonometric identity the latter equation can be written in the form

$$f = A_0 \cos (\omega t - kz) + \frac{A_0 M}{2} \{\cos [(\omega + \omega_m)t - kz]$$
$$+ \cos [(\omega - \omega_m)t - kz]\}. \tag{5.15}$$

The disturbance appears as the sum of three waves, each of different frequency. The first term is simply the carrier wave of constant amplitude A_0; the second and third terms contain the sum and difference, respectively, of the carrier and signal frequencies but with amplitudes dependent on the degree of modulation. They are called the upper and lower side frequencies. In the practical case in which $\omega \gg \omega_m$ the amplitude coefficient (5.4) is the envelope of the modulated wave shown in Fig. 5.7; M represents the modulation factor. Alternatively, the signal may be considered as being contained in the carrier and the two side frequencies. When the signal contains more than one frequency, it is evident that two groups of terms of the form $(\omega \pm \omega_m)$, called the side bands, will be present.

A number of modifications are useful in practical radiofrequency communication systems. These include single side band, double side band, and vestigial side band modulations. Since the side bands in amplitude modulation are symmetrical in frequency about the carrier, the upper and lower bands carry the same information. Thus one side band can be eliminated without loss of intelligence. Furthermore, since the carrier contains no information and serves only as a reference in the detection process, it too can be eliminated, provided a suitable reference signal can be generated at the detector. Such a system is called single side band. It has the obvious advantage of reducing the required bandpass by a factor of somewhat more than 2 with a concomitant reduction in power. This method, however, is somewhat cumbersome for most instrument applications. Other methods [12] involve suppression of only the lower side band (American television

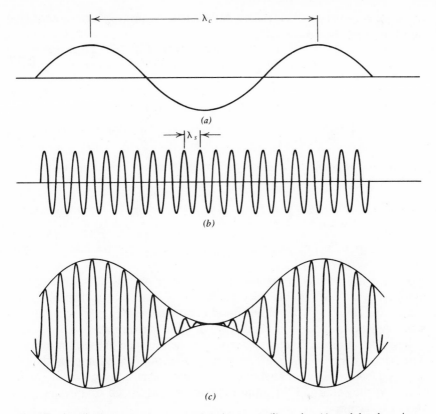

Fig. 5.7 Amplitude modulation: (*a*) modulating wave; (*b*) carrier; (*c*) modulated carrier.

standards), partial suppression of the carrier only, and double side band. In the latter case both side bands are allowed, but the carrier is completely suppressed to produce an envelope that varies at twice the modulation frequency.

Frequency Modulation

Frequency modulation is one form of the more general method called angle modulation [11]. In principle it is possible to allow the instantaneous frequency of a harmonic wave to vary, say as $\cos \omega_m t$. To avoid time-dependent products that would produce different results for the same signal the usual practice in frequency modulation is to take $\int \omega(t)\, dt$ as the argument of the harmonic function [10]. Thus, letting

$$\omega(t) = \omega_0(1 + M_f \cos \omega_m t), \tag{5.16}$$

where ω_0 is constant, M_f is the modulation factor, and ω_m is the modulating frequency, (5.2) becomes

$$f = A \cos\left[\omega_0 t + \frac{\omega_0}{\omega_m} M_f \sin \omega_m t\right]. \tag{5.17}$$

The spatial term and the constant of integration are omitted for simplicity. By a straightforward trigonometric expansion, letting $\omega_0 M_f = a_m$,

$$f = A\left[\cos \omega_0 t \cos\left(\frac{a_m \sin \omega_m t}{\omega_m}\right) - \sin \omega_0 t \sin\left(\frac{a_m \sin \omega_m t}{\omega_m}\right). \tag{5.18}$$

Finally, introducing expansions in terms of Bessel functions of the first kind, $J_n(a_m/\omega_m)$,

$$f = A\left\{J_0\left(\frac{a_m}{\omega_m}\right)\cos \omega_0 t + J_1\left(\frac{a_m}{\omega_m}\right)[\cos(\omega_0 + \omega_m)t - \cos(\omega_0 - \omega_m)t]\right.$$
$$\left. + J_2\left(\frac{a_m}{\omega_m}\right)[\cos(\omega_0 + 2\omega_m)t + \cos(\omega_0 - 2\omega_m)t] + \cdots\right\}. \tag{5.19}$$

Again the disturbance is resolved into a carrier of constant frequency and amplitude and side frequencies made up of sum and difference terms. Unlike the situation in amplitude modulation, there is an infinite number of side frequencies and a considerably wider band is required.

Bessel functions arise in many wave interactions and are well known [6]. The negative sign occurring in the second term of (5.19) implies that the side frequency is π out of phase from its counterpart. Since power is proportional to the square of the amplitude, the negative sign disappears in the power spectrum.

An angular modulated wave is characterized by constant amplitude and instantaneous frequency variations, as illustrated in Fig. 5.8 for the simple case of sinusoidal modulation. However, the number and amplitudes of the side orders vary according to the modulating frequency and to the degree of modulation. For certain values of modulation the carrier content is reduced to nearly zero. The frequency domain is usually observed with a spectrum analyzer which plots the power in the spectrum as a function of

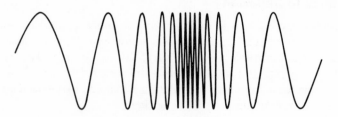

Fig. 5.8   Sinusoidal frequency modulation.

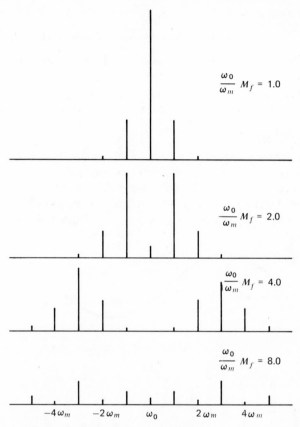

Fig. 5.9 Power spectrum of a frequency-modulated wave for various values of the index $(\omega_0/\omega_m)M_f$.

frequency. A typical plot appears somewhat as shown in Fig. 5.9. In the absence of distortion a sinusoidal modulating signal produces components that are symmetrical on either side of the carrier, and the frequency deviation is defined as the maximum departure of frequency from the unmodulated carrier. It is one-half the total frequency excursion. Since side band suppression results in a composite of frequency and amplitude modulation, conservation of bandwidth is best achieved by reducing the deviation.

Phase Modulation

Another form of angular modulation is obtained by allowing the initial phase angle θ to vary sinusoidally; that is, by setting

$$\theta = \theta_0(1 + M_p \cos \omega_m t), \tag{5.20}$$

where θ_0 is a constant and M_p is the modulation factor. Thus

$$f = A \cos (\omega_0 t + \theta_0 + \theta_0 M_p \cos \omega_m t). \qquad (5.21)$$

On comparison with (5.17), phase modulation is seen to differ from frequency modulation only in the coefficients of the sinusoidal modulation term and a phase difference of $\pi/2$. Since the factor $1/\omega_m$ can generally be introduced by appropriate circuitry, phase modulation is not discussed further.

Pulse Modulation

A more recent technique that is particularly useful for operations involving digital data at radiofrequency rates makes use of pulse techniques to modulate a high frequency carrier. Readily controllable parameters are the amplitude (PAM), duration or width (PWM), and position (PPM), illustrated in Fig. 5.10. PPM is equivalent to a time or frequency pulse modulation. It

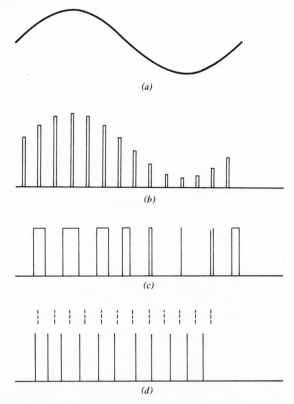

Fig. 5.10   Pulse modulation: (*a*) input signal wave; (*b*) pulse amplitude modulation; (*c*) pulse width modulation; (*d*) pulse position modulation.

can be shown that if the amplitude sampling rate exceeds twice the highest frequency contained in the signal wave the original signal can be reconstructed [13]. If the sampling pulses are sufficiently short, the unallocated time can be shared with other information channels. The process is called multiplexing. Pulse-width or pulse-time modulation offers the additional advantage that a signal can be reconstructed free of noise, provided the pulse amplitudes are moderately stronger than the noise. Because they require a very wide band, most pulse systems are limited to the very high frequencies.

In still another method, called pulse-code modulation (PCM), the signal is sampled at regular intervals and quantized into discrete amplitude levels which are converted to coded groups. As a rule binary coding is used so that the number of levels is 2^n, where n is the number of bits allowed in the code. Thus a three-bit code permits quantizing to eight levels and a four-bit code, to 16 levels. The maximum error is half the quantizing interval. Obviously the more levels used, the more precise the reconstruction. Such systems are error-free, provided the signal-to-noise ratio is high enough (20 dB, as a rule of thumb) that noise peaks are not mistaken for pulses.

It is evident in all types of modulation that side frequencies are an important consideration. In actuality the modulating signal is seldom even approximately harmonic and continuous. However, it can be shown by the methods of Fourier analysis that any finite wave train can be represented by an appropriate linear summation of harmonics of the types discussed. Details of the methods can be found in many works in applied mathematics.

4 ELECTROMAGNETIC WAVE GENERATION AND MODULATION

The Electromagnetic Spectrum

Electromagnetic energy exists as a state of excitation established by the presence and motion of electric charges. Classically it is described by the Maxwell field equations. The term "field" in this context is simply a region in which the directions and intensities of the electric and magnetic forces are defined at every point in the region. A time-variant magnetic field produces and is accompanied by an electric field; conversely, a time-variant electric field produces and is accompanied by a magnetic field. Taken together, the disturbance is called an electromagnetic field whose wavelike properties can be used to describe interactions with matter and with other fields.

The essential features of all electromagnetic waves are the same, regardless of frequency. The known spectrum (Fig. 5.11) extends continuously from the very long wavelengths associated with power distribution lines to the high-energy gamma rays produced by electron synchrotrons and observed

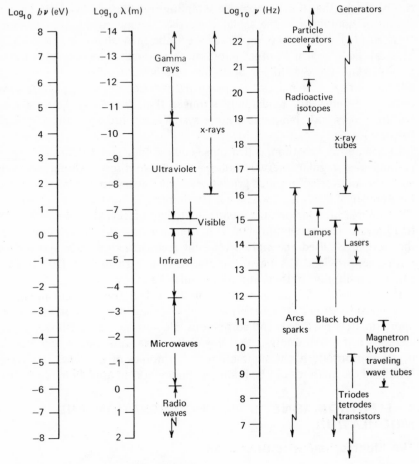

Fig. 5.11   The electromagnetic spectrum.

in cosmic radiation. Although it is possible to treat low-frequency generation and modulation on the basis of field theory, it is not usually profitable. The lower end of the radiofrequency spectrum is taken in the neighborhood of 10^4 Hz at a wavelength of 3×10^4 m. At the other end of the spectrum radiation still exhibits wavelike properties, but it is necessary to take into account its particlelike aspects in terms of quantized units of energy, $h\nu$, where h is Planck's constant. By convention the region between these two extremes is arbitrarily divided into octaves, as shown in Fig. 5.11. There is considerable overlapping between the very high radiofrequencies and the infrared regions and again between the far-ultraviolet and x-ray regions.

Such artificial classifications are significant only with respect to the physical apparatus employed in generation, transmission, or detection.

To the extent that Maxwell's equations are valid classical phenomena such as interference, refraction, and diffraction are invariant with frequency, provided the linear dimensions are scaled in proportion to wavelength [1]. However, interactions between radiation and matter are generally frequency-selective. The phase velocity of an electromagnetic wave is given by $v = (\mu\epsilon)^{-1/2}$, where μ and ϵ are, respectively, the permeability and permittivity of the medium in which the fields exist. In vacuum, and to a very close approximation in air, $v = (\mu_0\epsilon_0)^{-1/2} = c$, the velocity of light. The wavenumber $k = \omega/v = \omega(\mu_0\epsilon_0)^{1/2}$ is real and there is no attenuation of the wave. In the optical region the ratio c/v is called the index of refraction.

From a somewhat oversimplified point of view every source of electromagnetic energy can be considered as an array of one or more harmonic oscillators of the type represented by the LRC circuit of Fig. 5.12a. It is simply the tank circuit of the audio- or radiofrequency oscillator discussed in Chapter IV. Such a circuit supports current and voltage waves as long as electrical energy is supplied at a rate equal to that at which it is dissipated, by internal losses, radiation, or conduction. If $R = 0$, the circuit oscillates

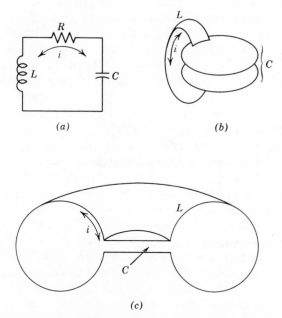

Fig. 5.12 Resonant circuits: (a) low frequency LRC circuit; (b) a high frequency circuit; (c) a microwave cavity.

indefinitely at a single frequency given by

$$v = \frac{1}{2\pi\sqrt{LC}}$$

At the lower end of the frequency scale the inductors and capacitors become so large physically that it is often more convenient to use rotating mechanical devices such as alternating current generators and choppers. Electric and magnetic fields exist even when the frequency is so low that it approaches direct current. However, the electromagnetic fields are weak and interactions are most easily treated in terms of potentials across or currents flowing in circuit elements.

To increase the resonant frequency of an oscillating circuit, it is necessary to use successively smaller values of inductance and capacitance. Ultimately, as the region of ultrahigh radiofrequencies is reached, the ac circuit is reduced to a single loop that constitutes the inductance of the leads and the internal shunt capacitance of the active element. In tubes and transistors designed for high-frequency operation these quantities are reduced to minimum values determined by geometry and required power levels. The circuit may be considered equivalent to that shown in Fig. 5.12b. Since high-frequency currents are restricted primarily to the surfaces of conductors, a considerable reduction in inductance can be attained by enlarging the conducting areas of the leads. Such a concept is illustrated in the cross-sectional view of Fig. 5.12c. It is essentially a cavity within which tubes or transistors of "planar" construction can be inserted. The leads and electrodes then function as a continuation of the resonant cavity. It still behaves as an oscillator but with inductance and capacitance distributed throughout the circuit. Unlike the basic circuit of Fig. 5.12a the electromagnetic field is confined to the cavity and it cannot radiate.

At low and intermediate radiofrequencies the time required for charge carriers to travel between electrodes is negligible, compared with the period of oscillation. As the operating frequency is raised, this effect, called transit time, becomes more important. It causes an increase in the effective input conductance in shunt with the resonant tank circuit and a phase shift in output current with respect to input potential. The result is a considerable loss of efficiency and finally a complete cessation of oscillation at high frequency. Transit-time effects can be minimized by the use of small electrodes and close electrode spacing. Power dissipation, however, is severely limited. Fortunately, advantage can be taken of finite transit time in electron tubes to obtain ultra-high-frequency operation through direct interactions between electron beams and cavity fields. Tubes in this category include klystrons, traveling-wave tubes, backward-wave oscillators, and magnetrons.

The lowest practical wavelength limit for direct generation of microwaves in electron cavity devices is in the neighborhood of 10^{-3} m. Although radiation at wavelengths in the fractional millimeter range can be obtained by a process called harmonic generation, oscillators of molecular dimensions are the next important class on an ascending frequency scale. Vibrations and rotations of molecules and atoms at elevated temperatures give rise to electromagnetic radiation that is generally classified as infrared. On the basis of the materials and detection used, this region is arbitrarily subdivided into the far infrared (10^{-3} to 5×10^{-6} m), the intermediate infrared (5×10^{-6} to 1.5×10^{-6} m), and the near infrared (1.5×10^{-6} to 7×10^{-7} m). On the basis of resonance absorption phenomena, four subdivisions of the same region are also made. These are, in order of decreasing wavelength, the rotation, fundamental vibration, overtone, and photographic regions.

Because of the extremely large number of molecules in a finite volume of matter, the coupling interactions between them, and the resulting perturbations, the radiation process is a complex one. The emission of electromagnetic energy is a quantum process that involves changes in vibrational and rotational quantum levels based on statistical and mechanical considerations beyond this discussion. Band spectra are characteristic of molecules containing more than one atom; that is, the radiation consists of many finite wave trains representing a range of frequencies that depends on the molecular and atomic structure.

Progressing through the electromagnetic spectrum, atomic spectra in the visible and near-ultraviolet regions represent radiation at definite frequencies arising from discrete jumps in electron energy levels. First the outer orbital electrons are involved and then the inner orbitals, which correspond to much higher energies. Finally, in the x- and γ-ray region the emission of radiation is associated with energetic reactions within the nucleus leading to transmutation of elements. Energy is usually measured in terms of the electron volt, the energy acquired by an electron in falling through a potential difference of 1 V.

Modulation of Radiofrequencies

Vacuum-tube and transistor oscillators for use at audio and intermediate radiofrequencies are described in Chapter IV. Essentially, they consist of circuits coupled between the grid and plate (or the equivalent transistor elements) in such a way that the grid and plate signals, referred to the cathode, are opposite in phase. Although the desired phase shift may be obtained from resistance-capacitance networks, as found in "twin-tee" and "Wien bridge" oscillators, resonant or tuned circuits are almost invariably used in sinusoidal radiofrequency generators. For long-term stability a mechanically resonant quartz crystal is commonly used in place of or in conjunction with the tuned circuit, the piezoelectric effect serving as the link between the mechanical and electrical circuits. The crystal and its holder may be represented by an equivalent circuit consisting of a series-resonant LRC shunted by the electrical capacitance of the mounting. It is characterized by high values of Q and stabilities of a few parts per million. Whatever the mode of operation, energy is stored in the circuit elements (or alternatively, in the field around them) and losses are replenished from the alternating component of plate current. Direct current plate potentials are introduced either by series or shunt feed. In the latter case a choke is used to isolate the power supply. A capacitor is also required to bypass radio frequency currents and to block direct currents from other portions of the circuit.

Amplitude Modulation Methods

In certain cases conventional oscillators can be directly modulated by superposing the modulating signal on the plate supply of the oscillator tube, as shown in the circuit of Fig. 5.13. With grid-leak bias the tube operates Class C* with high efficiency. The instantaneous amplitudes of oscillation

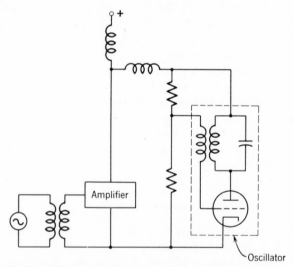

Fig. 5.13 Simplified schematic of an amplitude-modulated oscillator.

---

* A Class C amplifier is one in which bias is so adjusted that plate current flows during appreciably less than a half cycle. In tuned power amplifiers the grid is driven positive and draws current during the crest of the cycle. The output plate-cathode voltage is linear with excitation voltage up to the point of saturation.

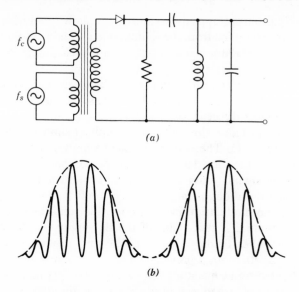

Fig. 5.14   Diode modulator: (a) simplified schematic; (b) output waveform.

faithfully follow the modulating signal, provided the effective Q of the tank circuit is reasonably low. High values of Q connote sharp resonance which discriminates against the side bands. This circuit has the disadvantage that frequency depends somewhat on the plate supply and thus on the modulation envelope. For the reason just given crystals do not perform satisfactorily in circuits of this type.

In the more general case modulation is carried out by applying two frequencies, the carrier and a signal, to a third circuit, called the modulator, in such a way that the carrier and the sum and difference frequencies appear at the output. The process is variously referred to as heterodyning, conversion, beating, and translation. To obtain the cross-product terms indicated in (5.15) it is evident that the circuit must have a nonlinear characteristic. This situation is in contrast to linear devices such as high quality sound systems which do not produce sum and difference frequencies (i.e., there is little or no intermodulation distortion).

The simplest nonlinear element is a solid-state diode. Carrier and modulating signals, applied as shown in Fig. 5.14a, are additive in the secondary winding of the input transformer. The lower frequency modulating signal can be considered as a variable bias that adds to or subtracts from the carrier amplitude in accordance with its instantaneous phase. After clipping the negative portion of the composite signal by rectifier action the negative half of each radiofrequency cycle is effectively reinserted in a low Q resonant circuit. The final output appears somewhat as shown in Fig. 5.14b. Since all of the power is supplied from the radiofrequency and modulating sources the simple diode modulator is useful only at low levels. Insertion loss is also considerable.

In power applications modulation is usually achieved in a power amplifier with suitable nonlinear characteristics. There are several methods in common use. One of the most direct involves superposing the modulating signal on the dc plate supply of an ordinary Class C amplifier shown in the simplified connection of Fig. 5.15. The equivalent plate supply potential thus varies in accordance with the sum. The radiofrequency output amplitude is linear with modulating signal, provided the grid bias and load impedance are adjusted so that the radiofrequency signal is just sufficient to cause saturation at the peak of the modulation cycle. Under this condition the equivalent plate supply potential is twice that of the dc supply. At the modulation troughs the amplifier tends to oversaturate and produce excessive grid dissipation. This situation is prevented either by the use of a series input resistance, shunted by a capacitor as shown, or by otherwise providing poor regulation in the radiofrequency driver. As in the discussion pertaining to the modulated oscillator, the loaded Q of the plate tank circuit must be low enough that the impedance at the upper side bands is substantially the same as that at the carrier frequency. In other words, the half-power band-width should be at least equal to twice the highest modulating frequency.

Viewed from the modulating signal source, the plate circuit impedance of the amplifier is given by the ratio of dc supply potential and dc plate current in the absence of modulation. To obtain complete modulation the modulating source should provide a signal with an amplitude and peak current equal to the respective values for the dc supply. Thus the modulator power requirement is one-half the dc power.

Modulating the collector supply of a transistor in a manner similar to that just discussed does not produce full modulation because a portion of

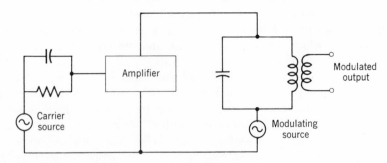

Fig. 5.15 Simplified schematic of plate modulation.

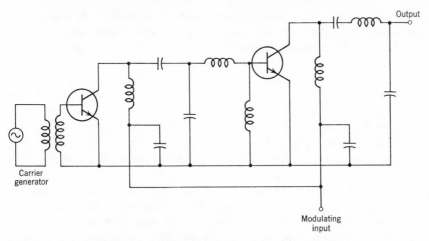

Fig. 5.16 Simplified schematic of a transistorized amplitude modulator.

the radiofrequency signal feeds through the transistor during troughs of the modulating signal [14]. Better characteristics are obtained by modulating the supply to at least two stages, as shown in Fig. 5.16. Here both the dc current and the signal current are supplied by the modulating source.

The large amount of power required for plate modulation is frequently a serious drawback. In many wideband applications, such as those that occur at the video frequencies, it is possible to obtain a modulated wave by superposing the modulating and carrier signals in the grid circuit of a Class C radiofrequency amplifier, as shown schematically in Fig. 5.17. Since the dc component of plate current is the same in both the presence and absence of modulation, the grid bias may be obtained by using a cathode resistor, suitably bypassed for both modulating and carrier frequencies. The fact that the grid is driven somewhat positive during a portion of the cycle requires that the sources have good regulation. To sustain power inputs at reasonably

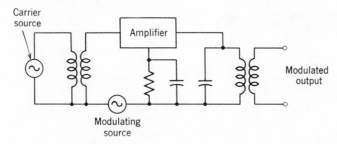

Fig. 5.17 Simplified schematic of grid modulation.

low values, beam and tetrode amplifiers are necessary. Grid modulation has the disadvantages of low plate efficiency and it introduces somewhat more nonlinearity than plate modulation.

Many other systems of amplitude modulation have been devised to take advantage of the nonlinear characteristics of both vacuum tubes and transistors. These include suppressor and screen-grid modulation of Class C amplifiers, as well as grid modulation that results from the dependence of transconductance on bias in the ordinary Class A amplifier. In addition, negative feedback is effective in reducing distortion and improving frequency response. Typically, a portion of the modulated output is rectified and fed back to the input circuit in proper phase.

There are various techniques for suppressing the carrier only, one side band only, or the carrier and one side band of amplitude modulated radio-frequency waves. Those most commonly used depend on direct filtering or on phase shifting and balance circuits. Filtering requirements are severe; quartz crystals, electromechanical band-pass filters, and passive LC networks designed for the purpose are available in many ranges. The latter are generally used for vestigial side band generation. For double side band modulation the carrier may be suppressed in balanced systems such as those in Fig. 5.18. The bridge circuit shown at (a) is available as an integrated

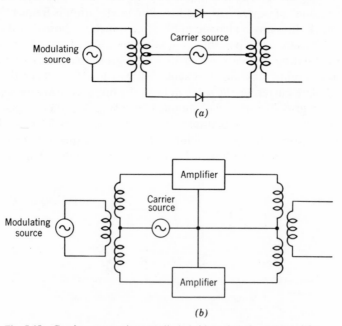

Fig. 5.18   Carrier suppression: (a) diode bridge; (b) balanced amplifiers.

circuit diode array. In the absence of a modulating signal the bridge is balanced and no radiofrequency output appears. A modulating signal upsets the balance by a biasing action on the diodes, which in turn permits a flow of radiofrequency current. To minimize distortion the amplitude of the radiofrequency should be several times that of the modulating signal. Series and ring-balanced configurations operate on similar principles. The circuit at (b) consists of two identical amplifiers in which the modulating signals are applied to the grids in opposite phase. Mixing with the carrier takes place in each tube, as previously described. The carrier, however, is applied in the same phase at each grid and effectively cancelled in the output transformer. A complete description of single side band modulation in which the carrier and one side band are suppressed by phase cancellation is considerably more involved. The modulator consists basically of two balanced pairs of the type shown in Fig. 5.18b. The circuit is so arranged that the radiofrequency signal applied at one of the pairs is shifted in phase by $\pi/2$. Each component of the modulating signal is likewise shifted in phase by $\pi/2$ with respect to the other pair. Mixing the outputs of both balanced pairs in a common tank circuit results in cancellation of the carrier and one side band. Any succeeding stages must operate in a linear mode to avoid intermodulation distortion.

Frequency- and Phase-Modulation Methods

The difference between frequency and phase modulation is largely a matter of semantics and implementation; for a given modulating frequency the contents are identical. In a frequency-modulated wave the index $(\omega_0/\omega_m)M_f$ [from (5.17)] varies inversely with the modulating frequency, whereas in a phase-modulated wave the index $\theta_0 M_p$ [from (5.21)] is independent of frequency. Thus the required bandwidth is larger for phase modulation than for frequency modulation. The phase mode, however, can be effectively converted to the frequency mode by passing the modulating signal through a frequency-selective network before modulation. In such a process, called "predistortion" by radio engineers, the amplitude of the modulating signal is made to decrease with increasing frequency content in a controlled manner. The usual practice in either phase or frequency modulation is to use a carrier of moderate frequency and modulate to a low index. By a secondary step of harmonic generation the index is then increased by the same factor as the frequency multiplication.

A direct and simple method of generating an angle-modulated signal is to vary the capacitance or the inductance mechanically in the tuned circuit of an oscillator. Such methods are useful when size and weight can be tolerated and simplicity is important. However, their speed of response is low. In the medium frequency range one or more resistive elements of an

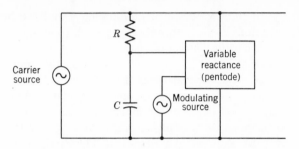

Fig. 5.19   Simplified schematic of a reactance tube modulator.

RC oscillator may be replaced with vacuum tube or transistor amplifiers. For a proper choice of operating conditions the oscillating frequency can be controlled over a considerable range.

A more common method used in frequency modulation is to shunt the tuned circuit with a variable reactance. In Fig. 5.19 a pentode, called a reactance tube (sometimes referred to as a quadrature circuit), draws reactive current in accordance with the amplitude of the modulating signal. With $R \ll X_c(X_c = 1/\omega_m C)$ the *RC* phase splitter provides a grid drive signal that is $\pi/2$ out of phase with respect to the plate-cathode potential. Thus the alternating plate current leads the plate potential by $\pi/2$ rad. In effect, this amounts to shunting the oscillator tank circuit with an equivalent capacitance of value $g_m RC$, where g_m is the transconductance of the tube. For modulating signals of moderate amplitude the variations in instantaneous radiofrequency are proportional to the amplitude of the modulating frequency. The resistive component of plate current in the reactance tube produces some amplitude modulation. It is usually removed by passing the modulated signal through a limiting device to produce a wave of constant amplitude. Practical use is restricted to frequencies below 10 MHz.

Various other methods for generating frequency-modulated signals follow similar lines of reasoning; for example, the reactive current through a series-connected capacitor and diode depends on the forward bias applied to the diode. As shown in Fig. 5.20, bias can be made to vary according to the

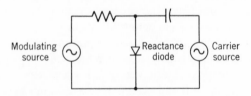

Fig. 5.20   Diode reactance control.

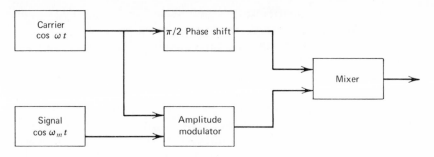

Fig. 5.21   The Armstrong method of angle modulation.

amplitude of the modulating signal by means of vacuum-tube or transistor amplifiers. Varactor diodes, in which capacitance varies in proportion to the applied potential, are also available.

The Armstrong method of frequency modulation employs amplitude modulation of the type discussed in Section 3. A portion of the unmodulated carrier is phase shifted by $\pi/2$ radians and added to the modulated carrier as illustrated in the block diagram of Fig. 5.21. From simple trigonometric identities it is easily shown that the resultant wave contains a phase term that depends on the modulation index and frequency. If the modulation index is small enough, the phase term can be approximated by $M \cos \omega_m t$, which has the same form as Eq. 5.21. The variation in amplitude can be effectively removed by using a suitable limiter circuit.

Ultrahigh-Frequency Generators

Negative-Grid-Modulated Devices

Oscillators for the ultrahigh-frequency range may be classified as negative-grid- or velocity-modulated. The negative-grid classification includes all the usual receiver-type tubes in which electron current is controlled by a signal impressed on a negatively biased grid. Although biasing conditions and the type of charge carrier differ, the same general classification applies to equivalent transistor circuits. It has already been mentioned that the lumped parameter concept must be abandoned at the ultrahigh frequencies. The usual point of departure occurs at such a frequency that a transmission line, although still electrically long, becomes physically short. Waves on such lines obey the wave equation and, under suitable conditions, reflections at the end of the line produce resonances of the type discussed in Section 2. If a quarter-wave line, or one that is an odd number of quarter wavelengths long, is short-circuited at the load end, the input impedance is high and varies with frequency in the same manner as a conventional resonant circuit.

A line shorter than a quarter wavelength presents a reactance that is inductive when short-circuited and capacitative when open-circuited; a line between a quarter and a half wavelength long presents a reactance that is capacitative when shorted and inductive when open. At high frequencies the effective Q and the impedance at resonance are considerably higher than can be obtained with lumped parameter circuits.

Some older types of tube used double-ended construction to permit connection to the center of a half-wave system with shorted ends. Since the lumped plate-grid capacitance is in effect divided between two quarter-wave sections, the frequency of oscillation is higher than in a single-ended quarter-wave section. Radiation losses are also lower for the same reason. More recent tube designs, such as are found in the "lighthouse," "disk-seal," or "planar" construction, have lead arrangements that make them suitable for coaxial lines or resonant cavities. Lead inductance is minimized by the use of large-diameter disks sealed into the glass envelope, as illustrated in Fig. 5.22. The planar construction, with the electrodes made as plane surfaces, permits very close spacing between grid and cathode and a consequent reduction in electron transit time. In power tubes that are capable of operating in excess of 3 GHz at peak pulsed outputs of more than a kilowatt the plate is made in the form of a solid block with thermal radiating fins. Metal and ceramic construction is also used for higher shock resistance and greater plate dissipation.

Solid-State Radiofrequency Devices

Recently *npn* power transistors* designed specifically for operation at 2 GHz have become commercially available. Like their electron-tube counterpart, they are hermetically sealed in a ceramic metal coaxial package

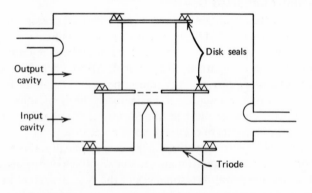

Fig. 5.22 Simplified outline of a disk-seal triode mounted in cavities.

* For example, RCA-2N5470.

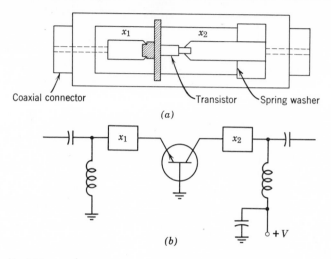

Fig. 5.23   Coaxial cavity and simplified circuit for a high-frequency transistor.

that can be used in coaxial, stripline, or lumped constant circuits. The base terminal is in the form of a large-diameter flange, electrically insulated from the collector and emitter stud terminals at either end. A suggested mounting arrangement and a circuit schematic are given in Fig. 5.23. Operating at a maximum collector-to-base potential of 55 V, the rated output power is 1 W at 2 GHz and 2 W at 1 GHz.

The frequency response of a transistor is limited by the drift and diffusion rates of charge carriers. A device not subject to these limitations is the tunnel diode [15, 16]. It exhibits a negative conductance that arises from quantum mechanical "tunneling" effects. The depletion region in a *pn* junction, usually of germanium, is made so thin that charge carriers can penetrate through the potential barrier with relative ease. In the absence of bias there is no net current, but as the bias is increased the current increases and passes through a maximum determined by the manufacturing process. As bias is further increased, the current drops to the "valley," as shown in Fig. 5.24a, and thereafter takes on the characteristic of an ordinary diode under forward bias.

Because of its negative conductance characteristic the tunnel diode is ideally suited to the design of low-power sinusoidal, relaxation, and mono-stable oscillators. A simple sinusoidal oscillator circuit is shown in Fig. 5.24b. The frequency of oscillation is given by

$$\omega = \left(\frac{1}{L(C + C_1)} - \frac{g_d{}^2}{C_1(C + C_1)} \right)^{1/2}, \tag{5.22}$$

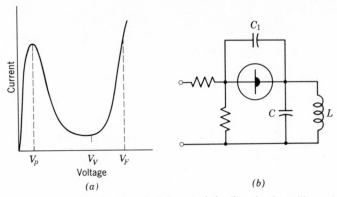

Fig. 5.24 The tunnel diode: (*a*) typical characteristic; (*b*) a simple oscillator circuit.

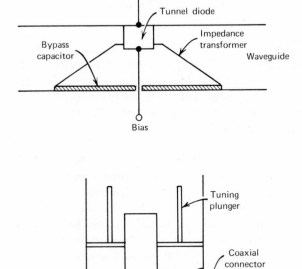

Fig. 5.25 Typical diode cavities: (*a*) waveguide mounting of tunnel diode; (*b*) cavity mounting.

where g_d is the conductance at the operating point and C, C_1, and L are, respectively, the capacitances and inductances shown. Theoretically the tunnel diode is capable of operating to thousands of gigahertz. The load inductance and package capacitance, however, tend to lower the maximum operating frequency. A variety of cavities [17], such as the one illustrated in Fig. 5.25a, have been designed to make the L and C parameters part of the microwave circuit. The impedance of the diode is low and driving from conventional power supplies is both difficult and inefficient.

Diodes that exhibit very thin depletion layers under avalanche conditions at microwave frequencies have also been made. With a suitable cavity [18, 19] they can be mechanically tuned over a frequency range in excess of one octave with only a modest variation in output power. One such resonant cavity consists of a tunable coaxial cavity with the diode at one end, as shown in Fig. 5.25b. Under typical bias conditions of 70 to 85 V and 17 to 18 mA diode current, the circuit can be tuned from 4 to 13 GHz. Power output is 45 mW.

Velocity Modulated Tubes

THE KLYSTRON OSCILLATOR [20, 21]

Several types of velocity-modulated electron device are used for generating microwave power [3, 22]. In all of them the electromagnetic field in a cavity or waveguide structure interacts directly with the electrons passing through it. Since the radiofrequency circuit is independent of cathode and anode, the problems of bypassing and decoupling are avoided.

A multicavity klystron is shown in the cross-sectional sketch in Fig. 5.26. With suitable radiofrequency connections it may be used as an amplifier

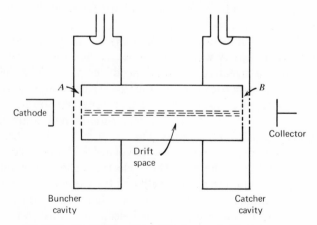

Fig. 5.26 Simplified outline of the two-cavity klystron.

or an oscillator. A high-velocity beam of electrons passes axially through two cavity resonators separated by a region called the drift space. Electrostatic focusing is used in some types; alternatively, an axial magnetic field produced by focus coils external to the tube is used to concentrate the electron beam in a more or less parallel bundle. For reasons that will become evident the input cavity is called the buncher. When it is excited by a radiofrequency signal to which it is resonant, a potential difference, varying at the resonant frequency, appears across the gap at A. An electron passing through the gap at the instant the radiofrequency potential is zero continues with unchanged velocity. An electron arriving at a somewhat later time when the radiofrequency potential is increasing in the positive direction undergoes acceleration and leaves the gap with an increased velocity. In a similar fashion an electron that had arrived at a somewhat earlier time is slowed down on leaving the gap. As a result of these actions the electrons tend to bunch together as they travel down the drift space toward the second cavity.

The bunching together of electrons at the second gap B, called the catcher, is tantamount to a cyclic variation of electron density, and the beam can be considered as a current-modulated beam. It excites oscillations in the catcher cavity in much the same way that pulses of plate current excite the tank circuit in a Class C amplifier. If the cavity is represented by an LC circuit, the AC component of current flowing through the shunt impedance represented by the gap induces a potential gradient (or electric field) across the gap. The energy extracted from the electron beam has a maximum value at the peak of the half cycle when the existing field is so directed that it tends to slow down the electrons during their passage through the gap. With proper values of accelerating potential, drift space length, and cavity dimensions, power amplification can be achieved. To convert such a device to an oscillator, a fraction of the radiofrequency signal appearing at the catcher is fed back to the buncher in proper phase.

The reflex klystron, illustrated schematically in Fig. 5.27, is an oscillator consisting of a single cavity which also serves as the anode. A repeller electrode operated at a negative potential produces an electric field which reflects the electron beam back through the cavity gap. Assuming oscillations in the cavity as a result of noise fluctuations in potential and beam current, the field across the gap produces a velocity-modulated beam as in the multicavity klystron. Those electrons that are accelerated in their passage through the gap penetrate deeply into the repeller field and trace out a long trajectory in returning to the gap. Those electrons that suffer retardation penetrate less deeply into the repeller field and trace out a shorter trajectory. (Plots of axial positions of the electrons as a function of time are called Appelgate diagrams.) As a result, bunched electrons return to the gap as a current-modulated beam. Again, if the bunches arrive at the gap at such

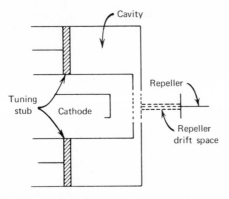

Fig. 5.27   Simplified outline of the reflex klystron.

points in the radiofrequency cycle that the existing electric field across the gap tends to decelerate the electrons, energy is delivered to the cavity field. Specifically, such a situation exists if the transit time in the repeller space is $(n + \frac{3}{4})$ cycles, where n is an integer. Figure 5.28 illustrates the dependence of frequency on reflector potential for three values of n in a typical tube operated at a constant resonator potential.

The frequency of oscillation in a reflex klystron is determined primarily by the resonant frequency of the cavity. Tuning over a moderate range can be achieved by mechanically flexing the cavity walls and/or simultaneously varying the gap spacing. With an external cavity a tuning plunger

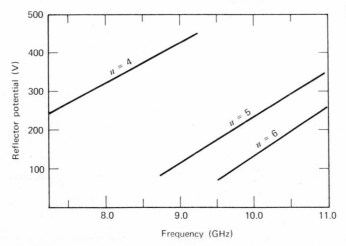

Fig. 5.28   Frequency dependence on reflector potential in a typical reflex klystron.

permits tuning over a frequency range of 2:1, provided the repeller potential is also varied to satisfy the conditions imposed by consideration of transit time. Oscillations can occur only for certain combinations of anode and repeller potentials, a fact that is often presented as a mode pattern diagram in a plot of repeller potential against resonator potential. These potentials can be varied to affect fine tuning or frequency modulation over a range of about 1%.

SLOW-WAVE OSCILLATORS

Devices with short electron interaction lengths, such as klystrons, are inherently narrow-band, high-Q systems. Another class of electron device employs slow-wave structures to decrease effectively the velocity of a radio-frequency wave with the speed of light to that of the electron beam [23–25]. Although it is basically an amplifier rather than an oscillator, the traveling-wave tube is described briefly for completeness. As indicated in Fig. 5.29a, an electron gun produces a pencil beam of electrons directed along the axis of a helix which carries the radiofrequency signal. The beam is normally

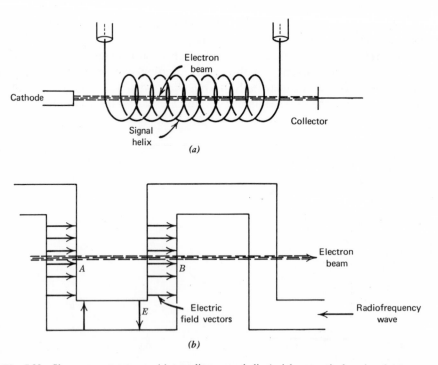

Fig. 5.29 Slow wave structures: (a) traveling wave helix (axial magnetic focusing field not shown); (b) a "folded" waveguide.

collimated by means of an axial magnetic field that is not shown. The axial component of the signal progresses with a velocity that is equal to the velocity of light times the ratio of helix pitch to circumference. When the electron velocity is approximately equal to the rate of advance of the electric field produced by the signal, energetic interactions take place. With electron energy delivered to the signal field, the signal wave on the helix increases in amplitude along the length of the helix. At the same time the electron beam is further subjected to velocity modulation along the entire length of the tube. Electron bunching, equivalent to current modulation in the electron beam, induces an added component to the wave on the helix. This, in turn, produces an axial electric field that lags the signal field by a quarter wavelength. As electrons travel down the tube, bunching becomes more complete and the induced wave grows exponentially in amplitude. At the end of the tube the resultant field, which is the sum of the signal and induced fields, lags the original signal by nearly a quarter wavelength. Since energy is extracted from the electron beam along the entire length, considerable power amplification is possible.

In the helix type of slow-wave structure, the velocity of the axial field is almost independent of frequency. Since it is a nonresonant device, considerably wider bandwidths can be obtained with the traveling-wave tube than with cavity resonators. In the frequency range of several gigahertz the gain is typically 30 dB or more and flat to within 3 dB over a frequency range of 2 to 1. Reflected waves arising from impedance mismatches can cause spontaneous oscillations, as discussed in Section 2. When designed for amplifier use, an attenuator in the form of a conducting coating is usually applied to the inner wall near the input end of the tube.

Other types of slow wave structure have also been designed. In particular, the axial wave velocity in a "folded" waveguide, such as that illustrated in Fig. 5.29b, is slow enough to permit interactions with a high-velocity electron beam directed through apertures in the guide. However, such an arrangement is dispersive in the sense that the wavelength varies with frequency. In the backward-wave tube advantage is taken of the narrower band pass to generate oscillations by positive feedback. Assuming a TE_{10} mode propagating to the left, the diagram shows the directions of the electric field at a given instant of time. The number of radiofrequency cycles required for an electron to travel from A to B, opposite to the propagation direction of the field, is $t_e v$, where t_e is the electron transit time and v is the wave frequency. The direction of the field at A is inverted and lags that at B by $t_w v$ cycles, where t_w is the transit time of the wave. Thus, when the electron reaches the region B, it encounters a field that lags the field it had been previously subjected to at A by $(t_e + t_w)v$ cycles. Because of the phase reversal in the wave, an electron velocity such that the lag is a half-cycle tends to cause bunching and velocity modulation of the beam as in the gap of a klystron. The effect is cumulative as the electron stream passes down the axis through a number of gaps. In practice, the electron velocity is adjusted so that the delay is slightly less than a half-cycle between gaps and the net delay at the collector end of the tube is approximately a half-cycle. On the average, over most of their path, the electron bunches encounter decelerating fields at each gap and deliver energy to the "backward" wave. The frequency of oscillation is given by

$$v = \frac{0.5[1 - (1/n)]}{t_e + t_w}, \tag{5.23}$$

where n is the number of gaps. Since the transit time of the wave t_w is determined by tube geometry, the generated frequency is controlled by the anode voltage through the electron transit time t_e. Tuning is possible over a frequency range of 2 to 1.

Slow-wave devices are fairly sophisticated and are useful in high-power broad-band applications. They are nominally designed for low duty-cycle pulsed service with anode potentials in the neighborhood of 20 kV or more. It is advisable to consult the manufacturer for recommendations on installation and operation.

Crossed-Field Devices

THE MAGNETRON OSCILLATOR

The magnetron was the first important microwave source developed to operate at high power levels. Basically it consists of a cylindrical cathode surrounded by a concentric set of resonant cavities with slots that open into an annular interaction space [3, 9]. Under the action of superposed, high-intensity, radial-electric and axial-magnetic fields, electrons emitted from the cathode spiral outward toward the slots in the anode structure. The degree of path curvature depends on the intensity of the magnetic field. That field which is just sufficient to prevent electrons from striking the anode is labeled the "cutoff field." Assuming that oscillations exist in the cavities (as the result of noise in the space charge), the instantaneous electric fields across the gaps appear somewhat as sketched in Fig. 5.30. If the magnetic field is above cutoff, some electrons in the neighborhood of a gap will have tangential components of velocity of the correct value to interact with the radiofrequency field. Further, if the accelerating electric field and the magnetic field are appropriately adjusted, some electrons will travel more or less tangentially between adjacent gaps in the interval during which the radiofrequency field changes direction, that is, in one half period. As a result electrons continue to give up energy to the oscillating field, slowing down in

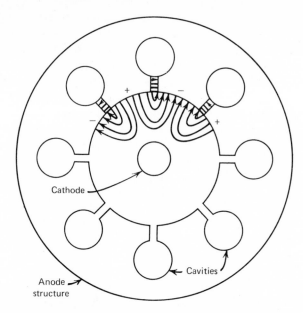

Fig. 5.30 Instantaneous electric fields in the magnetron.

the process until they strike the anode. Other electrons are radially accelerated by the radiofrequency field, but in the presence of the magnetic field they are rapidly turned back toward the cathode. These losses are compensated to some extent by inherent focusing. Electrons emitted out of step with the oscillating fields tend to be accelerated or decelerated to speeds of optimum interactions by the radial components of those fields. Magnetrons are normally designed for fixed-frequency operation but some tuning can be obtained by mechanically introducing a set of rods into the cavities or by coupling into an external tunable cavity.

A typical magnetron contains eight or more resonant cavities, each of which can resonate in a different mode, that is, with a different frequency and phase. In older designs alternate anode poles are "strapped" together by conducting rings to force operation into the π-mode. In this mode, which has the highest efficiency, the phase difference between the oscillating fields of adjacent gaps is restricted primarily to π rad. The capacitance between the straps loads the resonant cavities and lowers the frequency of the π-mode. Phase differences existing in other modes cause currents to flow along the straps which act as inductive shunts across the resonant circuit of the cavities. This raises the frequency of other modes and results in an effective separation of the π-mode from the others.

Several other schemes have been devised for constructing resonant cavities with adequate mode separation. In the "rising-sun" anode it is achieved by making the anode structure in the form of radial slots with alternate ones of different length. Radiofrequency fields appear between the vanes separating the slots just as they do across the gaps in Fig. 5.30. Interdigital lines in which the radiofrequency fields are developed across adjacent fingers have also been employed. Both structures avoid breakdown that occurs in high-power operation of the strapped structure at short wavelengths. The coaxial magnetron represents a more recent innovation to provide separation and damping of undesirable modes. The design incorporates a conventional vanelined anode surrounding the cathode and enclosed within a concentric cylindrical cavity operating in a TE_{011} mode. It is coupled to alternate resonators by means of slots in the cavity wall. Since energy is stored in the coaxial cavity rather than in the vane region, frequency is controlled by the cavity mode only, and the system may be tuned by a noncontacting plunger. Other modes can and do exist in coaxial cavities, but their analysis involves considerably more depth than can be presented here.

Magnetrons are high-power devices. Typically, powers range up to a few hundred watts constant wave at a few thousand volts to over a megawatt peak for pulsed operation, depending on duty cycle. Operation is sensitive to magnetic fields, anode potential, and load impedance. Many current models are supplied with permanent magnets as an integral part of the assembly. Field intensity and orientation are adjusted to optimum values at the factory. Performance data are ordinarily given in impedance charts called Rieke diagrams or in charts such as Fig. 5.31. For pulsed operation current and voltage pulses must be carefully shaped to the manufacturer's specification. Pulses are applied to the magnetron by discharging energy

	Min	Typical	Max	
Heater voltage		6.0		V
Peak anode potential	27.0	28.0	29.0	kV
Peak anode current		25.0		A
Pulse repetition rate		800		cps
Pulse duration		1.0		μsec
RF bandwidth		1.1	2.0	MHz
Frequency modulation			500	kHz
Peak power output	200	250		kW
Frequency	8600		9600	MHz

Fig. 5.31 Typical operating conditions of a tunable magnetron (Westinghouse WL-193).

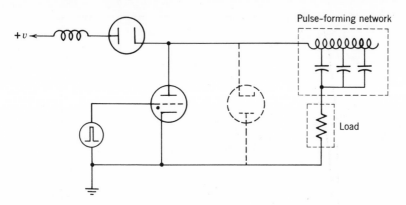

Fig. 5.32 Simplified line-type pulser circuit.

at a controlled rate through a pulse transformer specifically designed for the purpose. In the line-type pulser shown in Fig. 5.32 shaping is done in a pulse-forming network designed for specific pulse width and repetition rates. On the incidence of a synchronizing trigger the thyratron discharges the energy stored in the network through the transformer, thence to the magnetron. Vacuum-tube or "hard-tube" pulsers are also used to some extent. "Viewers" for coupling the current and voltage pulses to an oscilloscope are available as standard equipment.

Optical Sources

Blackbody Radiation

The oldest and still the commonest sources of energy in the optical region of the spectrum are glowing objects. Any solid (or liquid) object at a temperature above absolute zero radiates energy from the far infrared to the near ultraviolet, the intensity and spectral distribution depending on the temperature and nature of the body. Conversely, any object also absorbs energy from radiation incident on it. It is readily shown that the ratio of emissive power to absorbtivity is the same for all bodies in thermal equilibrium with their surroundings. This is known as Kirchhoff's law. Thus a body with a reflectivity of zero and an absorbtivity of unity is also the best possible radiator. Although no such material actually exists, the concept of an ideal model called a "blackbody" has considerable importance from both the theoretical and practical points of view. From theoretical considerations based on the quantized nature of radiation from a large number of elementary oscillators, the spectral radiant emittance W_λ, that is, the radiation emitted

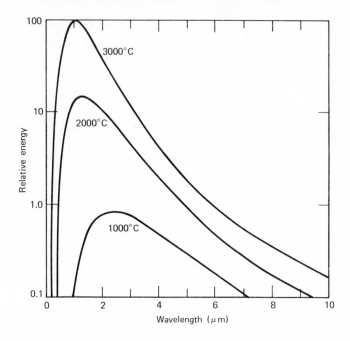

Fig. 5.33 Energy distribution of a blackbody source.

per unit surface area per unit wavelength interval, into a hemisphere, is given by

$$W_\lambda = \frac{2\pi h v^5}{C^3} \quad (e^{hv/kt} - 1)^{-1}$$

$$= \frac{2\pi h C^2}{\lambda^5} \quad (e^{hC/\lambda kt} - 1)^{-1}, \tag{5.24}$$

where T is the absolute temperature in degrees Kelvin, v and λ are, respectively, the frequency and wavelength of the emitted radiation, h ($= 6.62 \times 10^{-34}$ J-sec) is Planck's constant, C ($\approx 3 \times 10^8$ m/sec) is the velocity of propagation, and k ($= 1.38 \times 10^{-23}$ J/°K) is Boltzmann's constant. Equation 5.24 is known as the Planck radiation law. Some useful approximate equations of simpler mathematical form have been discussed by Erminy [26]. Figure 5.33 shows the dependence of emitted energy on wavelength for three values of temperature of an ideal blackbody. At any particular wavelength the ordinate represents the power radiated at that wavelength. Unlike radiofrequency sources, blackbody radiation always gives a continuous spectrum. As the temperature is increased, the emitted energy increases rapidly; at the wavelength of peak output the spectral radiance varies approximately as the fifth power of temperature. Also, the wavelength at which peak radiation occurs shifts toward the lower wavelengths with increasing temperature. The relation between the wavelength λ_m and temperature is given by differentiation of (5.24) by the Wien displacement law

$$\lambda_m T = \text{constant} (= 2.89 \times 10^3 \ \mu\text{m deg}), \tag{5.25}$$

where λ_m is expressed in meters and T is expressed in degrees Kelvin. The total radiant emittance into a hemisphere from an ideal blackbody is given by the Stefan-Boltzmann law, obtained by integrating (5.24) to yield

$$W = \sigma T^4, \tag{5.26}$$

where the Stefan-Boltzmann constant $\sigma = 5.67 \times 10^{-8} \ \text{W}/m^2 \ \text{deg}^4$.

Some detectors respond to the rate of photon arrival. In such cases the number of photons radiated per unit time spectral interval can be obtained by dividing each side of (5.24) by the energy of a photon, namely, $h\nu = hc/\lambda$.

The importance of the blackbody concept lies in the fact that its radiation is described in terms of fundamental constants. Properly designed cavities approach ideal conditions to a very close approximation [27–29]; for example, radiation entering a hollow enclosure through an aperture small compared with the size of the enclosure is reflected back and forth until it is completely absorbed, provided the reflectivity of the wall material is less than unity. If the enclosure is uniformly heated, the output radiation at a given temperature is the same in all directions. Practical sources of such shapes as those shown in Fig. 5.34 may be used as primary radiation standards for the calibration of radiometric instruments over a wide spectral range. They are usually constructed of suitably blackened steel, aluminum, or copper. A typical recessed construction provides a nominal 10 to 15° field of view at a cavity emissivity of 0.99. Temperatures range from a low of 50 up to 1900°C and may be controlled to a fraction of a degree by means of a high-gain servo system. In some models the cavity is protected by a curtain of dry argon gas or by baffle plates.

One ingenious design of a black body with an operating range of $-40°$ to $+60°$C employs thermoelectric heat pumping for uniform and stable temperature control [30]. The radiator consists of a blackened honeycomb cavity array with a 12° steradian field of view and an emitting area of 65 cm². The hexagonal honeycomb structure is commercially available in aluminum. With a cell depth of only 2.5 cm, its emissivity is given as higher than 0.995 over the range of 4 to 40 μm.

Few of the sources that are useful for instrumentation behave like ideal blackbodies. Some materials, such as carbon, tungsten, iron, and platinum,

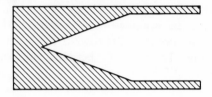

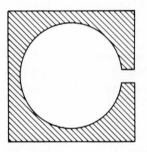

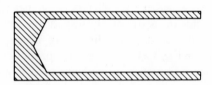

Fig. 5.34   Typical blackbody cavities.

are so nearly nonselective that they are called gray bodies. The spectral distribution of their radiation is nearly the same as that produced by a blackbody but at a lower power level [31, 32]. Carbon has the highest melting point of any known element and has been used in electrically heated filaments for many years. However, because of its high rate of evaporation, it must be operated at temperatures considerably below maximum in order to obtain satisfactory life. Tantalum carbides also have high melting points but are subject to the same difficulty. Tungsten has the highest melting point and lowest vapor pressure of any of the common metals, and strip filaments made from it provide reliable working standards over a range of 0.25 to 4.0 μm. Even though most modern lamps contain an inert atmosphere of argon and nitrogen at somewhat less than atmospheric pressure to retard evaporation of the filament, some blackening of the envelope eventually occurs. In a more recent innovation a small quantity of iodine is introduced into a lamp envelope designed for operation at an elevated temperature [33]. Iodine reacts with tungsten vapor, and the resulting product disintegrates at the tungsten filament rather than on the lamp wall. Such lamps are smaller than conventional lamps of the same power rating.

Other sources, such as gases at elevated temperatures, gases excited by electrons, luminescent materials, and lasers, are highly wavelength-selective. Nearly all modern sources employ electrical energy in one form or another. Although many of them emit over a very wide wavelength range, it is convenient to group them as infrared, visible, or ultraviolet emitters.

Infrared Sources

Infrared radiation lies between the radio and visible regions of the electromagnetic spectrum and possesses characteristics common to both. Unlike radiofrequency resonant circuits that emit waves with a very narrow frequency spread, few infrared sources emit radiation with any degree of monochromaticity. In other words, the coherence length is so short in all but special cases that the radiation is said to be noncoherent. The much shorter wavelengths, however, often permit the use of optical techniques with attendant simplicity of apparatus [34–36]. In addition to military ranging and communications and continuous process analysis, infrared radiation is widely used in studies of chemical reactions and crystal and molecular structures whose dimensions are of the order of magnitude of the wavelength of the radiation.

Because it is emitted by all hot bodies and produces heat on absorption (as does any electromagnetic wave), infrared radiation is often (and erroneously) referred to as heat radiation. Unlike heat, it is propagated through vacuum, most gases, and, in varying degrees, through many dielectric materials. Tungsten filament lamps are efficient generators of infrared and are widely used in spectrographic work. From 75 to 85% of the input power appears as heat and as infrared radiation between the limits of 0.76 and 5.0 μm. Longer wavelengths are absorbed by the glass bulb and dissipated by conduction and convection or reradiated at wavelengths corresponding to the emission from hot glass. Some special lamps are essentially ordinary lamps designed for low efficiency in the visible. Others employ quartz bulbs to withstand high-temperature operation [37]. In one example a coiled tungsten filament is contained within a quartz tube of small diameter. At 100 W/in. of lighted length the operating temperature is approximately 4000°F. Lamps of any reasonable length can be made but are restricted to horizontal burning.

With certain high-current incandescent sources the dynamic characteristics of the filament must be considered [38]. Tungsten metal exhibits a positive coefficient of resistance; the resistance of a cold filament is typically $\frac{1}{15}$ that of the same filament when hot. As a result, the initial current surge, sometimes called the inrush current, can attain large values. Furthermore, nonuniform heating caused by thermal inertia and local cooling at support structures can produce severe distortion and even rupture of the filament. In starting single-rod and strip-filament lamps, for example, precautions should be taken to ensure that the filament is brought to operating temperature slowly enough that thermal equilibrium is at least roughly maintained.

The Nernst glower is widely used as a source of near-infrared radiation [39]. It consists of a sintered bar or hollow tube of zirconia mixed with yttrium oxide that becomes electrically conductive at elevated temperatures. It is started by an auxiliary heater coil placed close to the glower and often backed by a reflector. Ordinarily operated at 1800°K in air, its power requirements are 90 W at 75 V.*

Since it exhibits a negative temperature coefficient, a series ballast is required. Output can be maintained at a constant level with a servo system that contains a photoelectric monitor and a saturable core reactor or multi-contact relay with stepwise adjustment of series resistance. A phase-control method has been described in which the load power in a silicon-controlled rectifier is controlled by the firing angle of a unijunction transistor [40]. Nernst glowers have the disadvantages of low mechanical strength and a limited number of heat-cool cycles.

Silicon carbides† bonded in the form of small-diameter cylinders are also convenient sources of energy in the near infrared. At an electrical power input of 180 W at 50 V they typically attain a temperature of 1200°C for a useful life of about 250 hr. Higher temperature operation causes sublimation of material from the surface and rapid deterioration.

Another useful source of infrared is the miniature cartridge-type heater with axial leads.‡ Resistance wire wound on an insulating core and packed in magnesium oxide with an Inconel metal sheath offers some advantage in efficiency [41]. Surface sandblasting, followed by a coating of Zapon black carbonoid lacquer, which is reduced to ash in operation, produces an emissivity that approaches unity in the 10-μm region. Although life at continuous operation is only about 10 hr at 1150°C, an improvement of about 10 times may be expected for every 120°C reduction in temperature. The thermal time constant is about 18 sec.

---

* "Insulcon" manufactured by Stupakoff Ceramic Company.

† "Globar" manufactured by Carborundum Corporation.

‡ "Firerod" manufactured by Watlow Electric Manufacturing Company.

Many arcs approximate black-body sources of high radiance. Most of the emitted energy, however, falls in the visible part of the spectrum. The wavelength distribution of carbon arcs can be altered by the addition of metallic salts and the desired spectra filtered out by optical filters. In the concentrated arc the cathode is formed as a coaxial hole in a tungsten cylinder and filled with zirconia [42]. High luminance is produced in the axial direction. Since the discharge takes place in an argon atmosphere, line spectra are superposed on the continuous background spectrum. A fused-quartz mercury arc with the outer glass envelope removed is also frequently used as a source of infrared radiation.

Because of the large thermal capacities involved, incandescent solids cannot be directly modulated at any appreciable rate. Fine-filament lamps can be operated at a few cycles per second and at somewhat higher rates in circuits that provide high-voltage starting. Power is severely limited, however. Higher power systems invariably employ mechanical or electro-mechanical beam interruption [43]. Since the frequency response of many infrared detectors is relatively low, the required chopping rates are more often limited by the detector than by mechanical considerations. Feedback stabilization has been employed to provide continuously variable chopping over the range of 8 to 3000 Hz [44]. Another mechanical method depends on the fact that rough surfaces strongly scatter short-wavelength radiation [45, 46]. If a rough-surfaced "mirror" in the optical path is oscillated, periodicity is introduced into the long-wavelength specularly reflected beam.

In the 8- to 12-μm region dimensional tolerances become such that frustrated total internal reflection can be used to produce amplitude modulation at frequencies above 6 kHz. In one device that has been described the modulation cell consists of two 20° germanium wedges arranged with a narrow air gap between the two slant faces [47]. If radiation from one element is incident on the gap at any angle exceeding critical, a fraction of the radiation will penetrate the gap and enter the other element. The penetration is a function of the wedge spacing and decreases from 100% to a negligible fraction as the gap width is increased by the order of a wavelength. For radiation at 10 μm a variation of 1 μm in gap width produces 67% modulation. A six-element stack of piezoelectric transducers is used to drive one wedge relative to the other.

Gaseous discharges (see Section 4) at moderate pressure permit pulsed and audiofrequency modulation when used in appropriate circuits. For near-infrared work the cesium vapor lamp emits resonance lines at 0.85 and 0.89 μm. The output is about five times that of tungsten for the same input power. The electrodes require an initial "warm-up," after which ionization of the cesium vapor is initiated by a high-voltage pulse. After starting, the arc can be maintained at a low level by direct current supplied through a ballast resistor. Modulation is then effected by superposing the modulating signal through a low-impedance transformer. Since the arc enclosure operates at an elevated temperature, it is enclosed in an outer evacuated envelope.

Gallium arsenide and gallium phosphide *pn* junctions emit radiation in the near-infrared region of the spectrum when operated under forward bias [48, 49]. An infrared emitter* designed for pulsed or continuous operation has a peak emission at 910 nm with a width at half-power of 60 nm. The output is 6 mW average at 1.4 V and is confined to a cone of 0.5°.

Injection laser diodes† of the same material $Ga(As_{1-x}Px)$ are fabricated with optically parallel ends to form a Fabry-Perot resonator. Under high forward bias a copious supply of charge carriers is injected into the junction [50–52]. As a result, an inversion region exists with a high population of conduction-band electrons and valence-band holes. Strong recombination produces quanta which, in their passage back and forth through the cavity, stimulate the generation of additional quanta at the energy peaks in the standing wave pattern. Peak emission occurs at a wavelength of 905 ± 5 nm with a width at half power of 0.5 nm. Designed for pulse operation at a repetition rate not to exceed 1 kHz and 0.2 μsec pulse width, its minimum peak power output is 1 W at a peak forward current of 30 A. Arrays of series-connected diodes in one package are capable of generating up to 100 W‡ peak-power output into a solid angle of 0.5 sr. Good heat sinking and/or cooling is required to maintain the operating temperature within rated limits [53].

The high currents required for operating laser diodes can be obtained from pulse-forming networks and cold cathode krytron switch tubes. Trigger generators and pulse transformers are normally used to obtain the high-voltage grid drive. In one type of pulse generator reported the electrode functions of the krytron are modified to operate like a free-running gas-tube oscillator while retaining the advantages of high current and short switching times [54]. The time interval between pulses is determined by the charging time of the energy storage capacitor.

Sources of Visible Radiation

INCANDESCENT SOURCES

The visible region of the electromagnetic spectrum nominally encompasses the wavelength interval from 400 nm to slightly more than 700 nm, a region in which blackbody sources above 3000°C radiate strongly. Though generally deficient at the blue end of the wavelength scale, most infrared sources emit

* For example, RCA developmental type TA 7008.
† For example, RCA developmental type TA 2628.
‡ For example, Laser Diode Labs., Model LD205.

visible light. For optical instrumentation incandescent lamps are by far the most commonly used sources. They are inexpensive, simple to operate, and can be obtained in a wide variety of standard and precision designs ranging from the $\frac{1}{4}$ W "grain-of-wheat" lamp upward in size and power consumption. The list is far too lengthy to include an adequate treatment here. A summary of modern types of tungsten lamp that are useful in optical instruments has been given by Carlson and Clark [55].

The radiation emitted by incandescent solids is continuous over the emission spectrum. The intensity, however, particularly at the shorter wavelengths, is limited by the melting point of the material used. Incandescent gases and vapors also emit visible radiation as a result of molecular collision processes. Although much higher temperatures can be attained with gases, their use is severely restricted because of instabilities in practical sources.

LUMINESCENT SOURCES

Another important category of visible sources is based on the phenomenon of luminescence, that is, on the emission of light that cannot be attributed solely to thermal excitation. Luminescence emission appears in many materials under a wide variety of conditions and is designated as chemi-, tribo-, radio-, photo-, electro-, or cathodoluminescence, according to the source of primary excitation. Among these the latter three account for the majority of modern practical sources.

Luminescent phenomena are also classified according to the persistence of emission. Fluorescence refers to the re-emission of radiant energy during and for a short time (less than 10^{-3} sec) after removal of the primary excitation. Phosphorescence refers to emission that persists for longer periods (10^{-3} sec). Solid materials that exhibit a strong afterglow are called phosphors, a term that has been extended to include, somewhat loosely, any luminescent solid. Some phosphors, such as the sulfides and phosphides of lead, are essentially nonluminescent in the pure state but can be "activated" by the addition of minute quantities of silver, copper, manganese, and other impurities. They are readily excited by ultraviolet irradiation at a wavelength in the neighborhood of 365 nm. In other phosphor materials, such as the tungstates and phosphates of calcium, photoemission is enhanced by the controlled addition of impurities called sensitizers. As a group, the latter types are most sensitive to irradiation at wavelengths in the neighborhood of 250 nm. They are used extensively in the manufacture of fluorescent lamps.

The emission from many photoluminescent phosphors can be quenched by infrared irradiation and increased temperature. Neither of these more complicated phenomena nor the role of impurity activation and sensitization is completely understood. Nevertheless, in a superficial sense, activation centers may be likened to simple harmonic oscillators which are excited to higher energy states through processes initiated by the absorption of photons. In a process of "trapping" and energy transfer the return to lower energy states after a finite period of time is accompanied by the release of photons, usually with somewhat lower energies corresponding to longer wavelength emission. The difference between the absorbed and emitted photon energies appears as heat. Since the amount of heat released is small, phosphors are frequently referred to as cold sources. By a suitable selection of additive mixtures and impurity concentrations a wide range of colors has been specifically designed for fluorescent lighting [56]. Some of the more useful phosphors are listed in Table 5.1. Zinc silicate emits in a relatively narrow spectral band centered at 525 nm and, with barium silicate, is one of the most efficient. The latter, which emits in a band centered near 350 nm in the ultraviolet, is called a "blacklight" source.

A variety of cathodo-luminescent phosphors are employed as screens in cathode-ray tubes to convert the energy of impinging electrons to visible radiation [57]. In standardized tubes blends or cascade layers designated by JEDEC* numbers are formed on glass face plates by one of several techniques. The commonest method for single layers involves gravitational

Table 5.1   Typical Fluorescent Phosphors for Lighting

Color	Composition	Wavelength of Peak Emission (nm)
White	Calcium silicate—magnesium tungstate— zinc silicate; calcium halophosphate; calcium zinc orthophosphate	590
Daylight	Calcium halophosphate—magnesium tungstate—strontium pyrophosphate; calcium zinc orthophosphate—barium titanium phosphate; calcium silicate—calcium tungstate—zinc silicate	460 580
Blue	Calcium tungstate; magnesium tungstate; strontium pyrophosphate	440
Green	Calcium halophosphate—magnesium tungstate—zinc silicate	546
Red	Calcium silicate	650
Blacklight	Barium silicate	365
High-pressure mercury vapor discharge	Calcium zinc orthophosphate	600 680

* Joint Electron Device Engineering Councils.

Table 5.2   Typical Cathode Ray Tube Phosphors

JEDC Number	Composition	Persistence	Color and Wavelength of Peak Emission (nm)	
P1	Zinc orthosilicate	Medium	Green	525
P2	Zinc cadmium sulfide	Long	Green-yellow	535
P11	Zinc sulfide	Short	Blue	460
P15	Zinc oxide	Extremely short	Ultraviolet	391
		Very short	Green	510
P16	Calcium-magnesium silicate	Very short	Ultraviolet	383
P24	Zinc oxide	Very short	Green	510
P22	Zinc sulfide	Short	Blue	450
	Zinc orthosilicate	Medium	Green	525
	Zinc phosphate	Medium	Red	638

settling from a water suspension containing a silicate binder and an electrolyte such as barium acetate to stimulate gelation of the silicate. Spray dusting and slurry application followed by spinning are also employed. As a final step, the screens of most standard direct-view tubes are aluminized to increase display brightness. Added stability is also claimed.

The intensity of light emitted by a typical cathode ray screen is relatively low compared with more conventional sources. However, the ease with which a luminous spot can be modulated in both intensity and position is advantageous in many applications. Thus the buildup of phosphorescence, persistence, and resolution are most important. All of these parameters are interrelated in a complex way and depend on manufacturing methods as well as on the mode of operation and history. A few of the phosphors commonly used in cathode-ray tubes are listed in Table 5.2. The zinc and zinc-cadmium sulfides and selenides are most efficient for accelerating potentials in the 5- to 15-kV range. Persistence characteristics and curves of spectral emission, which range from the ultraviolet for the P-16 to the near-infrared for one component of the tricolor P-22, can be found in handbooks such as the RCA tube manual.*

In applications in which scanning is not required the structure† shown in Fig. 5.35 is a versatile source capable of modulation at high rates. It consists basically of a simple electron gun with a heavy-duty cathode and without

---

* Published by Radio Corporation of America, Commercial Engineering, Harrison, New Jersey.

† Sylvania Electric Products Experimental Tube.

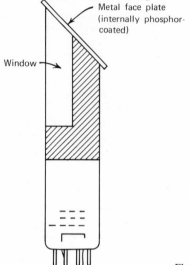

Fig. 5.35 Simplified outline of a modulated cathode ray tube light source.

deflection electrodes. An electrostatic focusing electrode operating in the range of 800 to 1800 V permits an adjustment of spot diameter from 1 mm to 1 cm. The maximum ultor potential is 15 kV. By mounting the phosphor plate at 45° to the tube axis advantage is taken of the higher radiant output from the electron-incident face. Additionally, since the metal plate on which the phosphor is coated also acts as a heat sink, higher beam currents can be used. The light output versus grid drive curve shown in Fig. 5.36 is typical of cathode-ray tubes. Complete modulation at rates in excess of 100 kHz can be obtained with a P-11 phosphor. All phosphors are subject to "burning" and care is required to ensure that screen heating is not excessive, particularly under constant beam current and long pulse operation.

Many photoluminescent materials also exhibit electroluminescence [58]. Among them zinc sulfide and related compounds are the most efficient and form the basis for most practical electroluminescent sources. Cells are fabricated in a wide variety of shapes by coating the phosphor in a suitable plastic or ceramic dielectric binder on a conducting substrate. A transparent electrode such as tin oxide is then applied to the light-emitting face. To obtain high fields (of the order of 10^5 V/cm) and to avoid undue absorption of emitted radiation, films are made as thin as possible while avoiding electrical breakdown. Cells are normally about 25 μm thick for ac operation at 120 V. The output intensity increases with both applied field and frequency [59].

Commercial electroluminescent lamps driven under controlled conditions (100 ± 3 V, 400 ± 2 Hz) have been used as low-level diffuse standards for such purposes as photomultiplier tube testing [60]. They have adequate homogeneity and are free of the bulb reflections, scattering, and filament aging that occur in tungsten lamps. The available spectral bands are 50 to 100 nm broad with spectral peaks ranging from blue (470 nm) to red (600 nm). Spectral distributions tend to shift toward longer wavelengths with increasing temperature. At or slightly above room temperature this effect levels off.

GAS DISCHARGE SOURCES

Luminescence also accompanies certain transitions from excited to lower energy states in atomic gases and in some metallic vapors. The spectra exhibit sharply defined lines that are characteristic of the gas and have an optical frequency given by the relation $v = (E_1 - E_2)/h$, where h is Planck's constant and E_1 and E_2 represent energy levels allowed by the rules of quantum mechanics. The energy levels correspond to positions of the outer orbital electrons in the atomic system and the energy differences, usually expressed in electron volts, are called the excitation potentials. Several excitation potentials may be allowed in a given atom but not all transitions

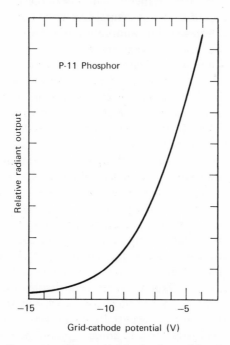

Fig. 5.36 Radiant output versus grid drive for the modulated source of Fig. 5.35.

are equally probable. Partly for this reason, the intensity of the spectral lines varies through the spectrum. Still higher energies are involved in ionization, namely, the complete removal of an outer shell electron and the radiant emission that occurs on recombination. Because of the larger number of allowed radiative transitions that can occur, the spectra contain many lines. The most easily produced spectral lines in a given gas correspond to spontaneous radiative transitions from the first excited state to the lowest energy ground state and are called resonance lines. In practical sources the generation of other transitions is enhanced by controlling the conditions under which the primary excitation takes place. Depending on the pressure and the type of gas, a wide range of colors can be obtained that extends from the ultraviolet through the visible to the near infrared.

The operation of practical gaseous discharge lamps depends on the fact that excited and ionized states can be produced by an electrical discharge passed between two electrodes immersed in a gas [61]. At atmospheric pressure a potential gradient of about 30,000 V/cm is required to initiate the discharge. Currents can attain extremely high values as a result of the dense ionization that follows breakdown and the discharge appears as an intense luminous arc. As the gas pressure is reduced, breakdown occurs at successively lower potential gradients. The discharge takes on a characteristic pattern composed of two principal luminous portions separated by relatively narrow dark spaces. The luminous regions are called the negative glow and the positive column, respectively; both are useful in the production of light. In tubular lamps with a length-to-diameter ratio of 20 or more the positive column occupies the greater portion of the tube near the anode end. This plasma consists of a mixture of excited atoms, ionized atoms, and electrons. Because the concentration of charge carriers is high, the potential drop in this region is low. In the vicinity of the electrodes, particularly near the cathode, the potential gradients are high.

Once started, the low pressure discharge is self-sustaining, provided the applied potential is sufficient to maintain an adequate flow of charge carriers. The mechanism is complex, but in essence accelerated electrons move toward the anode and maintain the gas atoms in excited and ionized states by elastic and nonelastic collision processes. Ions move toward the cathode and, at current densities that usually prevail in standard fluorescent lamps, positive-ion bombardment induces the emission of electrons under the influence of the relatively high field that exists at the cathode. The process is facilitated by the use of alkaline earth-metal oxides which are copious emitters of electrons by virtue of their low work functions. Since these materials are gradually used up, especially on starting, lamp life is limited by the number of start cycles [56]. In some circumstances the temperature of the cathode may be raised to a sufficiently high value to provide electrons by thermionic emission. The actual temperature of the gas is usually low (around 100°C, compared with 2000°C or higher for an incandescent lamp) but the equivalent electron temperature is very high. What amounts to the same thing, the electrons are highly mobile. As the number and energy of available charge carriers increase under the accelerating field, the rate of excitation increases and the process becomes cumulative. Thus low pressure discharges exhibit a negative resistance characteristic and some means of limiting current is required. For efficient ac operation a ballast in the form of a series inductance or a transformer with high magnetic leakage is ordinarily employed. Both have the advantage of producing a high voltage inductive "kick" that promotes easy ignition. Though less efficient, a series resistance is usually adequate for laboratory work. The appropriate value of resistance R can be calculated from the formula

$$R \geq \frac{V_S - V_L}{i},\qquad(5.27)$$

where V_S and V_L are, respectively, the supply potential and rated lamp drop and i is the rated current (rms values for ac operation).

The light output of a low-pressure positive-column discharge is approximately linear with current [62]. As shown in Fig. 5.37, a conventional fluorescent lamp can be intensity-modulated over a range exceeding 1000-to-1, provided an adequate supply of electrons is maintained. This is readily accomplished in lamps equipped with filaments by continuous heating from an auxiliary supply (say 6.3 V). For dc operation only the cathode need be heated. Since the tube drop varies by only a few volts over the entire dimming range, series elements such as variable resistors, vacuum tubes, or transistors may be used in place of or in addition to the normal ballast for current control. A photoflash trigger transformer is a convenient source of high potential for initiating discharge at low currents. It should be located near the lamp and the high-voltage lead brought into proximity with the envelope. Modulation rates are limited primarily by the recombination times of the ionized atoms and by phosphor response if such is contained in the tube. It is important to note that discharge lamps cannot be operated in parallel with a single ballast or current-control element. Because the negative resistance characteristic is seldom even approximately the same for any two lamps, the first to ignite will carry the entire current.

The elements most commonly used in gaseous discharge tubes are the inert gases: argon, neon, xenon, krypton, and metal vapors of mercury and sodium. Each produces a characteristic spectrum that depends at least in part on the gas pressure and temperature. Low-pressure metal vapor lamps generally contain a small quantity of inert gas, such as argon, to initiate discharge and vaporize the metal.

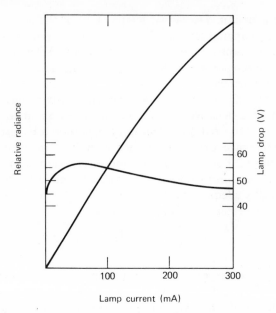

Fig. 5.37   Radiant output and voltage drop versus current in a tubular fluorescent lamp (T-8, 15 W).

The sodium D lines (589.0 and 589.6 nm) are widely used in polarimetry and refractometry. A typical laboratory lamp operates with a potential drop in the neighborhood of 20 V at 1 A. Because of the high melting point of sodium, the arc tube is enclosed in a Dewar flask to maintain operating temperature.

The conducting and radiating properties of mercury vapor discharges permit considerable versatility in lamp design and operation. The radiative atomic transitions at low pressure yield spectral lines that cover the ultraviolet and visible regions. A particularly intense ultraviolet line occurs at 253.7 nm. It is primarily responsible for the high efficiency of fluorescent lamps in which ultraviolet radiation is converted to lower frequency visible radiation. As the vapor pressure is raised, the probability of excitation by collision increases, provided the electron temperature is maintained. This implies higher operating potentials to provide the requisite potential gradient. Some band structure as well as additional lines also appear in the spectrum. With the exception of a moderately intense line at 1.01 μm, none of the infrared lines is of much importance.

With a further increase in pressure there is a transition from atomic to nuclear phenomena accompanied by a broadening of the spectral peaks and complete absorption of the prominent 253.7-nm line of mercury. Super-high pressure lamps* are characterized by highly concentrated arcs, high currents, and high operating temperatures. The visible spectrum consists of four strong lines (404.6, 435.8, 546.0, and 577.0/597.0 nm) superposed on a weak continuum and six broadened lines in the ultraviolet (313.0 to 366.3 nm). At pressures of several atmospheres the striking potential is many times larger than the running potential (approximately 100 V at 5 A). Starting is typically accomplished by means of a high-voltage pulse produced in a Tesla coil or in a spark gap and transformer arrangement, as shown in Fig. 5.38. However, if the current to an operating lamp is interrupted, the lamp cannot be reignited until it has cooled sufficiently to allow the pressure to drop. Some versions incorporate a third auxiliary electrode sealed into the bulb adjacent to one of the main electrodes and connected by an external resistance to the other electrode. Because of the small volume of these lamps, ionization and vaporization of the mercury occur rapidly and full output is reached in a few seconds. The bulb is made of quartz to resist the thermal and mechanical stresses. Either water or forced-air cooling is required. At room temperature the pressure is a fraction of an atmosphere. Although fragile, the lamps are safe to handle. Under normal operating conditions, however, the internal pressure approaches 100 atm and adequate enclosures should be provided.

Xenon lamps of similar structure operate with a dc drop of about 14 V and 5 A. The output shows a broad continuum from somewhat less than 300 to more than 1000 nm with two broadened lines between 800 and 900 nm [63]. The gas is under a pressure of several atmospheres, even when not in operation, and such lamps should be handled with caution.

At the other end of the pressure scale, or as the electrodes are moved closer together, the negative glow and its associated dark (Faraday) space take over a proportionally greater volume of the space between electrodes until the positive column disappears; for example, the hollow cathode tube operates in the glow discharge region in which gas ionization is produced chiefly by positive-ion bombardment of the cathode. As a sharp line radiation source designed for use in atomic absorption spectroscopy and analysis, the

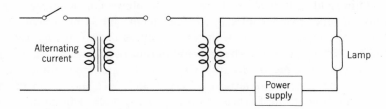

Fig. 5.38 Spark gap starting circuit for a high-pressure discharge lamp.

* PEK Labs 107/109 and GE AH-6.

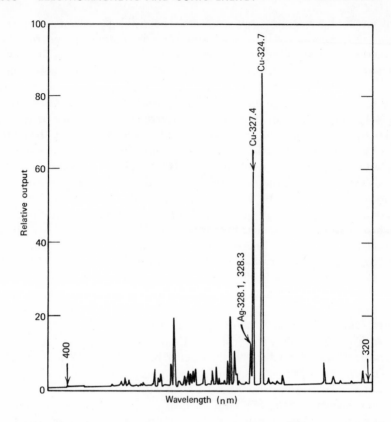

Fig. 5.39 Typical spectra of a hollow cathode source, copper cathode and neon filling (Westinghouse WL-22603).

basic structure consists essentially of a hollow cup-shaped cathode of a pure element and a rod anode external to the cup. Sealed-off tubes with cathodes of many of the elements are available in a choice of neon or argon gas filling and with quartz or Pyrex glass windows. One manufacturer* lists a line of tubes that includes 70 single-element and 34 multielement types. A typical copper spectrum with neon filling is shown in Fig. 5.39. Neon filling generally yields a higher spectral output because of a greater fraction of gas in the glow region. Because of sorption by sputtered cathode material, however, neon cleans up faster than argon and has a shorter operating life. Neon introduces interference spectra in the 330- to 370-nm and 500- to 650-nm regions, whereas argon introduces interference in the 400- to 500-nm

* Westinghouse Electric Corporation, Electronic Tube Division.

region. Wavelengths of the useful spectral lines lie between 196 nm for selenium and 780 nm for rubidium; both extremes are relatively weak. The individual line intensity of each element in a multielement cathode is usually lower than that produced by a comparable tube containing the pure element.

Depending on the cathode material and the type of gas filling, the maximum rated discharge currents range from 12 to 30 mA; tube drops range between 110 and 320 V. Since starting potentials are comparable to maintaining potentials, a 500-V dc supply with enough series resistance to limit the current to rated values is adequate for most purposes. At subnormal operating currents the discharge is subject to instability. At a current that is too high the increased potential drop increases the rate of gas cleanup and shortens life. Also the discharge may shift into an unstable glow region and cause destruction of the cathode as a result of excessive temperature.

In some recent designs the efficiency has been improved by the use of shielding and auxiliary high-current discharges [64]. Demountable hot-cathode sources of special design are claimed to be the most intense of any available source [65].

LASERS

All gaseous discharge and incandescent sources emit radiation that is essentially noncoherent and unpolarized. In the optical maser (microwave amplification by stimulated emission of radiation), more frequently called a laser, excited atoms are forced to emit electromagnetic waves with a greater or lesser degree of synchronism [66]. Despite their considerable differences in construction and operation, lasers and oscillators have two features in common, namely, a resonant structure that supports electromagnetic waves and a means for accepting energy from an external supply. In the laser excitation (or, as it is called, pumping) power is supplied by conventional light sources. The resonator consists basically of a pair of mirrors between which the optical waves are reflected back and forth. Since its first appearance some 10 years ago, an extensive body of references has evolved [67–72]. Consequently, only a superficial outline of the theory of operation is given here.

The basis of laser action is a material that provides a means of storing energy in a system of quantized energy states until released by a coherent trigger. The resultant wave passes back and forth through the medium and grows in amplitude until the stored energy is exhausted. In addition to the injection laser already mentioned, currently available commercial units fall into one of three classes.

1. The solid laser nominally consists of a rod of suitable crystalline material arranged between plane-parallel mirrors and excited by a flash discharge lamp. With peak power outputs ranging from a few kilowatts up

to millons of watts, it is useful when a very high flux is required for a very short time at low repetition rates.

2. The gas laser employs a self-contained gaseous discharge for pumping and continuous replenishment of energy states. Power outputs fall between a fraction of a watt and several watts. Both solid and gas types emit in narrow spectral bands consisting of one or more discrete wavelengths characteristic of the lasing medium.

3. More recent studies have shown that pulsed lasing action can also be obtained with organic dyes in liquids or plastics as the active medium.

Laser action in solid media [73] is determined by the energy-level structure of ionic impurities. At present, the most frequently used materials are (a) aluminum oxide (ruby) crystal doped with chromium ions, (b) neodymium glass and calcium fluoride doped with uranium, and (c) yttrium aluminum garnet doped with rare earths. Intense irradiation, or pumping, produces atomic transitions from the lowest energy ground state to an excited level. This process is followed by rapid nonradiative transitions to a metastable state, which, in the three-level system, is intermediate between the two. If the pumping is sufficiently intense, the increase in the number of atoms in the intermediate state is large compared with the number in the lowest energy state. In the four-level system is a second intermediate state that is virtually empty because of the high relaxation between it and the ground state. In either case a situation called population inversion is said to exist. Spontaneous transitions from the populated to the next lower energy level are accompanied by the release of quantized radiation of a frequency determined by the energy difference between the two levels (i.e., $\Delta E/h$). Because the radiation is constrained to the cavity, it stimulates additional transitions of the same frequency through a phenomenon related to resonance. If the population inversion is sufficiently high, the stimulated emission exceeds the spontaneous emission and a short, intense burst of monochromatic radiation is produced. To permit the extraction of radiant energy one of the end mirrors is made partially reflecting.

Most solid rod lasers are operated in a pulsed mode at repetition rates that are limited by power dissipation in the lasing material and/or the pumping source. Some models are available for continuous operation at reduced power, usually less than 500 mW. Recirculating water or other means of cooling is generally necessary. The efficiency and power output of pulsed lasers can be increased by a technique referred to as Q-spoiling. The concept of the Q of an optical cavity is carried over directly from the equivalent electrical circuit. During the pumping process the cavity is made lossy so that whatever stimulated emission exists occurs at a slow rate. On completion of the pumping cycle the Q is rapidly switched to a high value and

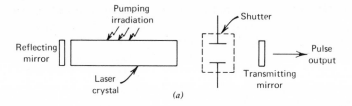

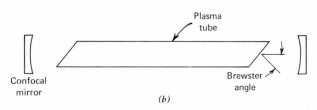

Fig. 5.40 Principles of laser construction: (*a*) *Q*-switched solid laser; (*b*) gas laser with confocal mirror arrangement.

stimulated emission proceeds at an extremely fast rate with a build-up time that is typically in the neighborhood of 10 nsec. In the various methods that have been devised this is accomplished by effectively changing the reflectivity of one cavity mirror by means of rotating mirrors, Kerr cell shutters, or mechanical choppers [74, 75] as illustrated in Fig. 5.40*a*.

Gas lasers employ dc or ac excitation of a capillary plasma supported within a high *Q* optical cavity consisting of either plane-parallel or confocal spherical mirrors [76–79], as shown in Fig. 5.40*b*. Both pumping and laser interaction occur within the positive column, which, as in low-pressure discharge lamps, occupies the greater portion of the tube length. Although many types of gas laser are commercially available and a far larger number of gas and molecular laser transitions are known [80], the helium-neon combination is by far the commonest. In this system the light-weight helium atoms are excited to metastable states by the electric discharge. As a result of collision processes energy is transferred to the neon atoms to produce population inversion in the latter. Radiation in the cavity stimulates nearly synchronous emission as the atoms relax to lower energy states. By allowing only a small transmission through one mirror, most of the energy is confined to the cavity and the process is self-maintained, a situation that is comparable to positive feedback in an electronic amplifier. The most probable, or dominant, transition in helium-neon yields the 3.39-μm spectral line in the infrared. This line is usually removed by the use of wavelength-selective optics oriented so that the 632.8-nm line enters and leaves the cavity at the Brewster angle. With this arrangement the emitted beam is plane-polarized and reflection of the undesired radiation at angles away from the tube axis minimizes stimulation at all but the one desired wavelength.

Alignment of the optical-cavity mirror terminations is critical. When the mirror is properly aligned within tolerances that are typically $\pm 0.005°$, oscillations of the TE_{00n} mode are favored. As in the vibrating string (see Section 2), several of these axial modes are possible if their wavelength separation is much smaller than the width of the spectral line produced by atomic transactions. In a cavity of length L the condition for resonance is that the round trip between mirrors be an integral number of wavelengths, or $n\lambda = 2L$, where n is an integer corresponding to an axial mode. Thus the wavelength separation between modes is given by $\Delta\lambda = \lambda^2/2L$ and the frequency separation is $\Delta v = c/2L$, where c is the velocity of light. The temperature-broadened helium resonance line has a half-width (the so-called Doppler half-width) that is typically 1500 MHz. As shown in Fig. 5.41, a high-gain cavity 1 m long might oscillate at five different frequencies with a frequency separation of approximately 300 MHz. The number is limited by the narrow bandwidth of the amplifier and the oscillation threshold. For all but very critical applications, such as those involving phase-locking techniques the output of the helium-neon laser is essentially monochromatic. The spectral width is many orders of magnitude narrower than can be produced by the best spectrometer.

Although glass and ion gas laser systems have been developed to a high degree of reliability, emission at shorter wavelengths is desirable for many

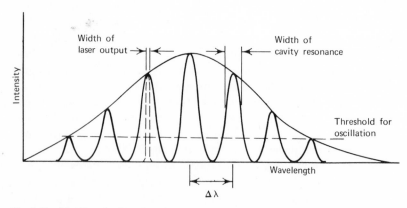

Fig. 5.41 The Doppler broadened gain envelope and cavity line widths in a gas laser.

applications. Some optical materials exhibit nonlinear effects that are suitable for the generation of second- and higher order harmonics at optical frequencies [81–84]. Since the nonlinear effect per unit wavelength is small, the intensity of the harmonic is governed by the coherence length over which the fundamental and harmonic can interact in phase. The most successful methods to date take advantage of birefringence in crystals, such as KDP (potassium dihydrogen phosphate) lithium niobate, and the more recently developed strontium barium niobate. Second harmonic generation with efficiencies up to 35 % have been obtained at a number of frequencies ranging from the infrared to the ultraviolet [85].

Stimulated pulsed emission from dilute solutions of organic dyes in liquids and solid plastics, such as polymethyl methacrylate, has been reported by several workers [86–89]. The active media, namely, xanthines, polymethines, and coumarin derivatives, can be excited by ruby laser emission or by flash lamps. In the latter case a short rise time is obtained by mounting the laser tube and flash lamp within the laser cavity and using re-entrant geometry to minimize inductance in the lamp circuit. The absorption of pumping light corresponds roughly to the inverse of phosphorescence. Laser action then develops from fluorescent transitions following the peak of pumping radiation and is characterized by lifetimes of the order of 10^{-9} sec. Absorption and emission curves typically show mirror symmetry but with a shift of emission spectra toward longer wavelengths. Most of the losses result from absorption in the region of overlap.

Liquids offer several advantages over pulsed solid lasers. For a given dye the liquid laser can be "tuned" over a significant portion of the visible spectrum by variation of dye concentration or by inserting dispersive elements in the cavity. In addition, liquids are self-healing, heat can be dissipated by recirculation, and laser action can be produced in relatively large volumes. On the other hand, spectral bandwidths are relatively broad and consequently the coherence length is extremely short.

Ultraviolet Sources

The upper wavelength limit of the ultraviolet spectrum is arbitrarily taken at 400 nm. From its proximity to the visible spectrum, radiation in this region is labeled near-ultraviolet. Radiation at much shorter wavelengths (far-ultraviolet) overlaps the soft x-ray spectrum, and any differentiation between the two is based more on the type of apparatus than on any particular characteristics of the radiation. Line and continuum sources in the near-ultraviolet are widely used for photoelectric scanning studies of absorption processes and in photographic absorption spectroscopy. High-intensity pulsed sources are used in flash photolysis techniques for detection of short-lived radicals and related phenomena. Ultraviolet radiation causes pronounced erythemal (sun tanning), germicidal, and ozone-producing effects, and caution should be exercised in its use.

Since ordinary glass does not transmit appreciably in the region below 350 nm, envelopes for ultraviolet sources are usually constructed with quartz or lithium fluoride windows. As shown in Fig. 5.33, the spectra of blackbodies and incandescent sources operated at 3000 K terminate rather abruptly at a wavelength of approximately 250 nm. Because of the limitation imposed by melting points of solids, much higher temperatures are not practical. To obtain radiation of shorter wavelengths one may consider gaseous discharges, sparks, and microwave-generated resonance phenomena. The design technology is highly specialized and the reader is referred to the literature for details.

Emission continua have been found in repetitive condensed discharges, known as Lyman discharges, in helium (60 to 100 nm, 105 to 400 nm), neon (74 to 100 nm), argon (107 to 160 nm), krypton (124 to 170 nm), and xenon (147 to 190 nm). Extension of the individual ranges by using two discharge tubes in series has also been reported. The discharge tube typically consists of a water-cooled capillary with aluminum tubular electrodes mounted in side arms at either end of the capillary [90, 91]. In a typical installation the tube is directly attached to a monochromator. Gas flows under low pressure through the capillary and entrance optical slit from which it is removed by differential pumping. The control variables are gas pressure, storage capacitance, power-supply potential, and pulse-repetition frequency. An excitation circuit for repetition rates of 1 to 5 kHz is shown in Fig. 5.42. The energy storage bank has a total capacity of 0.002 μF and is charged from a high voltage supply through a current-limiting resistor. The potential at which the tube fires is determined by the setting of the spark gap, which

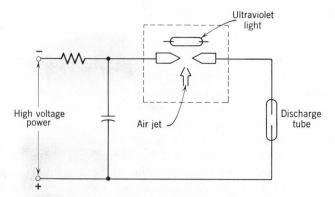

Fig. 5.42 Excitation circuit for a condensed discharge source.

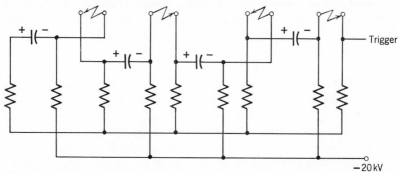

Fig. 5.43   Partial schematic of a short-flash spark discharge arrangement.

serves as a high voltage switch. Gap stability is achieved by the combination of low-level ultraviolet irradiation and a jet of compressed air. Hydrogen thyration modulators of the type shown in Fig. 5.32 have also been used for triggering the discharge.

The gas existing in Lyman sources imposes a limitation at short wavelengths because of unavoidable reabsorption of radiation [92]. By using a vacuum capillary and triggering the discharge with an auxilliary spark, a continuum can be generated that extends from the visible to 8 nm in the extreme ultraviolet [93]. Emission develops chiefly from the plasma in the neighborhood of the anode, which is made of a metal of high atomic number, uranium being the best. The essential elements are a completely coaxial discharge circuit of very low self-inductance and a triggering electrode that provides a "sliding" spark path [94] coaxial with the cathode. Radiation is emitted through a hole in the cathode. With a water-cooled anode support and a storage capacity of 0.05 μF charged to 20 kV rates up to 10 flashes/sec have been obtained.

The application of flash photolysis to kinetic spectroscopy of gases requires long reaction vessels and intense sources. The problem of unduly long flash durations (i.e., the time constant that result from single spark discharges of adequate intensities has been solved by dividing the total discharge energy between several discharge units [95]. By charging the energy storage capacitors in parallel and synchronously firing them in series, a $1/e$ flash duration of 2 μsec has been achieved. As shown in the partial schematic of Fig. 5.43, neighboring electrodes of different gaps have the same polarity and close spacing is possible. The capacitor bank is tightly packed and connected to electrodes through copper sheets to reduce self-inductance. With a pure nitrogen atmosphere at a pressure of 350 to 500 torr, the operating potential is 18 kV.

Another more recent technology for producing continua in the ultraviolet makes use of the very high temperatures that exist in gas plasmas heated by shock waves [96]. In what is called a "z-pinch" assembly ions are generated by a high voltage discharge between two disk electrodes separated by a cylindrical vessel filled with low-pressure gas. The resulting high current density in the axial direction gives rise to a magnetic induction field that encircles the axis. (By Ampere's law the field B within a long continuous plasma is given by $B = \mu_0 Jr/2$; J is the current density, $\mu_0 \approx 4\pi \times 10^{-7}$ is the permeability of the gas, and r is the radial distance to a point within the plasma.) Under the action of Lorentz forces the leading edge of the discharge is radially constricted to form a high velocity shock wave. (The inward radial force on an ion of charge q moving with a velocity u in the field B is given by the vector cross product $\mathbf{qu} \times \mathbf{B}$.) At maximum contraction the equivalent blackbody temperature may reach 60,000°K or higher and part of the energy is emitted as electromagnetic radiation. At the end of the discharge the gas expands and cools down rapidly. By using multiple storage capacitors, each with its own spark gap, with a stored energy of 4.85 kJ at potentials of 30 kV, pulses of half-width less than 0.2 μsec have been obtained. The optimum pressure for argon in a cylinder of 20-cm height and 20-cm diameter is approximately 0.03 torr. Other gases such as air, helium, krypton, and xenon have also been used but with somewhat less success.

The rare gases also emit continuous spectra with little or no structure when excited by microwave discharges at 2450 MHz [97–100]. The spectral continua are somewhat more restricted than those obtained with condensed discharges. The reported ranges are argon, 106 to 150 nm, krypton, 126 to 170 nm, and xenon, 150 to 200 nm. A typical discharge tube is 30 cm long, 1.2 cm in diameter, and has a lithium fluoride window sealed in one end [99]. Before filling, the tube is outgassed under high pressure and gettered with metallic barium contained in a side arm. Other designs employ continuous pumping and recirculation of the rare gas. Microwave lamps have the advantage of no internal electrodes which require outgassing and baking. In addition, inexpensive microwave ovens and medical diathermy units are available at powers up to 200 W. They operate in the 2450-MHz region and can be used with a variety of cavities and antennas that are also available.

Electrodeless microwave lamps also appear to be superior in many respects to hollow cathode structures for atomic absorption and fluorescence studies [101]. The discharge tube for these applications normally consists of a sealed quartz tube 2 to 7 cm long and containing a few milligrams of the desired metal or metal salt in an inert-gas atmosphere at a pressure of a few torr. Although the lamps can be operated at radiofrequencies, microwaves appear to be more efficient in the generation of intense spectra. Initiation of the discharge, which depends on the production of free electrons, is readily achieved with a simple Tesla coil. After an initial running-in period of 2 hr, a warm-up period of 5 min is usually sufficient. The techniques of lamp preparation are still relatively new and the parameters are not fully known. There seems little doubt, however, that microwave lamps will become increasingly important in the near future.

X- and γ-Ray Sources

Progressing through the ultraviolet spectrum and beyond, the optical phenomena so evident in the visible spectrum (refraction, diffraction, polarization, and reflection) become increasingly difficult to observe without highly specialized techniques. Radiation appears to be propagated as discontinuous bundles of increasingly greater energy content called x- and γ-ray quanta, respectively. The x-ray spectrum is frequently broken down into low energy (soft x-) and high energy (hard x-), collectively called Roentgen rays after their discoverer. A by-product produced in the collision of high-velocity electrons with atoms and in certain radioactive decay processes, such radiation is still considered part of the electromagnetic spectrum. The term "electron-volt," however, is more frequently used than frequency to specify energy. Because of the high penetrating power of x-radiation, particularly the hard variety, serious and possibly lethal injuries to personnel and damage to radiation-sensitive devices can result from improper use and inadequate safeguards. Qualified technical experts should be consulted for recommendations of equipment and operating procedures. Consequently only the most cursory review of x- and γ-ray sources is given here.

In addition to the well-known applications to medical diagnostics and nondestructive testing, x-radiation is widely used for chemical analyses and crystal diffraction studies [102–105]. Soft x-rays are strongly absorbed in micrometer layers of matter and are routinely used for light element determination, plasma diagnostics, and x-ray microscopy. Typically an x-ray generator consists of a source of electrons and a target electrode arranged somewhat as shown in Fig. 5.44. The electrons are accelerated through a potential difference of several kilovolts applied between the source and the target electrode on which they impinge. Tubes are classified as gas or high-vacuum, depending on the manner of producing electrons. In the former electrons are emitted from a cold cathode under the influence of positive-ion bombardment. This type has been largely supplanted by the high-vacuum type which employs an incandescent filament. For good efficiency the anode is usually a metal with a large atomic number, tungsten being in common use because of its high melting point, good thermal conductivity, and low vapor pressure. The target electrode is mounted on a block of material with high thermal conductivity, such as copper, to provide heat dissipation. For high power and continuous operation water cooling may

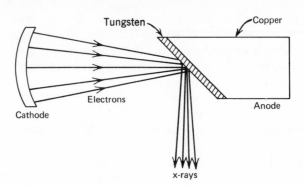

Fig. 5.44 Simplified structure of an x-ray tube.

be required. Alternatively, the electrode may be designed for continuous mechanical rotation.

The x-ray emission spectrum typically consists of a continuum containing all wavelengths greater than a minimum critical value. For a given target material this minimum wavelength, called the Duane-Hunt limit, corresponds to the maximum frequency v_{max} allowed by the relation $hv_{max} = eV$, where all of the electronic energy is converted to radiation. The term eV is the energy of an electron accelerated through a potential difference V and, as before, h represents Planck's constant. Thus the x-ray energy and its penetrating power depend on the accelerating voltage. In industrial radiography potentials from a few kilovolts to several megavolts are in common use. Ultor potentials of 15 to 30 kV are commonly used in cathode-ray and television picture tubes. Such devices are thus possible sources of soft x-radiation.

Superposed on the continuous spectra are extremely sharp lines similar to those found in optical spectra; these lines are called characteristic x-radiations and their wavelengths depend on the particular element used in the target [106]. The lighter elements emit only low-energy radiation in the far ultraviolet corresponding to plasma temperatures in the 10^6 K region. This effect is useful in direct electron probing measurements on materials that can be subjected to electron bombardment in high vacuum. Energy of these wavelengths is quickly absorbed by matter and tube windows of special materials are required. Beryllium is commonly used for wavelengths below 1 nm. Heavy elements emit higher energy radiation as a result of inner electronic shell ionization; x-radiation in this region is readily transmitted by materials of low atomic number and considerably more attention must be paid to shielding against unwanted radiation.

All isotopes of atomic number greater than 83 are radioactive. They disintegrate spontaneously to yield directly the very high energy γ-rays, x-rays, and other nuclei. More than 1000 radioactive nuclides have been produced, of which 10 or so are practically useful as sources of low-energy photons. The use of cyclotron-produced Fe-55, Co-57, and a few other nuclides listed in Table 5.3 is well established in industrial applications [104, 107–109]. Some, particularly those that decay by α-emission, are toxic and require sealing. Many are commonly available in the form of a disk capsule of welded steel with a gold backing to reduce transmission through the back. The nuclide is compacted with aluminum or a ceramic enamel and incorporated in a depression in the gold layer and faced with stainless steel. Such structures are robust and conform to most immersion standards. Some nuclides are sealed in glass beads and capillaries to form point and line sources.

Characteristic x-radiation can also be initiated by bombardment of matter with heavy charged particles, such as radioisotope-produced protons and α-particles [104]. Because of the large masses involved, absorption is high,

Table 5.3   Typical Nuclides

Nuclide	Half-Life (years)	Energy of Photon Emission (keV)	Mode of Decay
^{241}Am	458	60	α
		14–21	
^{109}Cd	1.27	88	Electron capture
		22	
^{57}Co	0.74	700	Electron capture
		136	
		122	
		14	
		6.4	
^{55}Fe	2.7	6	Electron capture
^{153}Gd	0.65	103	Electron capture
		97	
		70	
		41	
^{125}I	0.16	35	Electron capture
		27	
^{210}Pb	22	47	β
		11–13	
^{238}Pu	86.4	12–17	α
^{170}Tm	0.35	84	β
		52	

even in thin layers of light materials, and the excitation spectra are relatively pure. Although such techniques cannot compete with conventional x-ray equipment in flux output, the many available sources provide a degree of flexibility that is not possible with standard x-ray machines.

5   GENERATION OF ACOUSTICAL ENERGY

Acoustical Waves

Ultrasonics treats the study and application of acoustical waves above the limit of audibility, usually taken at about 20 kHz. Because such waves require physical media for their generation and propagation, the frequency spectrum is severely limited, compared with the electromagnetic spectrum. The distinction between the effects produced by waves of low and high energy forms a more natural basis for classification than does frequency. Low-energy waves are of such intensity that the elastic properties of materials in which they occur are not exceeded. They are widely used for nondestructive testing, determination of elastic constants, measurements of concentrations in solutions, and computer delay lines. High-energy waves produce nonlinear stress-strain relations and phenomena that involve cavitation and oxidation. They are used for emulsification, cleaning, and fatigue testing and in the study of chemical reactions due to acoustically induced electrolytic action and oxidation.

Ultrasonic waves are generated by transducers that convert mechanical, electrical, or even thermal energy into acoustical energy [110–112]. Many transducers, particularly those of low power, act reversibly and can also be used as detectors. They may be classified according to whether the primary vibratory motion occurs in fluid (gas or liquid) or solid materials, as indicated in Table 5.4. In gas and liquid devices steady mechanical forces, namely, fluid pressures, are converted into mechanical disturbances in media contained within, or associated with, some form of resonant structure. Generally the medium is also the one in which the desired ultrasonic interactions take place. When the primary vibration occurs in a solid material, the disturbances must be transmitted to the interacting material by contact, either directly or through another medium.

In nearly all cases involving the generation of sonic energy, the basic effects can be related to the oscillation of mass elements, such as pistons, that react with the medium in which the elements are immersed [4]. The resulting components of the disturbance then travel by wave motion as discussed in Section 2. The forced oscillation of a single lumped mass element M is analogous to the motion of a charge in an electrically resonant circuit. A mechanical circuit subjected to a periodic force of amplitude F and

Table 5.4 Classes of Ultrasonic Generators

Class	Mechanism	Frequency	Typical Application
Gas	Whistle	25 kHz	Foam control
	Siren	35 kHz	Aerosol coagulation
	Vortex	20 kHz	Fluidization
Liquid	Vibrating	30 kHz	Emulsification
	reed		Homogenization
Solid	Piezoelectricity	20 kHz	Measurement and
		10 MHz	control
			Communication
	Magnetostriction	20 kHz	Cleaning
		100 kHz	
			Machining
	Semiconductor	300 MHz	Experimental
	Resistive layers	10 GHz	

angular frequency ω exhibits a complex impedance defined by

$$Z_M = \frac{F}{\mu} = R_M + jX_M, \tag{5.28}$$

where μ is the velocity of the mass element, R_M is the damping coefficient, and the mechanical reactance is

$$X_M = \omega_M - \frac{1}{\omega C_M}. \tag{5.29}$$

The term C_M represents the displacement per unit restoring force and is called the compliance. By further analogy the quality of mechanical resonance is given by

$$Q_M = \frac{\omega_0 M}{R_M} = \frac{\omega_0}{\omega_1 - \omega_2}, \tag{5.30}$$

where ω_0 is the angular frequency at which the disturbance has a maximum value and ω_1 and ω_2 are the frequencies on either side of ω_0 at which the amplitude is reduced to $1/\sqrt{2}$ of the maximum value.

Except at very low frequencies, a mechanical system for generating acoustical energy seldom vibrates as a single unit. Rather the system consists of a set of driven mass elements distributed throughout its volume. The motions of the elemental volume elements, whether induced by shear or compressional forces, constitute an internal wave circumscribed by conditions that exist at the boundaries of the system. Since the wavelength is generally short in comparison to the cross section of the transducer, waves having plane wavefronts are readily produced in solid materials. Two important characteristics of a material are its elasticity and inertia. Elasticity appears in the relation between excess pressure across a plane section and the instantaneous gradient of displacement of the volume elements across that section. The ratio of the first to the second of these quantities is called the elastic modulus. Inertia appears in the form of the density ρ or mass per unit volume. Thus the specific acoustical impedance, or mechanical impedance per unit area, is defined by

$$Z_a = \frac{\rho}{u},\tag{5.31}$$

where p is the excess pressure over a transverse section due to wave action and u is the time rate of displacement of the volume elements constituting that section. The specific impedance is also analogous to electrical impedance.

From the wave equation of a progressive harmonic wave in an ideal homogeneous medium [the function f of (5.1) is replaced by particle or volume element displacement], the specific impedance reduces to

$$Z_a = \frac{K}{v} = \rho v = R_a,\tag{5.32}$$

where K is the appropriate bulk modulus of the material and v is the propagation velocity. In this case there is no reactive component and the real quantity $\rho v = R_a$ is called the characteristic impedance. It is associated with dissipation of energy. Definitions of the elastic constants and moduli for transverse and longitudinal waves in gases, liquids, and solids are given in Table 5.5. The formulas are based on the assumptions that the materials are isotropic and, except for the rod, of semi-infinite extent. As indicated for a few common materials, the characteristic impedance and velocity depend on the type of wave, the density, and the elastic constants. A transverse wave can exist only in a solid and travels at a speed in the neighborhood of one-half that of a longitudinal wave in the same material.

Coupling the generator to produce the desired wave motion in the material under study is one of the most exacting tasks in the application of acoustical energy. As in the analogous electrical transmission line, proper matching of source and load impedances is important. At the boundary separating two media, one of which may be considered as the source, the energy contained in a wave incident on the boundary is in general partially reflected and partially transmitted. For plane waves at normal incidence the transmission coefficient α_t (the ratio of transmitted to incident intensities)

Table 5.5 Ultrasonic Characteristics of Typical Materials

Material	Type of Wave	Modulus (K)	Typical Velocity (m/sec × 10^3)	Typical Characteristic Impedance (kg/m^2 sec × 10^6)
Gas	Longitudinal	γP_0	0.3 (air)	0.0004
Liquid	Longitudinal	$\dfrac{1}{B}$	1.5 (water)	1.5
Solid	Longitudinal	$\dfrac{Y(1 - \sigma)}{(1 + \sigma)(1 - 2\sigma)}$	2.3 (lead)	27.2
			6.4 (aluminum)	17.3
			1.3 (Teflon)	3.0
Solid (rod diameter 0.1)	Longitudinal	Y	1.2 (lead)	13.5
			5.1 (aluminum)	13.8
Solid (bulk)	Transverse	G	0.8 (lead)	9.0
			2.1 (aluminum)	8.4

γ Ratio of specific heat at constant pressure to that at constant volume.
P_0 Static pressure.
B Bulk compressibility (volume dilation/unit pressure differential).
Y Young's modulus (longitudinal stress/longitudinal strain).
σ Poisson's ratio (transverse strain/longitudinal strain, under longitudinal stress).
G Modulus of rigidity (shear stress/shear strain).

and the reflection coefficient α_r (the ratio of reflected to incident intensities) are given by

$$\alpha_t = \frac{4R_1 R_2}{(R_1 + R_2)^2} \quad \text{and} \quad \alpha_r = \left(\frac{R_2 - R_1}{R_1 + R_2}\right)^2, \tag{5.33}$$

where R_1 and R_2 represent the characteristic impedances of the respective media. Similar but more complex relations that involve the angles of reflection and transmission obtain at other than normal incidence.

The coefficient α_t has a maximum value of unity when the two impedances have the same value; there is no reflected wave at the boundary. If the impedances are unequal, a reflected wave will exist and its phase will depend on the relative magnitudes of the impedances on either side of the boundary; for example, a wave originating in a material of moderately low impedance such as a liquid suffers partial reflection at a liquid-metal interface without phase reversal. The amplitude of the wave transmitted into the metal will be larger than that of the incident wave. On the other hand, a wave originating in a metal will be reflected at a liquid-metal interface with a phase reversal of π rad and give rise to a standing wave pattern. The amplitude of the wave transmitted into the liquid will be considerably lower than that of the wave incident on the interface. Not only is the transmission efficiency reduced in the latter situation but the response to frequency and amplitude changes is severely restricted. In many configurations, particularly crystal transducers that employ plane-parallel interfaces, reflections and re-reflections may continue for a considerable period after drive power is removed [113]. This situation is equivalent to the familiar case of "ringing" in the electrical circuit or in a vibrating string.

In practice adequate coupling between two materials can generally be obtained if the characteristic impedances differ by not more than a factor of 2. For more critical applications matching can often be improved by the use of a third intervening medium of suitable impedance and thickness. The transmission coefficient of a plane-parallel sandwich comprised of two media of impedances R_1 and R_2, respectively, separated by a third medium of impedance R_3 and thickness l is

$$\alpha_t = \frac{4R_1 R_2}{(R_1 + R_2)^2 \cos^2 kl + (R_3 + R_1 R_2/R_3)^2 \sin^2 kl}, \tag{5.34}$$

where $k = 2\pi/\lambda$ is the wavenumber of the third medium. If the thickness of the intervening medium is an integral number of half wavelengths $(1 = n\lambda/2, kl = n\pi)$, the transmission coefficient is identical to that given by (5.33) and independent of the impedance of the intermediate layer. However, if the thickness is an odd number of quarter-wave lengths $(1 = (2n - 1)\lambda/4, kl = (2n - 1)\pi/2)$, (5.34) reduces to

$$\alpha_t = \frac{4R_1 R_2}{(R_3 + R_1 R_2/R_3)^2}. \tag{5.35}$$

Thus, if $R_3 = (R_1 R_2)^{\frac{1}{2}}$, α_t becomes unity and there is no reflection.

Fluid Generators

Although sirens and whistles are essentially gas-driven devices, many forms can also be used with liquids. In its simplest form the siren consists of a rotating disk containing a number of apertures or teeth spaced around its periphery [114]. When rotated in front of a similar stationary disk, the intermittent transmission of fluid under pressure produces acoustical waves of a frequency determined by the number of apertures and the rotational speed. Sirens are effective in producing high intensities at frequencies up to 35 kHz for such purposes as aerosol coagulation.

Whistles are essentially cavity resonators coupled to impinging fluid jets. Unstable flow patterns cause characteristic variations of pressure within the

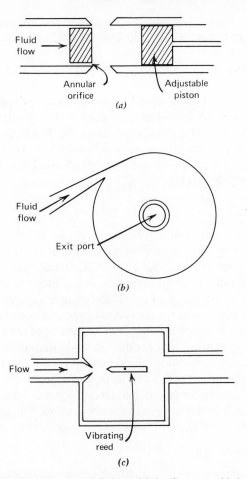

Fluid flow

Annular orifice

Adjustable piston

(a)

Fluid flow

Exit port

(b)

Flow

Vibrating reed

(c)

Fig. 5.45 Typical cavity resonators: (*a*) Golton whistle; (*b*) vortex whistle; (*c*) wedge resonator.

cavity. As in a toy whistle, the harmonic content is determined by the frequency of the pulsating flow rates. Some forms, such as the Galton and Hartmann generators (Fig. 5.45) have been used for many years. In them the jet nozzles are terminated so that the fluid strikes a circular concentric knife-edge at one end of a cylindrical cavity. The resonant frequency of the cavity can be controlled by a piston adjustment of the cavity depth.

The vortex whistle operates on a somewhat different principle [115, 116]. Fluid injected tangentially into a cylindrical volume closed at one end increases in rotational velocity as it progresses in a helical path toward a small-diameter axial port in the other end. The change from symmetric to asymmetric flow produces periodic fluctuations in motion and pressure that emanate from the exit port as acoustical waves. Frequency is approximately proportional to flow rate.

The wedge resonator is well suited to in-line liquid processing such as homogenization and emulsification. It consists basically of a resonant plate clamped at one or more nodal points. One edge is wedge-shaped and oriented in a jet emanating from a narrow rectangular slit parallel to the plate. Inherent instabilities in the jet stream cause the blade to vibrate at its resonant frequency, provided the pressure and velocity of the jet are properly adjusted. The upper frequency is limited by mechanical stresses and fatigue to the neighborhood of 30 kHz.

Solid Generators

The practical generation of ultrasonic waves in solids is based on the ability of certain materials to convert variations of electric- or magnetic-field intensities to internal stresses [117, 118]. Under suitable conditions these stresses induce dimensional variations in synchronism with the applied field. Depending on whether the field is electric or magnetic, the effects are broadly classified as piezoelectric or magnetostrictive, respectively. Electromagnetic generators in which moving coils or iron slugs are bodily vibrated are useful for high-power applications at audiofrequencies. Because of fundamental frequency limitations, however, they are not often used in the ultrasonic region. Thin metallic and plastic films can be driven like drumheads under electrostatic forces at frequencies approaching 50 kHz. Such techniques are useful in some optical mirror systems, but since the power output is extremely small these devices are not considered here.

Piezoelectric Transducers

The direct piezoelectric effect refers to the appearance of electric charge on the surface of certain anisotropic crystals subjected to mechanical stress [119]. The converse effect, that is, charge-induced strain, is the basis of acoustical wave generation. It is most prominent in natural crystals of quartz and tourmaline and in grown crystals of Rochelle salt, ammonium dihydrogen phosphate, and lead niobate. The crystals are normally cut in the shape of thin rectangular or circular plates. Since the piezoelectric properties are generally not isotropic, the various crystal cuts are specified with respect to right-handed rectangular coordinates related by standard rules to the crystallographic axes [120]; for example, a section normal to the optic* or Z-axis of a quartz single crystal is hexagonal. By convention the three axes joining opposite edges are defined as the X-axes and the three

---

* A unique direction in which light does not exhibit birefrigence.

axes drawn through opposite faces and normal to the respective X-axes are defined as the Y-axes. Plates cut with broad faces normal to an X-axis are called X-cut; those cut with faces normal to a Y-axis are called Y-cut. In some materials the plates may have other orientations. A 45° Y-cut, for example, implies a Y-cut that is rotated 45° about the X-axis.

X-cut quartz crystals are frequently used for generating compressional (longitudinal) waves. In this case an alternating electric field is applied by means of conducting electrodes formed on the broad faces. For one polarity of field strains appear as compression in thickness with simultaneous expansion in the Y-direction. On reversal of polarity the strains appear as expansion in thickness and compression in the Y-direction. In neither case does strain appear in the X-direction. Thus the crystal faces vibrate at a rate determined by the frequency of the electrical supply. For maximum amplitude the dimensions are chosen so that the crystal is mechanically resonant in a specified direction (i.e., thickness or length) at the desired frequency. At frequencies above a few megahertz the thickness required for resonance approaches a fraction of a millimeter. Since thin plates are extremely fragile and subject to dielectric failure under high fields, the usual practice is to use thicker crystals operating at one of the higher order odd harmonics. Because the piezoelectric effect is proportional to the applied field intensity, even-order harmonics appear as full waves with equal but opposing strains in each half wavelength. Thus there is no net displacement.

In addition to natural first-order piezoelectricity, all dielectrics exhibit a second-order electrostrictive effect. Electrostriction refers to a dimensional distortion that is proportional to the square of the applied field intensity. It is generally negligible, but in some materials, notably barium titanate, lead metaniobate, and lead zirconate-titanate, the effect is strongly pronounced. Such materials, called ferroelectrics, also exhibit piezoelectric properties when permanently polarized [81, 82]. This is usually accomplished in manufacture by heating the material with a suitable binder to a temperature at which electrostriction disappears (the Curie point) and subjecting it to a strong electric field during cooling. The result is a ceramiclike polycrystalline element that can be fabricated in a wide variety of shapes and sizes. Depending on design geometry and the direction of built-in polarization, plates may be operated in thickness, longitudinal, or shear modes, disks, in thickness or radial modes, and spheres and hemispheres, in radical modes. Compared with quartz, ceramics offer the advantages of better conversion efficiency, even well below resonance, and lower driving potentials. Since the internal damping resistance is relatively high, the mechanical Q is low, a fact that makes ceramics suitable for wide-band and pulse applications.

The performance of a piezoelectric transducer operated within its elastic limits is specified in terms of coefficients that appear in linear stress-strain tensors. They include dielectric constants, elastic moduli, and coefficients of coupling, charge, and voltage. Although a complete description is beyond the scope of the present discussion, the simplified relations that obtain for disks and rectangular prisms vibrating in the thickness mode are adequate for many purposes. In conformity with tensor notation, directions are identified by numerical subscripts corresponding to rectangular coordinates and rotations. Thus in a plate that is "poled" in the thickness or X-direction (Fig. 5.46a) K_1 refers to the dielectric constant measured in the X-direction and K_3 refers to the same parameter measured in Z-direction. Because of symmetry, $K_2 = K_1$. Electrical and mechanical interactions are indicated

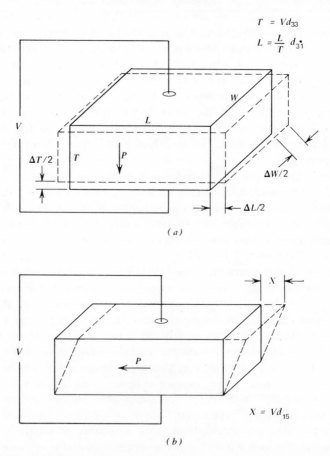

$$T = Vd_{33}$$

$$L = \frac{L}{T} d_{31}$$

(a)

$$X = Vd_{15}$$

(b)

Fig. 5.46 Deformations in piezoelectric transducers: (a) thickness mode; (b) shear mode.

by the use of double subscripts. The first gives the direction of the electric field associated with charge or applied potential and the second gives the direction of mechanical stress or strain. For operation in the shear mode (Fig. 5.46b) the poling electrodes used in fabrication are removed and replaced by electrodes on another pair of faces. The subscript 5 is used in the second place to indicate shear.

The piezoelectric charge coefficients d_{ij} are defined as the ratios of surface charge density to applied pressure. Thus d_{33} pertains to force applied in the direction of polarization and to the same surface on which charge is collected; d_{15} refers to shear with charge collected on the electrodes parallel to the polarization axis. The coefficients d_{ij} are also numerically equal to the ratios of mechanical strain to electric-field intensity. Values of d_{31} are typically about one-third those of d_{33}, which lie in the region of 10^{-10} m/V for ceramics and 10^{-12} m/V for quartz.

The voltage coefficients g_{ij} are defined as the ratio of electric-field intensity to the applied mechanical stress and are related to the charge coefficients d_{ij} by equations of the form

$$d = K\epsilon_0 g \tag{5.36}$$

and

$$k^2 = g\, dY \tag{5.37}$$

where ϵ_0 is the permittivity of free space, K and Y, respectively, represent the appropriate values of dielectric constant and Young's modulus, and k is the coupling coefficient (k_p is used for disks and thin-walled spheres vibrating in radial modes). The value k^2 is numerically equal to the ratio of electrical energy that is converted to mechanical energy, divided by the electrical input energy. Thus to obtain maximum energy transfer stiff materials with high values of both d and g are desirable.

Ceramic elements can be bonded to other materials with epoxy-resin adhesives or low-melting-point solders. To prevent depolarization adequate precautions should be taken to ensure that the soldering temperature does not exceed allowable limits. For resonant operation in the thickness mode sandwich-type mounting methods are frequently used. In one method the ceramic plate is cemented between two quarter-wave metal blocks with cross sections equal to that of the plate. The resonant angular frequency for blocks of length 1 is then given by

$$\omega = \frac{\pi}{l}\left(\frac{Y}{\rho}\right)^{\frac{1}{2}}, \tag{5.38}$$

where Y is Young's modulus and ρ is the density of the material. In another method, referred to as nodal point mounting, two similar ceramic elements are mounted back-to-back on opposite sides of a thin metal support plate.

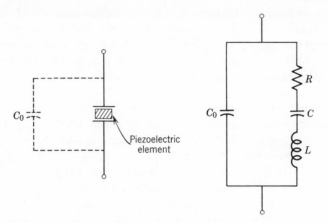

Fig. 5.47 Equivalent circuit of a piezoelectric transducer.

The outer faces of the element may again be terminated in quarter-wavelength sections. In either method the use of two different materials permits amplification of motion at one end with respect to the other by a factor $(Y_1\rho_1/Y_2\rho_2)^{1/2}$. The subscripts refer to the respective materials.

For wide-band operation where "ringing" cannot be tolerated one face of the transducer should be terminated in an infinite acoustic line of suitable impedance. If attenuation is high enough (as in a lossy line' so that end reflections are negligible, finite lengths of line are usually adequate. Other types of terminations, variously called horns, concentrations, or transformers, have also been used [121].

The equivalent circuit of a piezoelectric element consists of a mechanically resonant circuit in shunt with a capacitor C_0. The latter is simply the capacitance that exists between the electrodes. Under steady-state conditions the mechanical circuit can be represented by its electrical analog, as shown in Fig. 5.47, and the resonant frequency calculated from the relation

$$\omega = \left(\frac{1}{MC_M}\right)^{1/2} = \left(\frac{1}{LC}\right)^{1/2}, \qquad (5.39)$$

with values of L and C expressed in terms of the piezoelectric constants [122]. Alternatively, it is adequate for most purposes to use the "frequency constant" per unit dimensions usually supplied by the manufacturer for specific shapes and operating modes.

Maximum energy transfer at resonance is obtained by matching the impedance of the driver to that of the element, as by the transformer coupling shown in Fig. 5.48a. With a secondary winding of appropriate inductance

L_0, the parallel L_0C_0 circuit can be tuned to resonance. The mechanical resistance of a piezoelectric element is composed of two components: (a) useful expenditure of energy and (b) internal and mounting losses. Because of their relatively high internal friction, ceramics are characterized by rather broad resonance curves and can be operated at reduced output over a considerable frequency range. For wide-band operation the element presents an impedance that is chiefly capacitative, and it is best driven by the shunt-feed voltage source indicated in Fig. 5.48b.

Magnetostrictive Transducers

Magnetostriction refers to the deformation produced in certain materials subjected to an external magnetic field. Depending on the nature of the

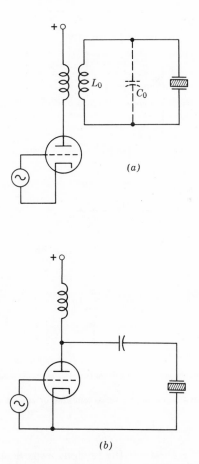

Fig. 5.48 Piezoelectric driving circuits: (a) transformer coupling; (b) shunt feed arrangement.

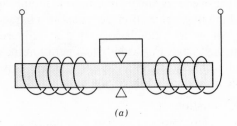

(a)

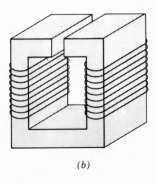

(b)

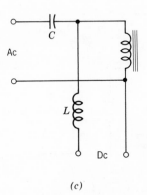

(c)

Fig. 5.49 Magnetostrictive transducers: (a) solenoidal drive; (b) typical magnetostrictive core; (c) typical drive circuit.

material, the deformation may be positive (elongation) or negative (contraction). For fields not intense enough to produce magnetic saturation, the mechanical strain is approximately proportional to the square of the magnetic flux density. Thus to obtain an alternating dimensional variation a static biasing field is required. Under this condition the incremental strain is proportional to the product of the incremental permeability and the amplitude of magnetic field. The proportionality constant is called the magnetostrictive strain coefficient. As in piezoelectrics, a coupling coefficient can also be defined. Because of the nonlinear character of the magnetization curve of most materials, however, it is highly dependent on the operating point. The magnitude of the magnetostrictive effect decreases at elevated temperatures and disappears completely at the Curie temperature.

Magnetostrictive transducers are used chiefly in high-power applications. Since much of the energy is dissipated in hysteretic and eddy current heating, a narrow hysteresis loop and high electrical resistivity are desirable. Metals such as nickel and various iron alloys and the nonmetal ferrites are in common use [123]. The resonant frequency of a half-wave rod clamped at its midpoint (i.e., a nodal point) is given by Eq. 5.38. Although it may be driven from relatively simple solenoidal windings, as illustrated in Fig. 5.49a, it suffers from high magnetic flux leakage. These losses can be avoided by using a closed magnetic circuit such as a toroid or a slotted core material, as shown in Fig. 5.49b. Magnetic bias can be obtained with a separate winding or by a permanent magnet inserted in the magnetic circuit.

Another commonly used method is illustrated in the circuit of Fig. 5.49c. The capacitor C, which is large enough to pass the exciting frequency, prevents dc bias current from flowing through the oscillator circuit. The inductance L offers resistance only to the flow of bias current. It should be large enough to prevent appreciable exciting current from reaching the dc supply.

To avoid eddy current losses the core is usually constructed of sheet laminations similar to the type used in transformers. Sintered ferrites have high inherent resistivities and negligible eddy currents.

Resistive Layer Transducers

Solid-state techniques have been applied to the generation of very high sonic waves in piezoelectric semiconductors such as gallium arsenide and cadmium sulfide. In essence very thin layers of high resistivity are formed at one end of a semiconductor bar by one of three processes: (a) depletion of carriers at pn or metal-n junctions by the application of reverse bias, (b) diffusion of impurities to a shallow depth below the surface, and (c) epitaxial growth of thin films on the surface. The piezoelectric properties of these layers can be exploited by electroding the top surface and applying a high-frequency exciting potential [124]. The resonant frequency depends on the thickness of the layer, which typically ranges between 10^{-6} and 10^{-8} m. Longitudinal waves at frequencies above 1 GHz have been generated. Because of constructional difficulties, such generators have found use to date only in laboratory investigations.

References

1. M. Born and E. Wolf, *Principles of Optics*, 3rd ed., Pergamon, New York, 1965.
2. D. Corson and P. Lorraine, *Introduction to Electromagnetic Fields and Waves*, Freeman, San Francisco, 1962.
3. A. H. Harvey, *Microwave Engineering*, Academic, New York, 1963.
4. R. B. Lindsay, *Mechanical Radiation*, McGraw-Hill, New York, 1960.
5. I. S. Sokolnikoff and R. M. Redheffer, *Mathematics of Physics and Modern Engineering*, McGraw-Hill, New York, 1958.
6. L. A. Pipes, *Applied Mathematics for Engineers and Physicists*, McGraw-Hill, New York, 1958.
7. E. Mayer, *J. Appl. Phys.* **17**, 1046 (1946).
8. A. Kiriloff, *Electronics* **33**, 96 (October 1960).
9. T. K. Ishii, *Microwave Engineering*, Ronald, New York (1966).
10. F. E. Terman, *Electronic and Radio Engineering*, McGraw-Hill, New York, 1955.
11. H. S. Black, *Modulation Theory*, VanNostrand, Princeton, New Jersey, 1953.
12. E. W. Pappenfus, W. B. Bruene, and E. O. Schoenike, *Single Sideband Principles and Circuits*, McGraw-Hill, New York, 1964.
13. Y. W. Lee, *Statistical Theory of Communication*, Wiley, New York, 1963.
14. RCA Silicon Power Circuits Manual, Series SP-50 (1967).
15. L. Esaki, *Phys. Rev.* **109**, 602 (1958).
16. S. P. Gentile, *Basic Theory and Application of Tunnel Diodes*, VanNostrand, Princeton, New Jersey, 1962.
17. R. F. Trambarulo and C. A. Burrus, *Proc. I.E.E.E.* **48**, 1776 (1960).
18. D. R. Melik and G. A. Foggiato, *Proc. I.E.E.E.* **56**, 1737 (1968).
19. E. Rivier, *Proc. I.E.E.E.* **56**, 1387 (1968).
20. J. J. Hamilton, *Reflex Klystrons*, Macmillan, New York, 1959.
21. G. J. Wheeler, *Introduction to Microwaves*, Prentice-Hall, Englewood Cliffs, New Jersey, 1963.
22. E. C. Okress, Ed., *Microwave Power Engineering*, Academic, New York, 1968.
23. M. R. Pearlman and R. H. Webb, *Rev. Sci. Inst.* **38**, 1264 (1967).
24. J. E. Rowe, *Nonlinear Electron-wave Interaction Phenomena*, Academic, New York, 1965.
25. R. M. Bevensee, *Electromagnetic-Slow Wave Systems*, Wiley, New York, 1964.
26. D. E. Erminy, *Appl. Opt.* **6**, 107 (1967).
27. C. S. Williams, *J. Opt. Soc. Am.* **51**, 564 (1961).
28. J. C. Fleming, *Appl. Opt.* **5**, 195 (1966).
29. H. Y. Yamanda, *Appl. Opt.* **6**, 357 (1967).

30. A. R. Karoli, J. R. Hickey, and R. E. Nelson, *Appl. Opt.* **6**, 1183 (1967).
31. M. R. Null and W. W. Lozier, *Ind. Control Sys.* **36**, 93 (May 1963).
32. A. T. Hattenburg, *Appl. Opt.* **6**, 95 (1967).
33. E. G. Zubler and F. A. Mosby, *Ill. Engr.* **54**, 734 (1959).
34. H. L. Hackforth, *Infrared Radiation*, McGraw-Hill, New York, 1960.
35. P. W. Kruse, L. D. McGlauchlin, and R. B. McQuistan, *Elements of Infrared Technology*, Wiley, New York, 1962.
36. G. T. Conn and D. G. Avery, *Infrared Methods*, Academic, New York, 1960.
37. T. M. Hard and R. C. Lord, *Appl. Opt.* **7**, 589 (1968).
38. W. R. Walker, *Ind. Control Sys.* **36**, 113 (August 1963).
39. W. Y. Ramsey and J. C. Alishouse, *Infrared Phys.* **8**, 143 (1968).
40. C. W. Hand, *Rev. Sci. Inst.* **38**, 983 (1967).
41. R. Carlon, *Appl. Opt.* **5**, 1281 (1966).
42. M. B. Hall and R. G. Nestor, *J. Opt. Soc. Am.* **42**, 257 (1952).
43. H. G. Lipson and J. R. Littler, *Appl. Opt.* **5**, 472N (1966).
44. C. Opal and W. B. Grandrud, *Rev. Sci. Inst.* **38**, 838 (1967).
45. R. J. Bell and T. E. Gilmer, Jr., *Appl. Opt.* **4**, 45 (1965).
46. S. I. Drasky and R. J. Bell, *Infrared Phys.* **5**, 137 (1965).
47. R. W. Astheimer, G. Falbel, and S. Minkowitz, *Appl. Opt.* **5**, 87 (1966).
48. B. Lax, *Solid State Design* **4**, 26 (November 1963).
49. J. Johnson and D. Porat, *Rev. Sci. Inst.* **38**, 1796 (1967).
50. R. H. Rediker, *Solid State Design* **4**, 19 (August 1963).
51. R. N. Hall, *Solid State Elect.* **6**, 405 (1963).
52. G. Burns and M. I. Nathan, *Proc. I.E.E.E.* **52**, 770 (1964).
53. H. K. Kessler, *Rev. Sci. Inst.* **37**, 517 (1966).
54. W. Koechner, *Rev. Sci. Inst.* **38**, 17 (1967).
55. R. Kingslake, Ed. *Applied Optics and Optical Engineering*, Vol. I, Academic, New York (1965), p. 43.
56. Bulletin TP-119, General Electric Co., Cleveland, O. (1967).
57. M. Fujinaka, *Proc. I.E.E.E.* **5**, 1635 (1967).
58. H. F. Ivey, *Advances in Electronics and Electron Physics*, Supp. 1, *Electroluminescence and Related Effects*, Academic, New York (1963).
59. L. D. Dickson, *Rev. Sci. Inst.* **38**, 1581 (1967).
60. S. Prydz and A. Ulset, *Appl. Opt.* **7**, 21 (1968).
61. L. B. Loeb, *Basic Processes of Gaseous Electronics*, University of California Press, Berkeley, 1961.
62. L. L. Blackmer and D. J. Stone, Jr., *Phot. Sci. Eng.* **1**, 172 (1958).
63. L. Klein, *Appl. Opt.* **7**, 677 (1968).
64. J. V. Sullivan and A. Walsh, *Spectrochim. Acta* **21**, 721 (1965).
65. J. I. Dinnan, *Anal. Chem.* **39**, 1489 (1967).
66. A. L. Schawlow and C. H. Townes, *Phys. Rev.* **112**, 1940 (1958).
67. K. Tomiyasu, *I.E.E.E. J. Quant. Elect.* **QE4**, 274 (1968).
68. K. Tomiyasu, *The Laser Literature, An Annotated Guide*, Plenum, New York, 1968.
69. H. A. Elion, *Laser Systems and Applications*, Pergamon, New York, 1967.

70. S. L. Marshall, Ed., *Laser Technology and Applications*, McGraw-Hill, New York, 1968.

71. E. L. Steele, *Optical Lasers in Electronics*, Wiley, New York, 1968.

72. A. Yario and E. I. Gordon, *Proc. I.E.E.E.* **51,** 4 (1963).

73. T. H. Maiman, *Nature* **187,** 493 (1960).

74. R. Daly and S. D. Sims, *Appl. Opt.* **3,** 1063 (1964).

75. G. Magyar, *Rev. Sci. Inst.* **38,** 517 (1967).

76. A. Javan, W. R. Bennett, Jr., and D. R. Herriott, *Phys. Rev. Letters* **6,** 106 (1961).

77. D. R. Herriott, *J. Opt. Soc. Am.* **52,** 31 (1962).

78. A. D. White and J. D. Rigden, *Proc. I.R.E.* **50,** 1697 (1962).

79. R. L. Field, Jr., *Rev. Sci. Inst.* **38,** 1720 (1967).

80. W. R. Bennett, Jr., *Appl. Opt.* **Supp. 2,** 3 (1965).

81. F. Jona and G. Shirane, *Ferroelectric Crystals*, Macmillan, New York, 1962.

82. J. C. Burfoot, *Ferroelectrics*, VanNostrand, London (1967).

83. P. A. Franken and J. F. Ward, *Rev. Med. Phys.* **35,** 23 (1963).

84. R. W. Minck, R. W. Terhune, and C. C. Wang, *Proc. I.E.E.E.* **54,** 1357 (1966).

85. E. G. Spencer, P. V. Lenzo, and A. A. Ballman, *Proc. I.E.E.E.* **55,** 2074 (1967).

86. P. P. Sorokin and J. R. Lankard, *I.B.M.J. Res. Dev.* **11,** 148 (1967).

87. B. H. Soffer and B. B. McFarland, *Appl. Phys. Letters* **10,** 266 (1967).

88. B. B. Snavely, O. G. Peterson, and R. F. Reithel, *Appl. Phys. Letters* **11,** 275 (1967).

89. O. G. Peterson and B. B. Snavely, *Appl. Phys. Letters* **12,** 238 (1968).

90. R. E. Huffman, Y. Tanaka, and J. C. Larrabee, *Appl. Opt.* **2,** 617 (1963).

91. R. E. Huffman, J. C. Larrabee, and Y. Tanaka, *Appl. Opt.* **4,** 1581 (1965).

92. B. C. Roquitte, *Appl. Opt.* **6,** 415 (1967).

93. H. Damany, J.-Y. Roncin, and H. Damany-Astoin, *Appl. Opt.* **5,** 297 (1966).

94. V. Feldman, M. Swartz, and L. Cohen, *Rev. Sci. Inst.* **38,** 1372 (1967).

95. K. H. Welge, J. Wanner, and A. Heindricks, *Rev. Sci. Inst.* **38,** 1728 (1967).

96. E. G. Niemann and M. Klenert, *Appl. Opt.* **7,** 295 (1968).

97. S. Murayana, *J. Appl. Phys.* **39,** 5478 (1968).

98. E. W. Schlag and F. J. Comes, *J. Opt. Soc. Am.* **50,** 866 (1960).

99. P. G. Wilkmson and E. T. Pyram, *Appl. Opt.* **4,** 581 (1965).

100. J. J. Sparapany, *Appl. Opt.* **4,** 303 (1965).

101. R. M. Dagnall and T. S. West, *Appl. Opt.* **7,** 1287 (1968).

102. F. Jaundrell-Thompson and W. J. Ashworth, *X-Ray Physics and Equipment*, Blackwell, Oxford, 1965.

103. J. Silman, *The Fundamentals of X-Ray and Radium Physics*, 4th ed., Charles C. Thomas, Springfield, Illinois, 1965.

104. *Proceedings of Second Symposium, Low Energy X- and Gamma Sources and Applications*, Oak Ridge National Laboratory, Oak Ridge, Tenn., March 1967.

105. *Proceedings of Annual Conference on Applications of X-Ray Analysis*, Plenum, New York, Vol. I, 1957, Vol. XI, 1968.

106. W. K. Robinson, W. D. Adams, and J. L. Dugan, *Am. J. Phys.* **36,** 683 (1968).

107. J. Kohl, R. D. Zentner, and H. R. Lukens, *Radioisotope Applications and Engineering*, VanNostrand, Princeton, New Jersey, 1961.

108. R. T. Overman, *Radioisotope Techniques*, McGraw-Hill, New York, 1960.

109. J. L. Summerville, Ed., *The Isotope Index*, Scientific Equipment Co., Indianapolis, 1967.
110. L. E. Kinsler and A. R. Frey, *Fundamentals of Acoustics*, 2nd ed., Wiley, New York, 1962.
111. J. R. Frederick, *Ultrasonic Engineering*, Wiley, New York, 1965.
112. J. Blitz, *Fundamentals of Ultrasonics*, Plenum, New York, 1967.
113. O. M. Stuetzer, *J. Acoust. Soc. Am.* **42,** 502 (1967).
114. C. H. Allen and I. Rudnick, *J. Acoust. Soc. Am.* **19,** 857 (1947).
115. B. Vonnegut, *J. Acoust. Soc. Am.* **26,** 18 (1954).
116. R. C. Chanaud, *J. Acoust. Soc. Am.* **35,** 953 (1963).
117. D. A. Berlincourt, D. R. Curran, and H. Joffa, *Physical Acoustics* Vol. IA, W. P. Mason, Ed., Academic, New York, 1964.
118. B. Carlin, *Physical Acoustics*, Vol. IB, W. P. Mason, Ed., Academic, New York, 1964.
119. J. F. Nye, *Physical Properties of Crystals*, Oxford, London, 1967.
120. Standards on Piezoelectric Crystals, *Proc. I.R.E.* **37,** 1378 (1949).
121. E. Eisner, *J. Acoust. Soc. Am.* **36,** 1 (1964).
122. E. Hafner, *Proc. I.E.E.E.* **57,** 179 (1969).
123. M. Preisinger, *I.B.M. J. Res. Dev.*, **10,** 321 (1966).
124. D. L. White, *Physical Acoustics*, Vol. IB, W. P. Mason, Ed., Academic, New York, 1964.

INDEX